The Open University

M208 Pure Mathematics

# LA1

## Vectors and conics

This publication forms part of an Open University course. Details of this and other Open University courses can be obtained from the Student Registration and Enquiry Service, The Open University, PO Box 197, Milton Keynes, MK7 6BJ, United Kingdom: tel. +44 (0)870 300 6090, e-mail general-enquiries@open.ac.uk

Alternatively, you may visit the Open University website at http://www.open.ac.uk where you can learn more about the wide range of courses and packs offered at all levels by The Open University.

To purchase a selection of Open University course materials, visit http://www.ouw.co.uk, or contact Open University Worldwide, Michael Young Building, Walton Hall, Milton Keynes, MK7 6AA, United Kingdom, for a brochure: tel. +44 (0)1908 858793, fax +44 (0)1908 858787, e-mail ouw-customer-services@open.ac.uk

The Open University, Walton Hall, Milton Keynes, MK7 6AA.

First published 2006.



Edited, designed and typeset by The Open University, using the Open University TEX System.

Printed and bound in the United Kingdom by Hobbs the Printers Limited, Brunel Road, Totton, Hampshire SO40 3WX.

ISBN 0 7492 0222 X

1.2

# Contents

# Introduction to the Linear Algebra Block

Attempts to answer problems in areas as diverse as science, technology and economics lead to systems of simultaneous linear equations in several variables, whose solutions give the required answer. Therefore, much effort has been devoted to solving simultaneous linear equations, a process which is not always straightforward, especially if the number of variables is large.

A specific example reveals the kinds of difficulties which may occur. Consider three rather similar pairs of linear equations in the variables $x$ and $y$:

$$\begin{cases} x + 3y = 5 \\ -2x + 6y = 2 \end{cases} \qquad \begin{cases} -x + 3y = 5 \\ -2x + 6y = 2 \end{cases} \qquad \begin{cases} -x + 3y = 1 \\ -2x + 6y = 2. \end{cases}$$

The first pair of equations has the unique solution $x = 2$, $y = 1$, whereas the second pair has no solutions, and the third pair has infinitely many solutions (for example, $x = -1$, $y = 0$, and $x = 0$, $y = \frac{1}{3}$). These different outcomes may be understood:

- algebraically, by studying the *matrix* of coefficients of the equations, and introducing a function of these coefficients, called the *determinant*;
- geometrically, by interpreting solutions of the equations as points of intersection of the corresponding pairs of straight lines drawn in an $(x, y)$-plane.

For simultaneous linear equations involving more than two variables, we can use a similar algebraic approach, and also a geometric one using a generalisation of the plane called *n-dimensional Euclidean space*, $\mathbb{R}^n$, whose elements are *points*, or *vectors*, of the form $(x_1, x_2, \ldots, x_n)$, where $x_1, x_2, \ldots, x_n$ are real numbers. Although it is possible to visualise objects in $n$-dimensional space only when $n = 1$, 2 or 3, this more general Euclidean space is a convenient environment in which to develop the theory needed to analyse the solutions of simultaneous linear equations.

A key tool in this theory is the concept of a *linear transformation* which, in its basic form, is a function from one Euclidean space to another that preserves certain aspects of their geometric structure. For example, the function

$$t(x, y) = (x + 3y, -2x + 6y)$$

is a linear transformation from $\mathbb{R}^2$ to $\mathbb{R}^2$ which is closely related to the first pair of equations above. Solving that pair of equations is equivalent to finding a point $(x, y)$ in $\mathbb{R}^2$ such that the function $t$ maps $(x, y)$ to the point $(5, 2)$. This suggests that we can obtain information about the solutions of simultaneous linear equations by studying the corresponding linear transformations. Moreover, there are results about linear transformations which can be used to understand the solution sets of quadratic equations in several variables. These turn out to be the familiar *conics* in $\mathbb{R}^2$ and the so-called *quadric surfaces* in $\mathbb{R}^3$.

But linear transformations arise in situations apart from that of solving equations. For example, many common geometric transformations have great importance in their own right; for example, they are needed to manipulate computer graphic images, as illustrated in the following diagrams.

effect of a rotation

effect of a reflection

effect of a shear

Finally, the range of available linear transformations can be increased greatly by introducing the notion of a *vector space*. This is a generalisation of $n$-dimensional Euclidean space, and it may be finite-dimensional or infinite-dimensional. The elements of a vector space are sometimes called *vectors*, but they can be very general objects; for example, we shall consider vector spaces whose elements are real functions, and introduce linear transformations between such vector spaces which arise from operations on real functions such as differentiation and integration. In this way, vector spaces and their associated linear transformations form a very general context in which many seemingly unrelated problems can be studied using similar techniques.

# Introduction

In this unit we look at some of the ways that we represent points, lines and planes in mathematics. You have already met some of these in the Introduction Block, so part of this unit will be revision. However, the idea of vectors may be new to you. This is an important concept which we shall need later in the block.

In Section 1 we revise coordinate geometry in two-dimensional Euclidean space, $\mathbb{R}^2$, and then extend these ideas to three-dimensional Euclidean space, $\mathbb{R}^3$. We discuss the equation of a plane in $\mathbb{R}^3$, but find that we do not have the tools to determine the equation of a plane, and leave this until Section 3.

In Section 2 we introduce the idea of a vector, and look at the algebra of vectors. Vectors give us a way of looking at points and lines, in the plane and in $\mathbb{R}^3$, which is sometimes more useful than Cartesian coordinates, although the two are closely related.

In Section 3 we introduce the idea of the dot product of two vectors, and then use it to determine the general form of the equation of a plane in $\mathbb{R}^3$.

In Section 4 we explain the origin of conics, as the curves of intersection of double cones and planes in $\mathbb{R}^3$. The focus–directrix definitions of the non-degenerate conics, the ellipse, the parabola and the hyperbola, are given. We observe that conics are precisely the subsets of the plane determined by an equation of degree two.

## Study guide

The sections should be studied in the natural order.

Section 1 is straightforward, and should not take long.

Sections 2 and 3 contain most of the new material in the unit. Your study of the unit should concentrate on these two sections, as they contain important ideas needed in future units in the block.

Section 3 is the audio section.

# 1 Coordinate geometry: points, planes and lines

After working through this section, you should be able to:

(a) recognise the *equation of a line* in the plane;

(b) determine the *point of intersection* of two lines in the plane, if it exists;

(c) recognise the *one-one correspondence* between the set of points in three-dimensional space and the set of ordered triples of real numbers;

(d) recognise the *equation of a plane* in three dimensions.

## 1.1 Points, lines and distances in $\mathbb{R}^2$

In coordinate geometry we generally use rectangular (or *Cartesian*) coordinate axes, as illustrated, to describe the Euclidean plane. We can represent any point in the plane *uniquely* by an ordered pair of coordinates $(a, b)$; that is, any point in the plane has precisely one possible pair of coordinates with respect to the chosen axes.

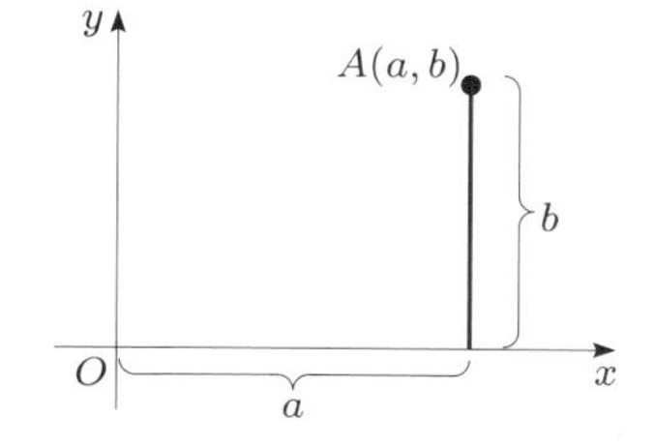


This gives a one-one correspondence between the points of the plane and ordered pairs of real numbers. Often we do not bother to distinguish explicitly between the points and their representation as ordered pairs; we simply write $(a, b)$ to denote the point $A$.

The plane together with an origin and a pair of $x$-, $y$-axes is often called *two-dimensional Euclidean space*, denoted by the symbol $\mathbb{R}^2$.

### Lines

The equation of any line in $\mathbb{R}^2$, except a line parallel to the $y$-axis, can be written in the form

$$y = mx + c, \tag{1.1}$$

See the first sketch below.

where $m$ is the *gradient* or *slope* of the line, and $c$ is its *$y$-intercept*; that is, $(0, c)$ is the point at which the line crosses the $y$-axis.

In the particular case that the line cuts the $y$-axis at the origin, its equation has the simple form

$$y = mx,$$

See the second sketch below.

as $c = 0$ in this case.

Another special case occurs when $m = 0$. Then the line is parallel to the $x$-axis, and its equation is of the form

$$y = c,$$

See the third sketch below.

where $c$ is the $y$-intercept.

Finally, the equation of a line parallel to the $y$-axis cannot be written in the form $y = mx + c$, but it can be written as

$$x = a, \tag{1.2}$$

See the final sketch below.

where $(a, 0)$ is the point at which the line crosses the $x$-axis.

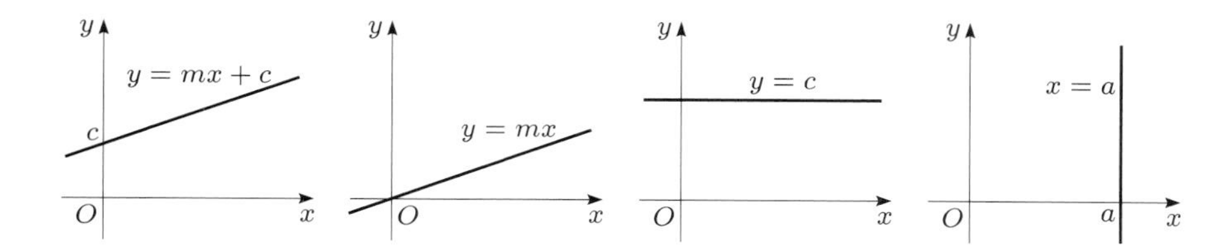


In both cases (1.1) and (1.2) above, the equation of a line in the plane can be written in the form

$$ax + by = c, \tag{1.3}$$

for some real numbers $a$, $b$ and $c$, where $a$ and $b$ are not both zero.

Thus any line in $\mathbb{R}^2$ has an equation of the form (1.3); conversely, any equation of the form (1.3) represents a line in $\mathbb{R}^2$.

**Equation of a line** The general equation of a line in $\mathbb{R}^2$ is

$$ax + by = c,$$

where $a$, $b$ and $c$ are real, and $a$ and $b$ are not both zero.

**Exercise 1.1** Determine the equation of the line with gradient $-3$ that passes through the point $(2, -1)$.

You may omit Exercises 1.1 and 1.2 if you feel confident about finding the equations of lines in the plane.

**Exercise 1.2** For each of the following pairs of points, determine the equation of the line through them.

(a) $(1, 1)$ and $(3, 5)$. (b) $(0, 0)$ and $(0, 8)$.

(c) $(0, 0)$ and $(4, 2)$. (d) $(4, -1)$ and $(2, -1)$.

## Parallel and perpendicular lines

We often wish to know whether two lines are *parallel* (that is, they never meet) or *perpendicular* (that is, they meet at right angles).

Two distinct lines, $y = m_1x + c_1$ and $y = m_2x + c_2$, are parallel if and only if they have the same gradient; that is, if and only if $m_1 = m_2$. For example, the lines $y = -2x + 7$ and $y = -2x - 3$ are parallel since both have gradient $-2$, whereas the lines $y = -2x + 7$ and $y = 2x - 3$ are not parallel since their gradients are not equal (they are $-2$ and $2$, respectively).

Two lines $\ell_1$ and $\ell_2$ with equations $y = m_1x + c_1$ and $y = m_2x + c_2$, respectively, where $m_1$ and $m_2$ are both non-zero, are perpendicular if and only if $m_1m_2 = -1$. If the lines are perpendicular, then one ($\ell_1$, say) must slope up from left to right and the other ($\ell_2$, say) must slope down from left to right, as shown in the margin.

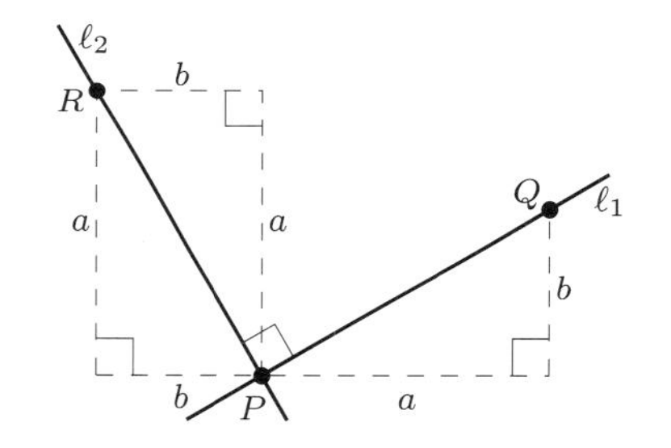


Let the lines intersect at $P$, and let $Q$ be a point on $\ell_1$ to the right of $P$. Suppose that $Q$ is $a$ units to the right of $P$ and $b$ units up from $P$, as illustrated. Let $R$ be the point on $\ell_2$ obtained by rotating $PQ$ anticlockwise through an angle of $\pi/2$; then $R$ is $b$ units to the left of $P$ and $a$ units up from $P$, as shown.

Then the gradient of $\ell_1$ is $m_1 = \dfrac{b}{a}$, and the gradient of $\ell_2$ is $m_2 = -\dfrac{a}{b}$.

It follows that $m_1m_2 = \left(\dfrac{b}{a}\right) \times \left(-\dfrac{a}{b}\right) = -1$.

The proof of the converse is similar.

Two distinct lines with equations $y = m_1x + c_1$ and $y = m_2x + c_2$, where $m_1$ and $m_2$ are both non-zero, are

- **parallel** if and only if $m_1 = m_2$ and $c_1 \neq c_2$;
- **perpendicular** if and only if $m_1m_2 = -1$.

**Example 1.1** Determine which of the following lines are parallel, and which are perpendicular to each other.

$\ell_1 :\ y = -2x + 4$ $\quad \ell_2 :\ 2x - 3y - 2 = 0$ $\quad \ell_3 :\ y - 2x = 9$

$\ell_4 :\ 2y + 3x + 5 = 0$ $\quad \ell_5 :\ x + \frac{1}{2}y + 2 = 0$ $\quad \ell_6 :\ 2y = 3x + 7$

**Solution** The gradients of the given lines are $-2$, $\frac{2}{3}$, $2$, $-\frac{3}{2}$, $-2$ and $\frac{3}{2}$, respectively. Thus the lines $\ell_1$ and $\ell_5$ are parallel, and the lines $\ell_2$ and $\ell_4$ are perpendicular. ■

**Exercise 1.3** Determine which of the following lines are parallel, and which are perpendicular to each other.

$\ell_1: y = -2x + 4$ $\quad \ell_2: 6x - 3y + 4 = 0$ $\quad \ell_3: 2y + x = 10$

$\ell_4: 6y - 3x + 5 = 0$ $\quad \ell_5: x - 2y + 2 = 0$ $\quad \ell_6: 2y + 4x + 7 = 0$

## Intersection of two lines

Two arbitrary lines in $\mathbb{R}^2$ may have a single point of intersection, may be parallel, or may coincide. The first two possibilities are illustrated below. Can we tell from the equations of the lines which of the three possibilities occurs?

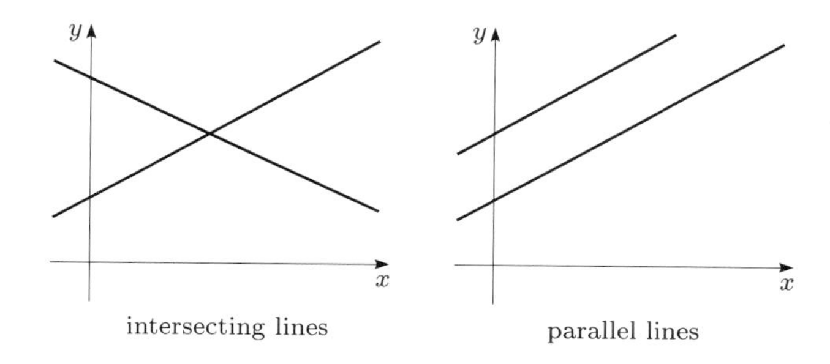


intersecting lines parallel lines

We deal with this question by considering some examples. Given the equations of two lines, it is often useful to sketch the lines, since this will not only show whether the lines do intersect, but it will give us some idea of the location of any point of intersection. Then, since the coordinates of the point of intersection must satisfy the equations of both lines, we can find these coordinates by solving the two equations as simultaneous equations in $x$ and $y$.

**Example 1.2** Determine whether the following pairs of lines intersect each other at a single point, are parallel, or coincide. If the lines intersect at a single point, find its coordinates.

(a) $y = x + 1$ and $y = 3x - 1$.

(b) $y = 2x - 2$ and $y = 2x + 1$.

(c) $y = \frac{1}{2}x - 2$ and $2y = x - 4$.

**Solution**

(a) These lines have gradients 1 and 3, and $y$-intercepts 1 and $-1$, respectively; this enables us to sketch the lines, as shown in the margin. Clearly the lines intersect, at some point in the right half-plane.

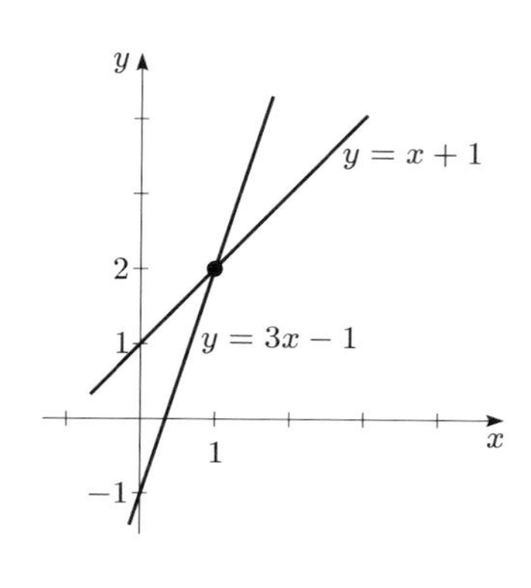


At the point of intersection,

$$y = x + 1 \quad \text{and} \quad y = 3x - 1;$$

thus $x + 1 = 3x - 1$, from which we deduce that $x = 1$.

Substituting this value of $x$ into either equation gives $y = 2$. So the point of intersection of the two lines is $(1, 2)$. (You can always check your solution of simultaneous equations by substituting your answer back into the original equations.)

(b) These lines both have gradient 2, and their $y$-intercepts are $-2$ and 1, respectively. We can thus sketch the lines, as shown in the margin.

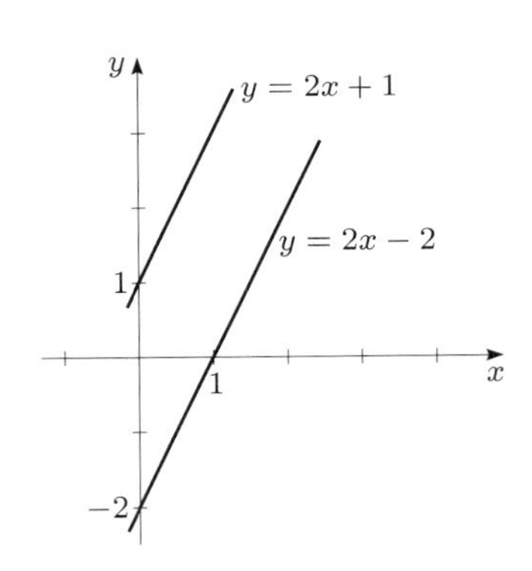


Since the lines have equal gradient and their $y$-intercepts are different, they are parallel and so do not intersect. (If we try to solve the equations $y = 2x - 2$, $y = 2x + 1$ as a pair of simultaneous equations, we are led to the contradiction that $-2 = 1$. Thus there can be no point $(x, y)$ that lies on both lines.)

(c) At first glance these two equations may appear to be different. However, if the second equation is divided throughout by 2 (which leaves unchanged the actual line that it represents), we obtain the first equation. So the two equations are equivalent: they represent the same line. (In a sense, the two lines intersect at each of their points.)

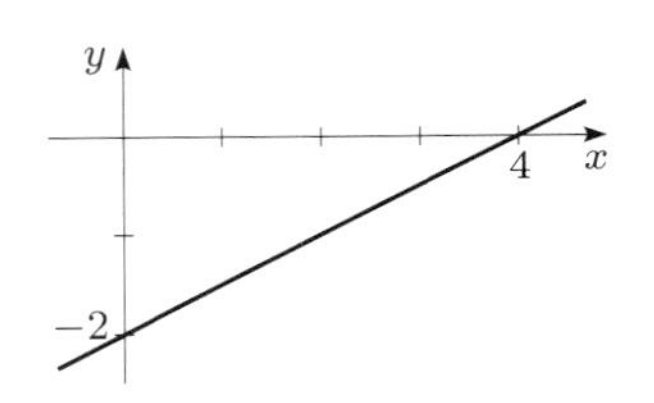


The line has gradient $\frac{1}{2}$ and $y$-intercept $-2$, so we can sketch it as shown in the margin. (Two lines coincide if the equation of one can be rearranged to be a multiple of the equation of the other.) ■

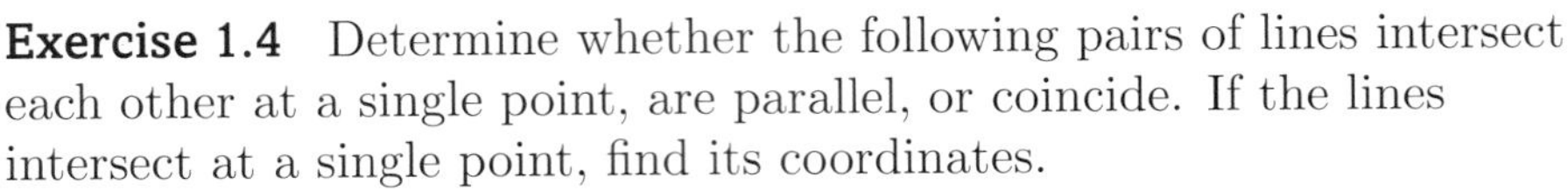

**Exercise 1.4** Determine whether the following pairs of lines intersect each other at a single point, are parallel, or coincide. If the lines intersect at a single point, find its coordinates.

(a) $y = \frac{1}{2}x + 1$ and $y = 2x - 1$. (b) $y = 2x - 1$ and $y = 2x + \frac{1}{2}$.

(c) $4y = 2x + 6$ and $6y = 3x + 9$. (d) $y = 7x - 1$ and $y = -x$.

## Distance between two points in the plane

Next, we find the formula for the distance between two points $P(x_1, y_1)$ and $Q(x_2, y_2)$ in the plane. In the diagram in the margin we have drawn $P$ and $Q$ in the first quadrant, but the formula we derive holds wherever the points are in the plane.

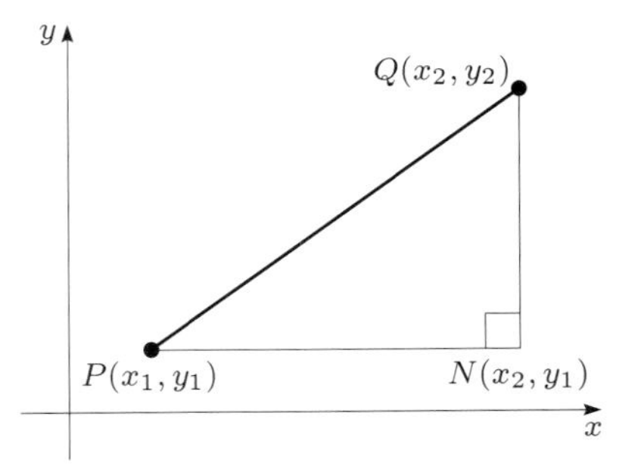


We can construct a right-angled triangle $PNQ$ as shown; the line $PN$ is parallel to the $x$-axis, the line $QN$ is parallel to the $y$-axis, the angle $PNQ$ is a right angle, and $PQ$ is the hypotenuse of the triangle.

The length of $PN$ is $|x_2 - x_1|$ and the length of $QN$ is $|y_2 - y_1|$. It follows from Pythagoras' Theorem that

For any real number $x$,
$$|x| = \begin{cases} x, & \text{if } x \geq 0, \\ -x, & \text{if } x < 0. \end{cases}$$

$$PQ^2 = PN^2 + QN^2,$$

so $PQ = \sqrt{(x_2 - x_1)^2 + (y_2 - y_1)^2}$.

**Distance Formula in $\mathbb{R}^2$** The distance between two points $(x_1, y_1)$ and $(x_2, y_2)$ in the plane is

$$\sqrt{(x_2 - x_1)^2 + (y_2 - y_1)^2}.$$

For example, it follows from the formula above that the distance between the points $(1, 2)$ and $(3, -4)$ is

$$\sqrt{(3-1)^2 + (-4-2)^2} = \sqrt{2^2 + 6^2} = \sqrt{40} = 2\sqrt{10}.$$

**Exercise 1.5** Find the distance between each of the following pairs of points in the plane.

(a) $(0, 0)$ and $(5, 0)$. (b) $(0, 0)$ and $(3, 4)$.

(c) $(1, 2)$ and $(5, 1)$. (d) $(3, -8)$ and $(-1, 4)$.

## 1.2 Points, planes, lines and distances in $\mathbb{R}^3$

We now study three-dimensional space, $\mathbb{R}^3$. This is a space with which you are familiar, of course, as 'the real world' is a three-dimensional space.

We define a coordinate system in three-dimensional space via three mutually perpendicular axes.

*Mutually perpendicular* means that any two of the axes are at right angles to each other.

First, we choose a point $O$ as the origin, and then we choose an $x$-axis and a $y$-axis at right angles to each other, as described earlier.

Next, we draw a third line through the origin, perpendicular both to the $x$-axis and to the $y$-axis; this line is called the $z$-axis. We choose the positive direction of the $z$-axis such that the $x$-, $y$- and $z$-axes form a so-called *right-handed system of axes*. This means that if you hold the thumb and first and second fingers of your right hand at right angles to each other, and label them $x$, $y$ and $z$ (in that order), you can turn your hand in such a way that your fingers point in the positive directions of the corresponding axes.

Finally, we choose a unit of distance along each axis.

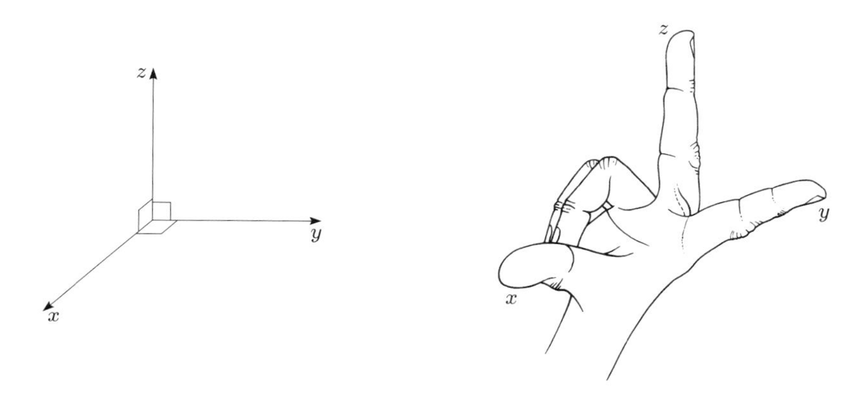


We have seen already that there is a one-one correspondence between the points of the plane and the ordered pairs $(a, b)$ of real numbers. Similarly, there is a one-one correspondence between the points of three-dimensional space and the ordered triples $(a, b, c)$ of real numbers. The point with coordinates $(a, b, c)$ is reached from the origin by moving a distance $a$ in the direction of the $x$-axis, a distance $b$ in the direction of the $y$-axis, and a distance $c$ in the direction of the $z$-axis.

For instance, the points with coordinates $(1, 2, 3)$ and $(1, -2, -3)$ are as shown in the diagram below.

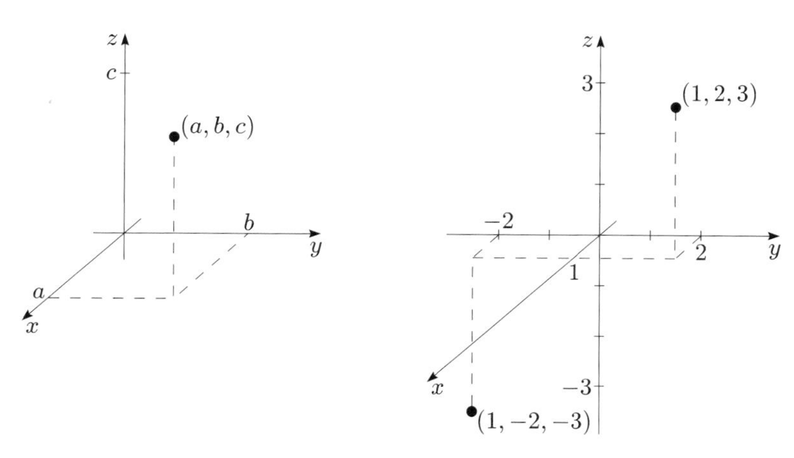

It may help you to visualise axes and coordinates in three dimensions by thinking of the corner of a room, with the $x$- and $y$-axes along the foot of the two walls, and the $z$-axis along the vertical join of the walls. To become familiar with this notation, choose axes as above for the room you are in, and determine the approximate coordinates of the corners of the room (using appropriate units of distance).

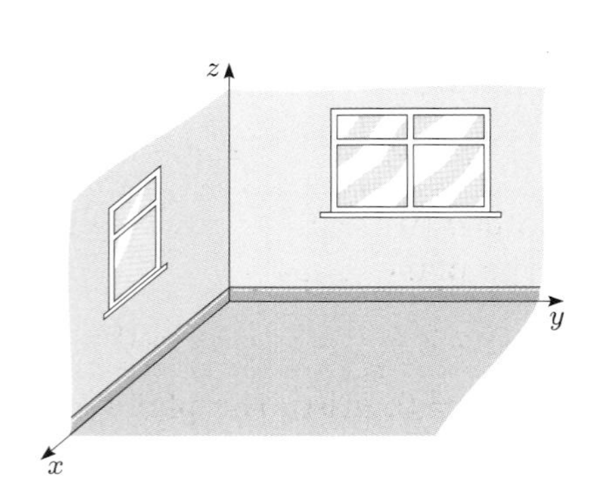


**Exercise 1.6** On a single diagram, sketch the $x$-, $y$- and $z$-axes and the points with coordinates $(-1, 2, -1)$ and $(0, 1, 2)$.

In view of the one-one correspondence between points in three-dimensional space and ordered triples of real numbers, often we do not distinguish between the points and their representation as ordered triples; thus we simply write $(a, b, c)$ to denote the point represented by this triple.

We call three-dimensional space, together with an origin and a set of $x$-, $y$- and $z$-axes, *three-dimensional Euclidean space.*

## Planes in $\mathbb{R}^3$

We now look at the general form of the equation of a plane in $\mathbb{R}^3$.

Three planes whose equations are easy to find are those that contain a pair of axes. For example, the $(x, y)$-plane is the plane that contains the $x$-axis and the $y$-axis. Points which lie in this plane are precisely those points $(x, y, z)$ in $\mathbb{R}^3$ for which $z = 0$, so the equation of the $(x, y)$-plane is

$$z = 0.$$

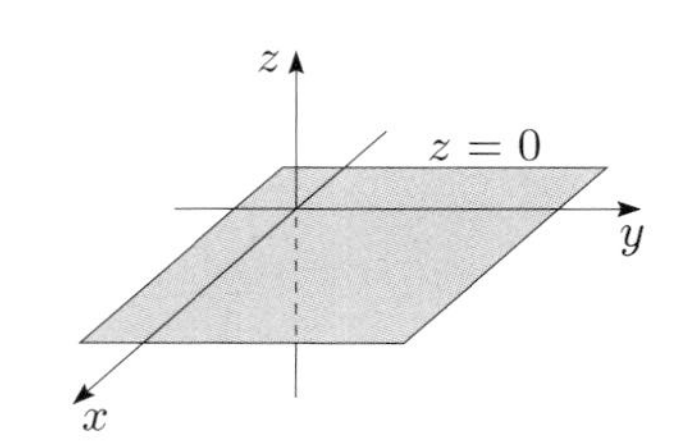


**Exercise 1.7** Find the equations of the $(y, z)$-plane and the $(x, z)$-plane.

**Exercise 1.8** Sketch the planes whose equations are as follows.

(a) $z = 2$ (b) $y = -1$

You have seen that the general form of the equation of a line in $\mathbb{R}^2$ is $ax + by = c$, where $a$, $b$ and $c$ are real, and $a$ and $b$ are not both zero. In $\mathbb{R}^3$ the analogue of this equation is the equation of a plane.

Subsection 1.1

We have already met the planes with equations $x = 0$, $y = 0$ and $z = 0$. Each of these equations is a special case of a more general equation

$$ax + by + cz = d,$$

where $a$, $b$, $c$ and $d$ are real, and $a$, $b$ and $c$ are not all zero. In fact, the equation of any plane in $\mathbb{R}^3$ is of this form.

**Equation of a plane** The general equation of a plane in $\mathbb{R}^3$ is

$$ax + by + cz = d,$$

where $a$, $b$, $c$ and $d$ are real, and $a$, $b$ and $c$ are not all zero.

We shall prove this in Subsection 3.2.

**Example 1.3** Determine the general form of the equation of a plane that passes through the origin.

**Solution** Let the plane have equation

$$ax + by + cz = d.$$

Since $(0, 0, 0)$ lies in the plane, its coordinates must satisfy the equation of the plane; thus

$$a \times 0 + b \times 0 + c \times 0 = d,$$

so $d = 0$. Also, the plane whose equation is

$$ax + by + cz = 0$$

clearly passes through the origin $(0, 0, 0)$.

Hence the general form of the equation of a plane that passes through the origin is

$$ax + by + cz = 0,$$

where $a$, $b$ and $c$ are real and not all zero. ■

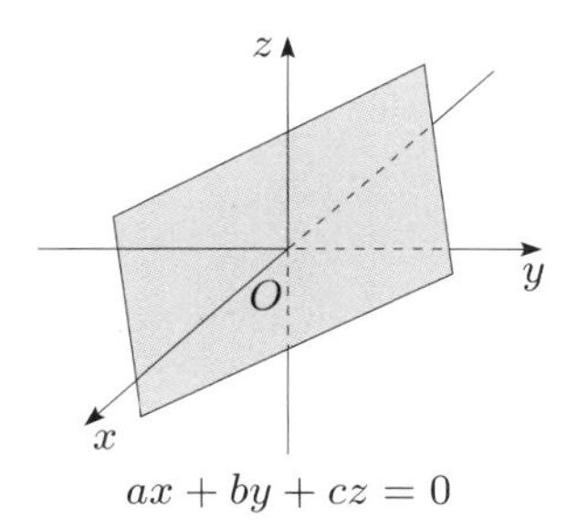

$ax + by + cz = 0$

The $(x, y)$-, $(y, z)$- and $(x, z)$-planes all pass through the origin, and their equations are all of this form.

**Exercise 1.9** For each of the following points, determine the general form of the equation of a plane that passes through the point.

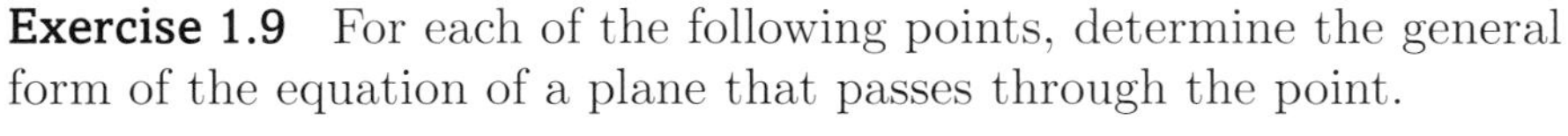
(a) $(1, 2, 3)$ (b) $(-1, -4, 2)$

## Intersection of two planes

We saw earlier that two arbitrary lines in $\mathbb{R}^2$ may intersect, be parallel, or coincide. In an analogous way, two arbitrary planes in $\mathbb{R}^3$ may intersect, be parallel, or coincide.

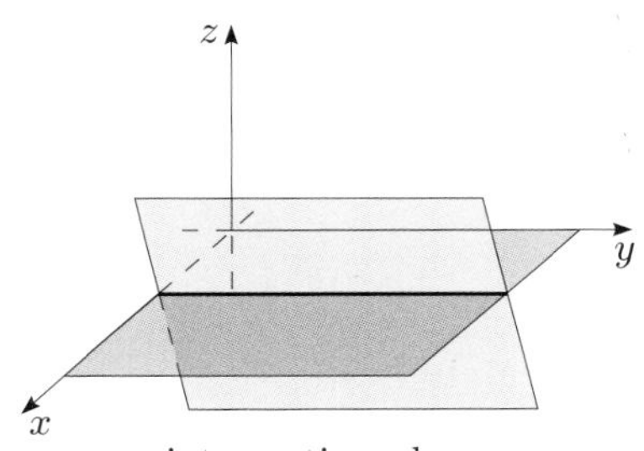

intersecting planes

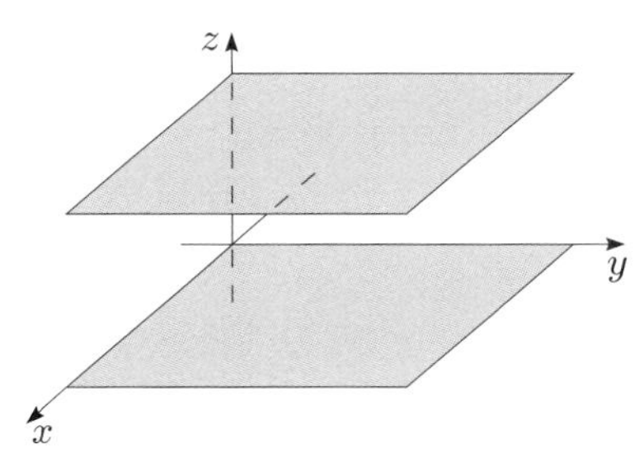

parallel planes

In general, if two distinct planes intersect, then the set of common points is a line that lies in both planes.

For example, the $(x, y)$-plane and the $(x, z)$-plane intersect in the $x$-axis, which lies in both planes.

Similarly, the planes $x - y = 0$ and $x + y + z = 1$ intersect in a line; the points $(x, y, z)$ on this line all satisfy both of the equations

$$x - y = 0 \quad \text{and} \quad x + y + z = 1.$$

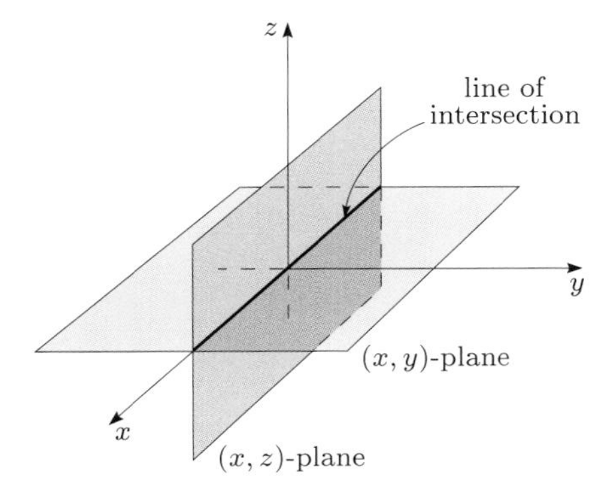


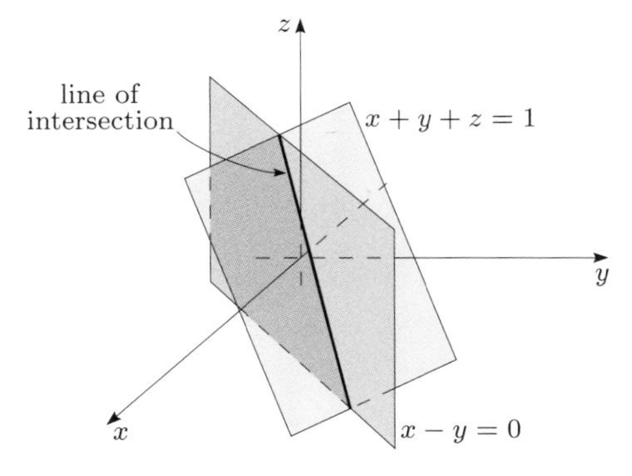

Two planes in $\mathbb{R}^3$ may be parallel, and so cannot intersect. For example, the plane with equation $z = 0$ is the $(x, y)$-plane, and the plane with equation $z = 1$ is a plane parallel to the $(x, y)$-plane, passing through the point $(0, 0, 1)$ on the $z$-axis. These two planes do not intersect; every point in the plane $z = 1$ lies at distance 1 above the plane $z = 0$.

Finally, two planes may coincide. For example, the planes with equations

$$2x - 4y + 6z = 1 \quad \text{and} \quad -x + 2y - 3z = -\tfrac{1}{2}$$

coincide, since the second equation is simply the first multiplied by the number $-\frac{1}{2}$.

In general, two planes are coincident if the equation of one can be rearranged to be a multiple of the equation of the other.

**Exercise 1.10** Determine whether the planes with equations $z = 2$ and $y = -1$ intersect, are parallel, or coincide. Illustrate your answer with a sketch.

Hint: You have already sketched these two planes in Exercise 1.8.

We shall return to a discussion of the intersection of planes in $\mathbb{R}^3$ later in the block.

Unit LA2

## Distance between points in $\mathbb{R}^3$

You saw earlier that the distance between two points $(x_1, y_1)$ and $(x_2, y_2)$ in the plane is given by

Subsection 1.1

$$\sqrt{(x_2 - x_1)^2 + (y_2 - y_1)^2}.$$

We can establish a similar formula for the distance between two points in $\mathbb{R}^3$, as follows.

Let $P(x_1, y_1, z_1)$ and $Q(x_2, y_2, z_2)$ be two points in $\mathbb{R}^3$. Let $M$ be the foot of the perpendicular from $Q$ to the plane through $P$ that is parallel to the $(x, y)$-plane; then $M$ has coordinates $(x_2, y_2, z_1)$. Next, let $N$ be the point in this plane with coordinates $(x_1, y_2, z_1)$.

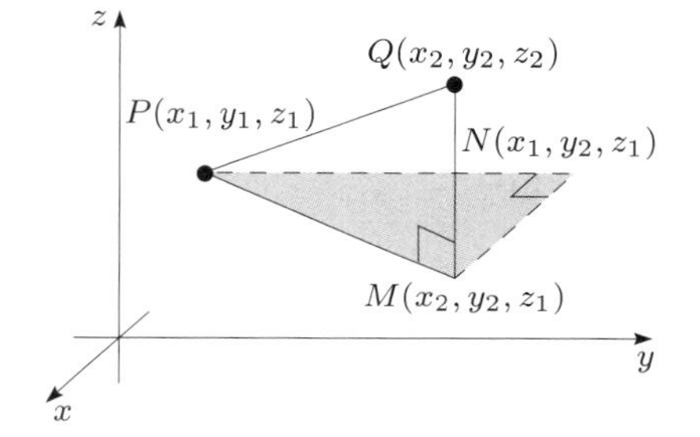


Then the triangles $PQM$ and $PMN$ are both right-angled triangles, with right angles at $M$ and $N$, respectively, as shown in the margin.

The length of $PN$ is $|y_2 - y_1|$, the length of $NM$ is $|x_2 - x_1|$, and the length of $MQ$ is $|z_2 - z_1|$. It follows from Pythagoras' Theorem that

$$PM^2 = NM^2 + PN^2,$$

so

$$PM^2 = (x_2 - x_1)^2 + (y_2 - y_1)^2.$$

This part of the discussion is similar to the derivation of the Distance Formula in $\mathbb{R}^2$ (see page 10).

Using Pythagoras' Theorem again, we obtain

$$PQ^2 = PM^2 + MQ^2,$$

so

$$PQ^2 = (x_2 - x_1)^2 + (y_2 - y_1)^2 + (z_2 - z_1)^2,$$

that is,

$$PQ = \sqrt{(x_2 - x_1)^2 + (y_2 - y_1)^2 + (z_2 - z_1)^2}.$$

**Distance Formula in $\mathbb{R}^3$** The distance between two points $(x_1, y_1, z_1)$ and $(x_2, y_2, z_2)$ in $\mathbb{R}^3$ is

$$\sqrt{(x_2 - x_1)^2 + (y_2 - y_1)^2 + (z_2 - z_1)^2}.$$

For example, it follows from this formula that the distance between the points $(1, 2, 3)$ and $(4, -2, 15)$ is

$$\sqrt{(4-1)^2 + (-2-2)^2 + (15-3)^2} = \sqrt{169} = 13.$$

**Exercise 1.11** For each of the following pairs of points in $\mathbb{R}^3$, find the distance between them.

(a) $(1, 1, 1)$ and $(4, 1, -3)$.

(b) $(1, 2, 3)$ and $(3, 0, 3)$.

# Further exercises

**Exercise 1.12** Determine the equation of the line through each of the following pairs of points. Show that both equations can be written in the form $ax + by = c$, for some real numbers $a$, $b$ and $c$, where $a$ and $b$ are not both zero.

(a) $(-2, -4)$ and $(1, 6)$.

(b) $(0, 0)$ and $(7, 3)$.

**Exercise 1.13** Determine the values of $k$ for which the lines

$$3x + 4y + 7 = 0 \quad \text{and} \quad 2x + ky = 3$$

are (a) parallel, (b) perpendicular.

**Exercise 1.14** Sketch the lines with the following equations, on a single diagram:

$$y = -3x, \quad y = \tfrac{1}{3}x + 2, \quad y - 3 = 3(x - 3).$$

**Exercise 1.15** Determine the coordinates of the points of intersection of the lines in Exercise 1.14.

**Exercise 1.16** Find the distances between the vertices of the triangle formed by the points of intersection found in Exercise 1.15.

**Exercise 1.17** Determine whether each of the pairs of planes given by the following equations intersect, are parallel, or coincide.

(a) $x = 1$ and $y = 2$.

(b) $z = 1$ and $z = 3$.

Illustrate your answer to each part with a sketch.

**Exercise 1.18** Determine the distance between the points $(1, -2, 3)$ and $(-2, 3, -1)$ in $\mathbb{R}^3$.

# 2 Vectors

After working through this section, you should be able to:

(a) explain what are meant by a *vector*, a *scalar multiple* of a vector, and the *sum* and *difference* of two vectors;

(b) represent vectors in $\mathbb{R}^2$ and $\mathbb{R}^3$ in terms of their *components*, and use components in vector arithmetic;

(c) use the Section Formula for the position vector of a point dividing a line segment in a given ratio;

(d) determine the equation of a line in $\mathbb{R}^2$ or $\mathbb{R}^3$ in terms of vectors.

## 2.1 Definitions

In this section we introduce an alternative way of describing points in the plane $\mathbb{R}^2$ or in three-dimensional space $\mathbb{R}^3$; namely, by using vectors.

You meet vectors such as velocity and acceleration in everyday life; these have in common the fact that to specify each fully, we must give both its size and also its direction. For example, if you are driving along a road, then you are interested both in how fast your car is moving (that is, its speed) and also in what direction. Physical quantities that are uniquely determined only if we know both their size and their direction are called *vectors*. We shall use the term *magnitude* for the size of the physical quantity represented.

For example, a velocity of $50\,\mathrm{km\,h^{-1}}$ north-east differs from a velocity of $90\,\mathrm{km\,h^{-1}}$ north-east, and both of these differ from a velocity of $50\,\mathrm{km\,h^{-1}}$ south-west.

By contrast, some physical quantities (such as temperature and volume) have only a magnitude—they have no direction associated with them. We call such quantities *scalars*.

> **Definitions** A **vector** is a quantity that is determined by its magnitude and direction. A **scalar** is a quantity that is determined by its magnitude.

We can *represent* a vector geometrically by a line segment in $\mathbb{R}^2$ or in $\mathbb{R}^3$. The length of the line segment is a measure of the magnitude of the vector, and the direction of the line is the same as the direction of the vector; we indicate the direction of the line with an arrow, as shown in the margin. A vector represented by a line segment from $A$ to $B$ is often written as $\overrightarrow{AB}$; the magnitude of the vector is proportional to the distance between $A$ and $B$, and the arrow indicates the direction of the vector.

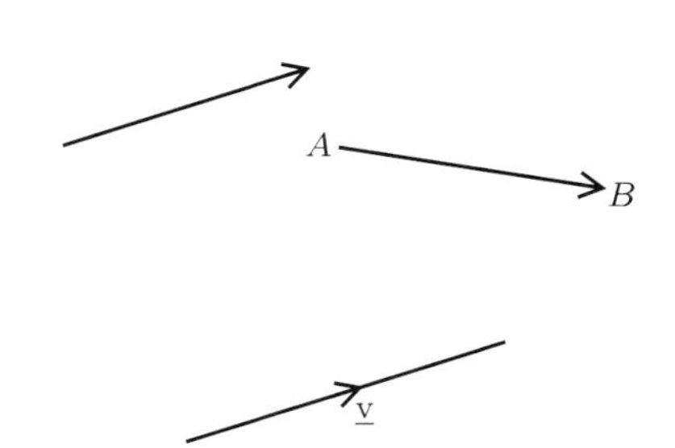


Often we use single letters, such as $\mathbf{a}$, $\mathbf{b}$, $\mathbf{p}$, $\mathbf{q}$ or $\mathbf{v}$, to denote vectors. Vectors are usually distinguished in print by the use of a bold typeface, or in hand-written work by underlining the letters (for example, $\underline{\mathrm{v}}$). This is a useful convention, as it reminds us that they are vector quantities.

We use two pairs of vertical lines to denote the magnitude of a vector; thus we denote the length of a vector $\mathbf{v}$ by the symbol $\|\mathbf{v}\|$.

There is just one vector which does not fit conveniently into the above definition; namely, the zero vector. This arises quite naturally, however.

For, just as we can imagine a car travelling at 50 km/h NE, it makes sense to say that a car is stationary; in this case, the magnitude of the velocity of the car is zero, but we can assign any direction that we please to its velocity.

We abbreviate north-east to NE, and so on.

**Definition** The **zero vector** is the vector whose magnitude is zero, and whose direction is arbitrary. It is denoted by the symbol $\mathbf{0}$.

In order to gain a feeling for how we should build up an arithmetic for vectors that agrees with our intuition, we shall now look at some geometric examples of vectors in the plane.

For convenience, we shall use compass bearings to describe the directions of the vectors.

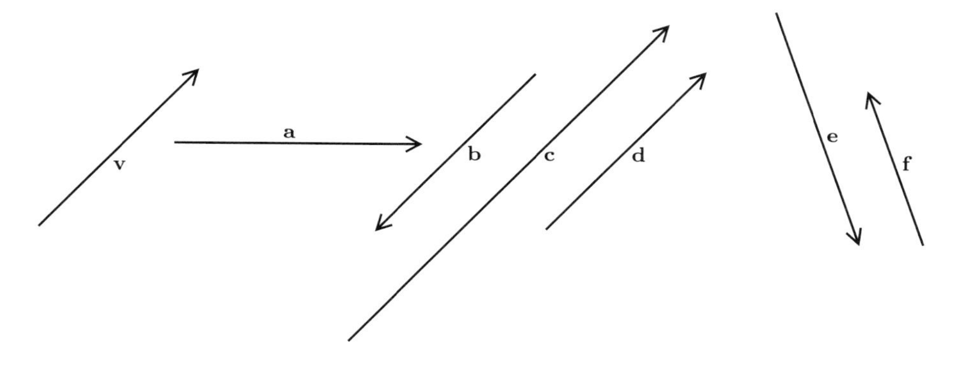


In the diagram above, $\mathbf{v}$ is the vector 3 cm NE. This vector is different from the vectors $\mathbf{a}$, $\mathbf{b}$, $\mathbf{e}$ and $\mathbf{f}$ as its direction differs from their directions. Also, $\mathbf{v}$ is a different vector from $\mathbf{c}$ although it has the same direction as $\mathbf{c}$, since its magnitude is different from that of $\mathbf{c}$. However, $\mathbf{v}$ and $\mathbf{d}$ are the same vector, since they have the same magnitude and direction.

The geometric representations of equal vectors do not need to start at the same point and finish at the same point. They need only be the same length and in the same direction.

**Definition** Two vectors $\mathbf{a}$ and $\mathbf{b}$ are **equal** if

they have the same magnitude ($\|\mathbf{a}\| = \|\mathbf{b}\|$)

and

they are in the same direction.

We write $\mathbf{a} = \mathbf{b}$.

Now, although the vectors $\mathbf{v}$ and $\mathbf{b}$ are unequal, they are closely related: they have the same magnitude (3 cm), and their directions are exactly the opposite of each other (NE and SW). We say that $\mathbf{b}$ is 'minus $\mathbf{v}$', and write this as $\mathbf{b} = -\mathbf{v}$. If we write $\mathbf{v}$ in terms of a line segment $AB$ in the form $\overrightarrow{AB}$, then $-\mathbf{v}$ can be expressed as $\overrightarrow{BA}$.

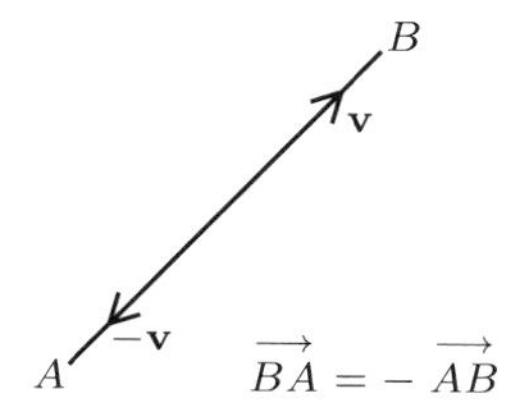


**Definition** The **negative** of a vector $\mathbf{v}$ is the vector with the same magnitude as $\mathbf{v}$, but the opposite direction. It is denoted by $-\mathbf{v}$.

## Multiplication by a scalar

In the collection of vectors sketched above, although $\mathbf{v}$ is not equal to $\mathbf{c}$, the vectors $\mathbf{v}$ and $\mathbf{c}$ are closely related: $\mathbf{c}$ is a vector in the same direction as $\mathbf{v}$, but it is twice as long as $\mathbf{v}$. Thus it is natural to write $2\mathbf{v}$ for $\mathbf{c}$, since we can think of a journey represented by $\mathbf{c}$ as being a journey $\mathbf{v}$ followed by a second journey $\mathbf{v}$.

In an analogous way, we can write $-\frac{3}{2}\mathbf{f}$ for $\mathbf{e}$, the vector whose magnitude is $\frac{3}{2}$ times that of $\mathbf{f}$ and whose direction is that of $-\mathbf{f}$.

> **Scalar multiple of a vector** Let $k$ be a scalar and $\mathbf{v}$ a vector. Then $k\mathbf{v}$ is the vector whose magnitude is $|k|$ times the magnitude of $\mathbf{v}$, that is, $\|k\mathbf{v}\| = |k|\,\|\mathbf{v}\|$, and whose direction is
>
> the direction of $\mathbf{v}$ if $k > 0$,
>
> the direction of $-\mathbf{v}$ if $k < 0$.
>
> If $k = 0$, then $k\mathbf{v} = \mathbf{0}$.

**Exercise 2.1** For each of the vectors shown below, decide whether it is a multiple of any of the other vectors; if it is, write down an equation of the form $\mathbf{v}_1 = k\mathbf{v}_2$ that specifies the relationship between them.

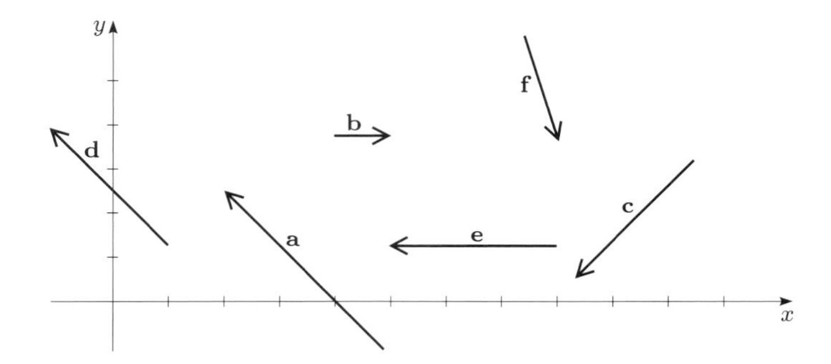


**Exercise 2.2** For the vector $\mathbf{d}$ in Exercise 2.1, sketch $3\mathbf{d}$ and $-2\mathbf{d}$.

## Addition of vectors

We saw above that the vector $2\mathbf{v}$ can be regarded as the vector $\mathbf{v}$ 'followed by' the vector $\mathbf{v}$; we can also quite naturally describe this vector as being the 'sum', $\mathbf{v} + \mathbf{v}$, of the vector with itself.

Analogously, if $\mathbf{p}$ is the vector 2 cm E and $\mathbf{q}$ is the vector 3 cm NE, we can think of the 'sum' $\mathbf{p} + \mathbf{q}$ of the vectors as follows. Starting from a given point, $O$ say, draw the vector $\mathbf{p}$; starting from its finishing point, draw the vector $\mathbf{q}$. Then if the final point reached is $S$, $\mathbf{p} + \mathbf{q}$ is the vector $\overrightarrow{OS}$.

> **Triangle Law for addition of vectors** The sum $\mathbf{p} + \mathbf{q}$ of two vectors $\mathbf{p}$ and $\mathbf{q}$ is obtained as follows.
>
> 1. Starting at any point, draw the vector $\mathbf{p}$.
> 2. Starting from the finishing point of the vector $\mathbf{p}$, draw the vector $\mathbf{q}$.
>
> Then the sum $\mathbf{p} + \mathbf{q}$ is the vector from the starting point of $\mathbf{p}$ to the finishing point of $\mathbf{q}$.

There is an equivalent way of visualising the sum of vectors geometrically. Instead of following $\mathbf{p}$ with $\mathbf{q}$ to find the third side of a triangle, as above, we obtain exactly the same vector if we draw $\mathbf{p}$ and $\mathbf{q}$ with the same starting point, complete the parallelogram of which these are adjacent sides, and take the diagonal of the parallelogram from the common starting point (see the following diagram).

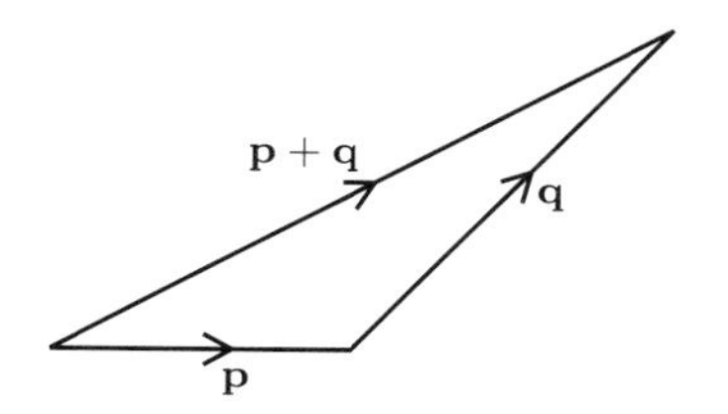

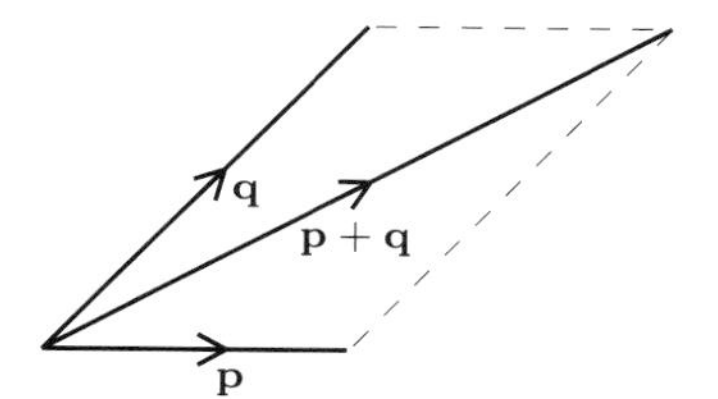


**Parallelogram Law for addition of vectors** The sum $\mathbf{p}+\mathbf{q}$ of two vectors $\mathbf{p}$ and $\mathbf{q}$ is obtained as follows.

1. Starting at the same point, draw the vectors $\mathbf{p}$ and $\mathbf{q}$.
2. Complete the parallelogram of which these are adjacent sides.

Then the sum $\mathbf{p}+\mathbf{q}$ is the vector from the starting point of $\mathbf{p}$ and $\mathbf{q}$ to the opposite corner of the parallelogram.

The order in which we add vectors does not matter: the sum $\mathbf{q}+\mathbf{p}$ is precisely the same vector as the sum $\mathbf{p}+\mathbf{q}$. It turns out also that the sums $(\mathbf{p}+\mathbf{q})+\mathbf{r}$ and $\mathbf{p}+(\mathbf{q}+\mathbf{r})$ are equal. Thus addition of vectors is commutative and associative.

We omit the proof.

Finally, we can define subtraction of vectors in terms of addition and scalar multiplication. For example, if $\mathbf{p}$ and $\mathbf{q}$ are the vectors 3.8 cm E and 2.4 cm NE, respectively, then $-\mathbf{q}$ is the vector 2.4 cm SW, and we define the difference $\mathbf{p}-\mathbf{q}$ to be the vector obtained by drawing first $\mathbf{p}$ and then $-\mathbf{q}$.

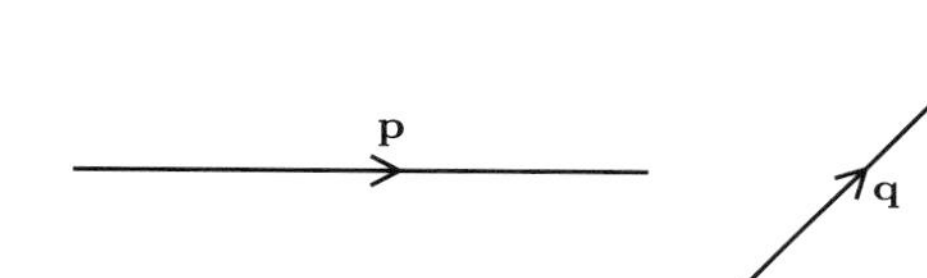

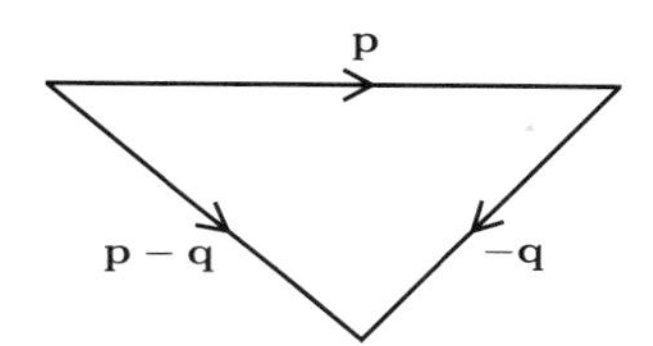


**Definition** The **difference**, $\mathbf{p}-\mathbf{q}$, of two vectors $\mathbf{p}$ and $\mathbf{q}$ is

$$\mathbf{p}-\mathbf{q}=\mathbf{p}+(-\mathbf{q}).$$

In general, $\mathbf{q}-\mathbf{p}$ does not equal $\mathbf{p}-\mathbf{q}$; in fact, as you would expect,

$$\mathbf{q}-\mathbf{p}=-(\mathbf{p}-\mathbf{q}).$$

Since the vector $-\mathbf{q}$ has the same magnitude as $\mathbf{q}$ but the opposite direction, we can draw $\mathbf{p}-\mathbf{q}$ by using either of the two constructions which we use for adding vectors.

**Exercise 2.3** For the vectors $\mathbf{p}$ and $\mathbf{q}$ shown in the margin, sketch $\mathbf{p}+\mathbf{q}$, $\mathbf{p}-\mathbf{q}$ and $2\mathbf{p}+\frac{1}{2}\mathbf{q}$.

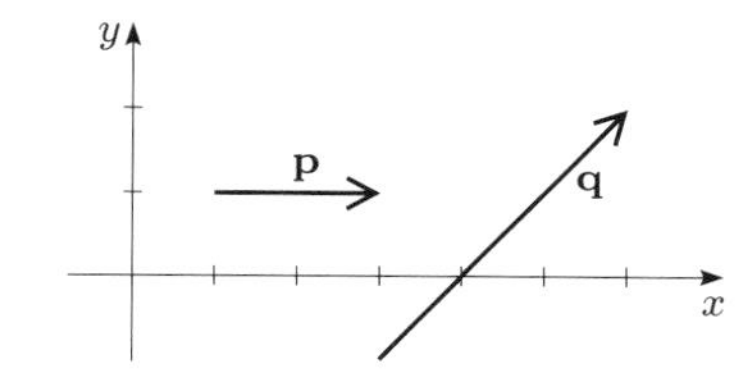


## 2.2 Components and the arithmetic of vectors

We introduce now a different method of representing vectors, which will make the manipulation of vectors much easier. Thus we shall avoid having to solve problems involving vectors by drawing the vectors and making measurements, which is very time-consuming and never very accurate.

We can think of a vector as a translation, that is, as representing a movement by a certain amount in a given direction. Then we can use the Cartesian axes in the plane or in $\mathbb{R}^3$ to describe the translation.

For example, consider the vector $\mathbf{v}$, in $\mathbb{R}^2$, shown below. In view of the Triangle Law for adding vectors, we can think of $\mathbf{v}$ as the sum of two vectors, one of magnitude 3 units in the direction of the positive $x$-axis and one of magnitude 4 units in the direction of the positive $y$-axis.

In this sense, we can associate the ordered pair of real numbers $(3, 4)$ with the vector $\mathbf{v}$.

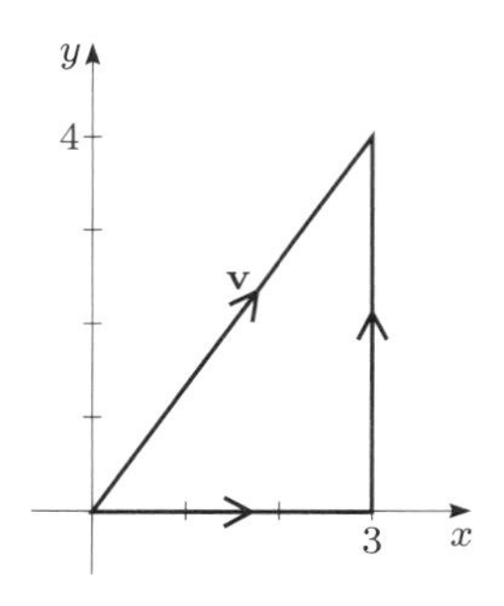


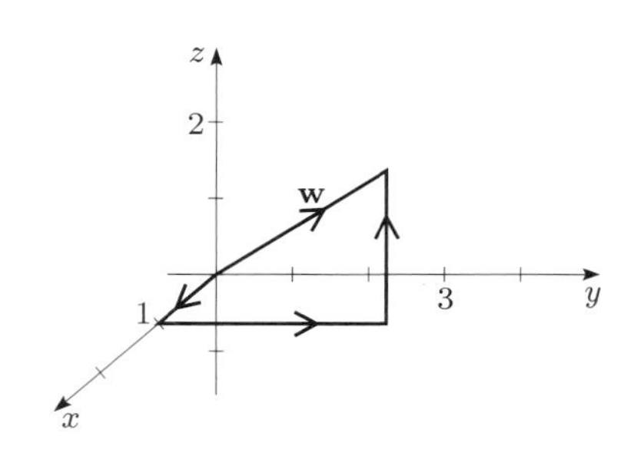


Similarly, in $\mathbb{R}^3$, the vector $\mathbf{w}$ shown above can be considered as the sum of three vectors, one of magnitude 1 in the direction of the positive $x$-axis, one of magnitude 3 in the direction of the positive $y$-axis, and one of magnitude 2 in the direction of the positive $z$-axis.

So we can associate the ordered triple of real numbers $(1, 3, 2)$ with the vector $\mathbf{w}$.

Thus we can express a vector in $\mathbb{R}^2$ in terms of multiples of *unit vectors* in the directions of the $x$- and $y$-axes, and a vector in $\mathbb{R}^3$ in terms of multiples of unit vectors in the directions of the $x$-, $y$- and $z$-axes. This expression of a vector as a sum of vectors in standard directions is called *decomposition of the vector into components*.

A **unit vector** is a vector of magnitude 1 unit.

This representation of a vector in terms of components will be useful in Section 3.

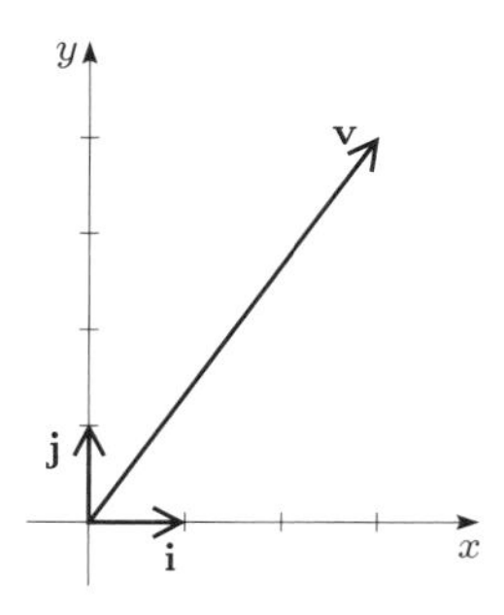


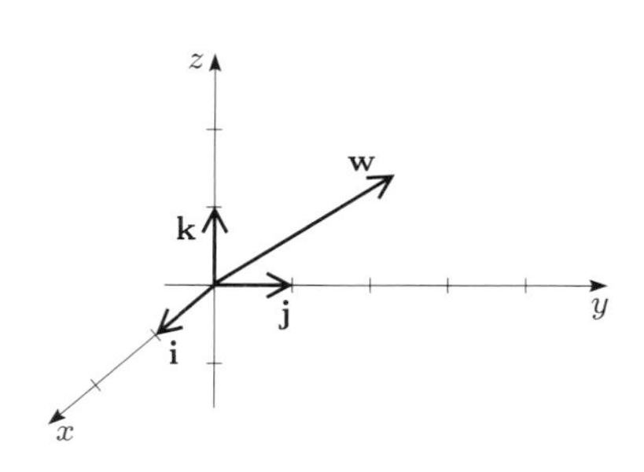


**Definitions** In $\mathbb{R}^2$, the vectors $\mathbf{i}$ and $\mathbf{j}$ are unit vectors in the positive directions of the $x$- and $y$-axes, respectively. Any vector $\mathbf{p}$ in $\mathbb{R}^2$ can be expressed as a sum of the form

$$\mathbf{p} = a_1\mathbf{i} + a_2\mathbf{j}, \quad \text{for some real numbers } a_1, a_2;$$

often we write $\mathbf{p} = (a_1, a_2)$, for brevity. The numbers $a_1$ and $a_2$ are the **components** of $\mathbf{p}$ in the $x$- and $y$-directions, respectively.

Thus we can express the above vector $\mathbf{v}$ as $3\mathbf{i} + 4\mathbf{j}$, or simply as $(3, 4)$.

In $\mathbb{R}^3$, the vectors $\mathbf{i}$, $\mathbf{j}$ and $\mathbf{k}$ are unit vectors in the positive directions of the $x$-, $y$- and $z$-axes, respectively. Any vector $\mathbf{p}$ in $\mathbb{R}^3$ can be expressed as a sum of the form

$$\mathbf{p} = a_1\mathbf{i} + a_2\mathbf{j} + a_3\mathbf{k}, \quad \text{for some real numbers } a_1, a_2, a_3;$$

often we write $\mathbf{p} = (a_1, a_2, a_3)$, for brevity. The numbers $a_1$, $a_2$ and $a_3$ are the **components** of $\mathbf{p}$ in the $x$-, $y$- and $z$-directions, respectively.

Thus we can express the above vector $\mathbf{w}$ as $\mathbf{i} + 3\mathbf{j} + 2\mathbf{k}$, or simply as $(1, 3, 2)$.

It is important to remember that the above expression of a vector as an ordered pair or an ordered triple of real numbers simply describes the components of the corresponding translation; it does not mean that we are identifying the vector with the point whose Cartesian coordinates are that pair or triple.

**Exercise 2.4** Sketch the following vectors in $\mathbb{R}^2$ on a single diagram:

$$2\mathbf{i} - 3\mathbf{j}, \quad -3\mathbf{i} + 4\mathbf{j}, \quad -2\mathbf{i} - 2\mathbf{j}.$$

In the above discussion we expressed vectors in $\mathbb{R}^2$ and in $\mathbb{R}^3$ in terms of components relative to unit vectors that are mutually perpendicular. In general, however, we do not need to restrict ourselves in this way. In fact, we can express a vector in $\mathbb{R}^2$ in terms of *any* two vectors that are not parallel (that is, whose directions are not the same or exactly opposite), and a vector in $\mathbb{R}^3$ in terms of *any* three non-coplanar vectors. These ideas will be the cornerstone of our work in the subsequent units of this block.

A set of vectors in $\mathbb{R}^3$ is *coplanar* if there is some plane in $\mathbb{R}^3$ that contains all the vectors of the set.

Now that we can describe vectors in terms of their components, we return to the operations on vectors which we described geometrically in Subsection 2.1, in order to describe the same operations in terms of components.

The following observations follow immediately from the definition of components.

> **Definitions**
>
> Two vectors, both in $\mathbb{R}^2$ or both in $\mathbb{R}^3$, are **equal** if and only if their corresponding components are equal.
>
> The **zero vector** in $\mathbb{R}^2$ is $\mathbf{0} = 0\mathbf{i} + 0\mathbf{j} = (0, 0)$, and the zero vector in $\mathbb{R}^3$ is $\mathbf{0} = 0\mathbf{i} + 0\mathbf{j} + 0\mathbf{k} = (0, 0, 0)$.

We have described addition of vectors already. To add two vectors $\mathbf{p}$ and $\mathbf{q}$ using the Triangle Law, we first draw the vector $\mathbf{p}$; then, starting from the finishing point of $\mathbf{p}$, we draw the vector $\mathbf{q}$. The sum $\mathbf{p} + \mathbf{q}$ is the vector from the starting point of $\mathbf{p}$ to the finishing point of $\mathbf{q}$.

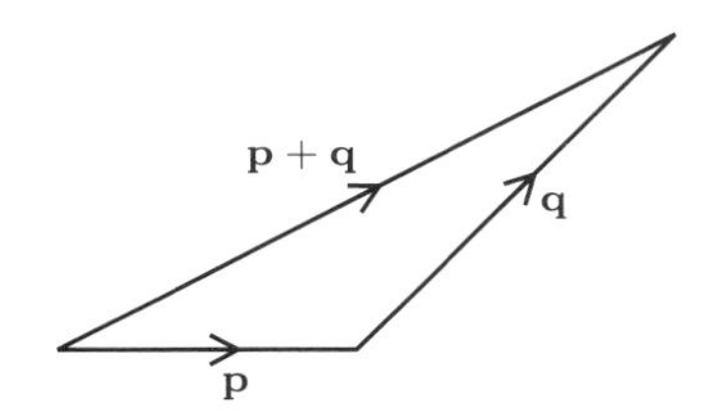


In order to see how addition can be described in terms of components, we look at the sum of two vectors in the plane. Let $\mathbf{p}$ and $\mathbf{q}$ be the vectors

$$\mathbf{p} = a_1\mathbf{i} + a_2\mathbf{j} = (a_1, a_2), \quad \mathbf{q} = b_1\mathbf{i} + b_2\mathbf{j} = (b_1, b_2).$$

Recall that we can think of a vector as a translation.

Then a translation $\mathbf{p}$ followed by a translation $\mathbf{q}$ can be described in terms of the following four successive translations:

- move $a_1$ units in the direction of the positive $x$-axis; (This translation is vector $a_1\mathbf{i}$.)
- then $a_2$ units in the direction of the positive $y$-axis; (This is $a_2\mathbf{j}$.)
- then $b_1$ units in the direction of the positive $x$-axis; (This is $b_1\mathbf{i}$.)
- then $b_2$ units in the direction of the positive $y$-axis. (This is $b_2\mathbf{j}$.)

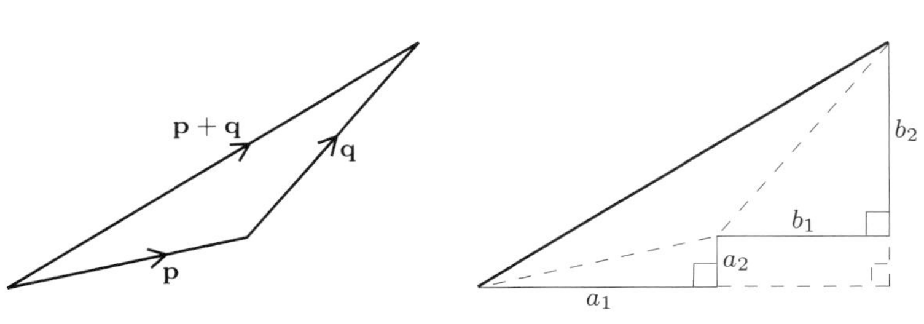


Since the order in which we perform translations does not matter, the net effect is a translation of $a_1 + b_1$ units in the positive direction of the $x$-axis, followed by a translation of $a_2 + b_2$ units in the positive direction of the $y$-axis. In other words, the sum $\mathbf{p} + \mathbf{q}$ is the vector

$$(a_1, a_2) + (b_1, b_2) = (a_1 + b_1, a_2 + b_2).$$

There is a corresponding formula in $\mathbb{R}^3$.

**Addition of vectors** To add vectors in $\mathbb{R}^2$ or in $\mathbb{R}^3$ given in component form, add their corresponding components:

$$(a_1, a_2) + (b_1, b_2) = (a_1 + b_1, a_2 + b_2); \qquad (2.1)$$

$$(a_1, a_2, a_3) + (b_1, b_2, b_3) = (a_1 + b_1, a_2 + b_2, a_3 + b_3). \qquad (2.2)$$

There are analogous formulas for vectors expressed in terms of the unit vectors **i** and **j**, or **i**, **j** and **k**.

For example, the sum of the vectors $(1, -3)$ and $(4, 2)$ in $\mathbb{R}^2$ is the vector $(1 + 4, -3 + 2) = (5, -1)$, and the sum of the vectors $(2, -1, -3)$ and $(-2, 3, 2)$ in $\mathbb{R}^3$ is the vector $(2 - 2, -1 + 3, -3 + 2) = (0, 2, -1)$.

In equations (2.1) and (2.2), the symbol + is used with two different meanings. On the left-hand side of each equation, + denotes addition of vectors, and on the right-hand side, + denotes addition of real numbers. It is sensible to use the same symbol, as addition of vectors obeys the same rules as addition of real numbers.

**Exercise 2.5** Determine the following sums of vectors in $\mathbb{R}^2$:

$$(3, 2) + (1, -5), \quad (5, -2) + (-5, 2), \quad (4, 1) + (0, 0),$$
$$((1, 3) + (4, 2)) + (-3, 1), \quad (1, 3) + ((4, 2) + (-3, 1)).$$

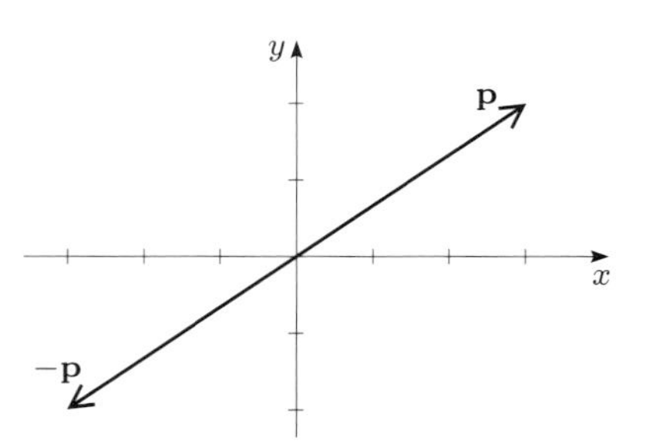


You saw in Exercise 2.5 that the sum of $(5, -2)$ and $(-5, 2)$ is the zero vector. In general, in $\mathbb{R}^2$ the sum of the vectors $\mathbf{p} = (a_1, a_2)$ and $(-a_1, -a_2)$ is the zero vector, so that in terms of its components, the vector $-\mathbf{p}$ is $(-a_1, -a_2)$. Similarly, in terms of components, the negative of the vector $\mathbf{p} = (a_1, a_2, a_3)$ in $\mathbb{R}^3$ is $-\mathbf{p} = (-a_1, -a_2, -a_3)$. For example, if $\mathbf{p} = (1, -3)$, then $-\mathbf{p} = (-1, 3)$; and if $\mathbf{p} = (2, -1, 3)$, then $-\mathbf{p} = (-2, 1, -3)$.

We can then express the difference $\mathbf{p} - \mathbf{q}$ of two vectors $\mathbf{p}$ and $\mathbf{q}$ in terms of components since, as we saw earlier, $\mathbf{p} - \mathbf{q}$ is defined to be $\mathbf{p} + (-\mathbf{q})$.

Subsection 2.1

For example, if $\mathbf{p} = (4, 1)$ and $\mathbf{q} = (2, -1)$, then $-\mathbf{q} = (-2, 1)$ and

$$\mathbf{p} - \mathbf{q} = (4 - 2, 1 + 1) = (2, 2).$$

Similarly, if $\mathbf{p} = \mathbf{i} + 2\mathbf{j} - 3\mathbf{k}$ and $\mathbf{q} = 2\mathbf{i} - \mathbf{j} + \mathbf{k}$, then $-\mathbf{q} = -2\mathbf{i} + \mathbf{j} - \mathbf{k}$ and

$$\mathbf{p} - \mathbf{q} = -\mathbf{i} + 3\mathbf{j} - 4\mathbf{k}.$$

**Negative of a vector** To find the negative of a vector in $\mathbb{R}^2$ or in $\mathbb{R}^3$ given in component form, take the negatives of its components:

$$-(a_1, a_2) = (-a_1, -a_2) \quad \text{and} \quad -(a_1, a_2, a_3) = (-a_1, -a_2, -a_3).$$

There are analogous formulas for vectors expressed in terms of the unit vectors **i** and **j**, or **i**, **j** and **k**.

**Subtraction of vectors** To subtract a vector in $\mathbb{R}^2$ or in $\mathbb{R}^3$ given in component form, subtract its corresponding components:

$$(a_1, a_2) - (b_1, b_2) = (a_1 - b_1, a_2 - b_2);$$
$$(a_1, a_2, a_3) - (b_1, b_2, b_3) = (a_1 - b_1, a_2 - b_2, a_3 - b_3).$$

**Exercise 2.6** For each of the following pairs of vectors $\mathbf{p}$ and $\mathbf{q}$, write down $-\mathbf{p}$, $-\mathbf{q}$ and $\mathbf{p}-\mathbf{q}$.

(a) $\mathbf{p}=(3,-1)$ and $\mathbf{q}=(-1,-2)$.

(b) $\mathbf{p}=-\mathbf{i}-2\mathbf{j}$ and $\mathbf{q}=2\mathbf{i}-\mathbf{j}$.

(c) $\mathbf{p}=-\mathbf{i}+2\mathbf{k}$ and $\mathbf{q}=\mathbf{i}-2\mathbf{j}-\mathbf{k}$.

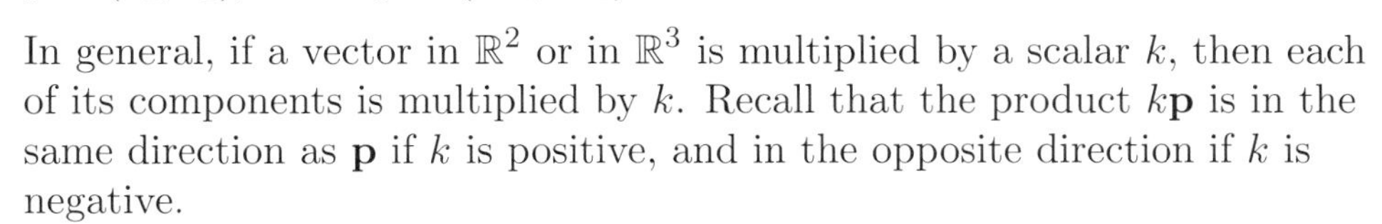


The other operation that we described geometrically earlier was multiplication by a scalar. For example, the vector $2\mathbf{p}$ has magnitude twice that of $\mathbf{p}$ and has the same direction; so, in terms of components, if $\mathbf{p}=(a_1,a_2)$, then $2\mathbf{p}=(2a_1,2a_2)$.

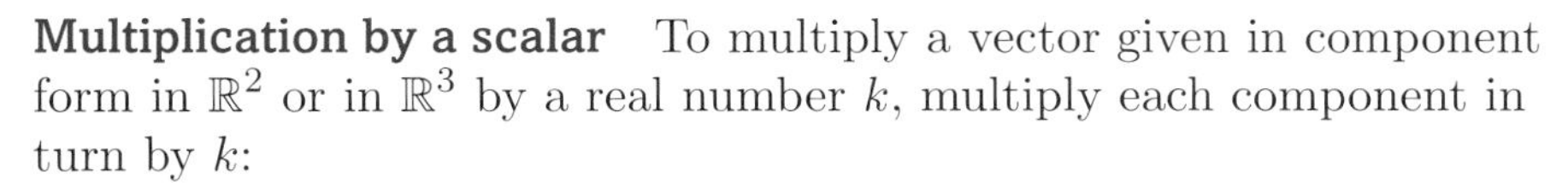

In general, if a vector in $\mathbb{R}^2$ or in $\mathbb{R}^3$ is multiplied by a scalar $k$, then each of its components is multiplied by $k$. Recall that the product $k\mathbf{p}$ is in the same direction as $\mathbf{p}$ if $k$ is positive, and in the opposite direction if $k$ is negative.

**Multiplication by a scalar** To multiply a vector given in component form in $\mathbb{R}^2$ or in $\mathbb{R}^3$ by a real number $k$, multiply each component in turn by $k$:

$$k(a_1,a_2)=(ka_1,ka_2) \quad \text{and} \quad k(a_1,a_2,a_3)=(ka_1,ka_2,ka_3).$$

There are analogous formulas for vectors expressed in terms of the unit vectors $\mathbf{i}$ and $\mathbf{j}$, or $\mathbf{i}$, $\mathbf{j}$ and $\mathbf{k}$.

For example, if $\mathbf{p}=(2,-1)$, then $2\mathbf{p}=(4,-2)$ and $-3\mathbf{p}=(-6,3)$.

**Exercise 2.7** For each of the following pairs of vectors $\mathbf{p}$ and $\mathbf{q}$, determine $2\mathbf{p}$, $3\mathbf{q}$, $2\mathbf{p}+3\mathbf{q}$ and $2\mathbf{p}-3\mathbf{q}$.

(a) $\mathbf{p}=(3,-1)$ and $\mathbf{q}=(-1,-2)$.

(b) $\mathbf{p}=-\mathbf{i}+2\mathbf{k}$ and $\mathbf{q}=\mathbf{i}-2\mathbf{j}-\mathbf{k}$.

The set of ordered pairs (triples) of real numbers, together with the operations of addition of ordered pairs (triples) and multiplication of an ordered pair (triple) by a scalar, is an example of the algebraic structure known as a *vector space*, which we shall study later in the block.

Unit LA3

**Definitions** The **vector space** $\mathbb{R}^2$ is the set of ordered pairs of real numbers with the operations of addition and multiplication by a scalar defined as follows:

$$(a_1,a_2)+(b_1,b_2)=(a_1+b_1,a_2+b_2);$$
$$k(a_1,a_2)=(ka_1,ka_2), \quad \text{where } k\in\mathbb{R}.$$

Similarly, the **vector space** $\mathbb{R}^3$ is the set of ordered triples of real numbers with analogous operations of addition and multiplication by a scalar.

## Position vectors

Finally, we relate the method of specifying points in the plane as an ordered pair of real numbers (that is, via the Cartesian coordinate system) to vectors.

In order to do this, we use those vectors whose starting point is the origin; such vectors are called *position vectors*. For example, the position vector $(2,-1)$ is the vector shown in the margin.

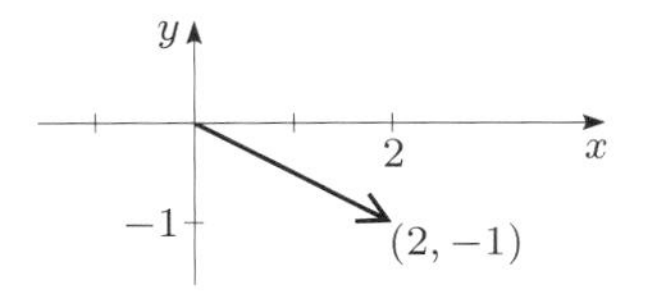

**Definition** The **position vector**

$$\mathbf{p} = a_1\mathbf{i} + a_2\mathbf{j} \quad \text{(often written as } \mathbf{p} = (a_1, a_2), \text{ for brevity)}$$

is the vector in $\mathbb{R}^2$ whose starting point is the origin and whose finishing point is the point with Cartesian coordinates $(a_1, a_2)$.

The position vector $\mathbf{p} = a_1\mathbf{i} + a_2\mathbf{j} + a_3\mathbf{k}$ (often written as $\mathbf{p} = (a_1, a_2, a_3)$) in $\mathbb{R}^3$ can be defined in a similar way.

Thus there is a one-one correspondence between the points of the plane and the set of position vectors in $\mathbb{R}^2$. We shall make use of this in Subsection 2.3 to simplify the solution of various geometric problems in the plane.

**Exercise 2.8** Let $\mathbf{p}$ and $\mathbf{q}$ be the position vectors $(5, 3)$ and $(1, 4)$, respectively.

(a) Determine the position vectors $\mathbf{p} - \mathbf{q}$, $\mathbf{p} + \mathbf{q}$ and $\frac{1}{2}\mathbf{p} + \frac{1}{2}\mathbf{q}$.

(b) Sketch $\mathbf{p}$, $\mathbf{q}$ and each of the position vectors that you found in part (a).

## 2.3 Lines

Earlier, we found the equation of a line in the $(x, y)$-plane in the form

$$ax + by = c,$$

for some real numbers $a$, $b$ and $c$, where $a$ and $b$ are not both zero. We now find an equivalent equation for a line in terms of vectors.

Let $P$ and $Q$ be two given points with position vectors $\mathbf{p}$ and $\mathbf{q}$, and [illegible]y $\ell$ the line that passes through $P$ and $Q$. How can we find the [illegible] vector $\mathbf{r}$ of a point $R$ on $\ell$ that lies between $P$ and $Q$?

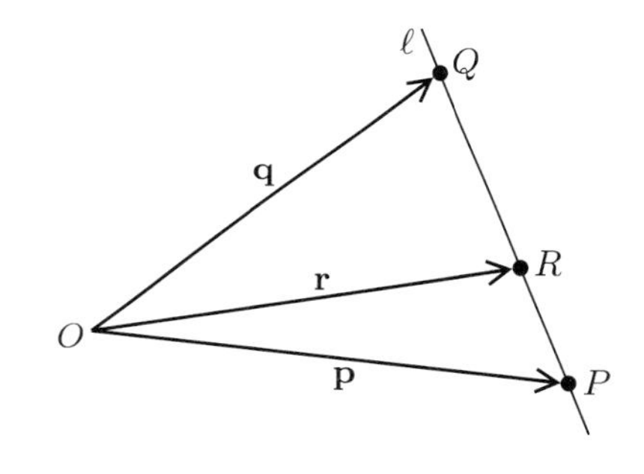


[illegible] use the Triangle Law for the addition of vectors to find expressions for the vectors $\overrightarrow{PQ}$ and $\overrightarrow{RQ}$; this gives

$$\begin{aligned}\overrightarrow{PQ} &= \overrightarrow{PO} + \overrightarrow{OQ} \quad \text{(by the Triangle Law, where } O \text{ is the origin)}\\ &= -\overrightarrow{OP} + \overrightarrow{OQ} = -\mathbf{p} + \mathbf{q} = \mathbf{q} - \mathbf{p}\end{aligned}$$

and

$$\begin{aligned}\overrightarrow{RQ} &= \overrightarrow{RO} + \overrightarrow{OQ} \quad \text{(by the Triangle Law)}\\ &= -\overrightarrow{OR} + \overrightarrow{OQ} = -\mathbf{r} + \mathbf{q} = \mathbf{q} - \mathbf{r}.\end{aligned}$$

Since $\overrightarrow{PQ}$ and $\overrightarrow{RQ}$ are parallel, the vector $\mathbf{q} - \mathbf{r}$ is parallel to the vector $\mathbf{q} - \mathbf{p}$, so it must be a multiple of $\mathbf{q} - \mathbf{p}$; that is,

$$\mathbf{q} - \mathbf{r} = \lambda(\mathbf{q} - \mathbf{p}), \quad \text{for some real number } \lambda.$$

Two vectors are *parallel* if they are in the same direction or in opposite directions.

We can rearrange this equation in the form

$$\mathbf{r} = \mathbf{q} - \lambda(\mathbf{q} - \mathbf{p}),$$

or

$$\mathbf{r} = \lambda\mathbf{p} + (1 - \lambda)\mathbf{q}. \tag{2.3}$$

This is a general formula for the position vector of a point on the line segment $PQ$, in the following sense: each point on $\ell$ between $P$ and $Q$ corresponds to a particular value of $\lambda$ between 0 and 1, and vice versa.

In equation (2.3),

$$\text{when } \lambda = 0, \quad \mathbf{r} = 0\mathbf{p} + 1\mathbf{q} = \mathbf{q},$$
$$\text{when } \lambda = 1, \quad \mathbf{r} = 1\mathbf{p} + 0\mathbf{q} = \mathbf{p},$$

and

$$\text{when } \lambda = \tfrac{1}{2}, \quad \mathbf{r} = \tfrac{1}{2}\mathbf{p} + \tfrac{1}{2}\mathbf{q} = \tfrac{1}{2}(\mathbf{p} + \mathbf{q}).$$

This is the *midpoint* of the line segment $PQ$.

Equation (2.3) also makes sense when $\lambda > 1$ and when $\lambda < 0$, and not just when $\lambda$ lies between 0 and 1. In fact,

if $\lambda > 1$, then $R$ lies on $\ell$ beyond $P$,
if $0 < \lambda < 1$, then $R$ lies on $\ell$ between $P$ and $Q$,
if $\lambda < 0$, then $R$ lies on $\ell$ beyond $Q$.

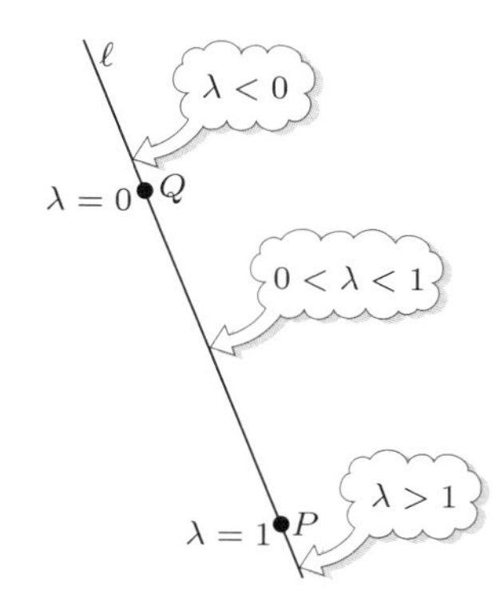


Thus each point on the line $\ell$ has a position vector of the form of equation (2.3), for some value of $\lambda$. In other words, we can regard equation (2.3) as the *vector form of the equation of the line* $\ell$, with $\lambda$ as a parameter.

> **Vector form of the equation of a line** The equation of the line through the points with position vectors $\mathbf{p}$ and $\mathbf{q}$ is
>
> $$\mathbf{r} = \lambda\mathbf{p} + (1 - \lambda)\mathbf{q}, \quad \text{where } \lambda \in \mathbb{R}. \tag{2.3}$$

**Exercise 2.9**

(a) Let $P$ and $Q$ be the points with position vectors $\mathbf{p} = (3, 1)$ and $\mathbf{q} = (2, 3)$, respectively. Write down the vector form of the equation of the line $\ell$ through $P$ and $Q$.

(b) Determine the points on $\ell$ whose position vectors are given by equation (2.3) when $\lambda$ takes the values $\frac{1}{3}$, $\frac{3}{2}$ and $-\frac{1}{2}$.

(c) On a single diagram, sketch $P$, $Q$, the line $\ell$ through $P$ and $Q$, and the three points that you found in part (b).

The vector form of the equation of the line $\ell$ passing through the points $(3, 1)$ and $(2, 3)$ is

$$\mathbf{r} = \lambda(3, 1) + (1 - \lambda)(2, 3),$$

that is,

$$\mathbf{r} = (2 + \lambda, 3 - 2\lambda), \quad \text{where } \lambda \in \mathbb{R}.$$

We can use this equation to determine whether or not a given point lies on the line $\ell$. For example, the point $(5, -3)$ lies on $\ell$ if there is some real number $\lambda$ such that

$$(5, -3) = (2 + \lambda, 3 - 2\lambda).$$

Equating the corresponding components, we see that this condition reduces to a pair of simultaneous equations that must be satisfied by such a number $\lambda$:

$$5 = 2 + \lambda \quad \text{and} \quad -3 = 3 - 2\lambda.$$

These have the solution $\lambda = 3$, and hence the point $(5, -3)$ does lie on the line $\ell$.

**Exercise 2.10** Let $P$, $Q$ and $\ell$ be as in Exercise 2.9.

(a) Determine the value of $\lambda$ corresponding to the point $(4, -1)$ in the vector form of the equation of $\ell$: $\mathbf{r} = \lambda(3, 1) + (1 - \lambda)(2, 3)$.

(b) Use the vector form of the equation of $\ell$ to prove that the point $\left(\frac{1}{2}, \frac{1}{2}\right)$ does not lie on $\ell$.

We can obtain another useful result from our derivation of equation (2.3). We saw above that

$$\overrightarrow{RQ} = \lambda\overrightarrow{PQ};$$

it follows that

$$\begin{aligned}\overrightarrow{PR} &= \overrightarrow{PQ} - \overrightarrow{RQ} \quad \text{(by the Triangle Law)}\\ &= \overrightarrow{PQ} - \lambda\overrightarrow{PQ}\\ &= (1 - \lambda)\overrightarrow{PQ}.\end{aligned}$$

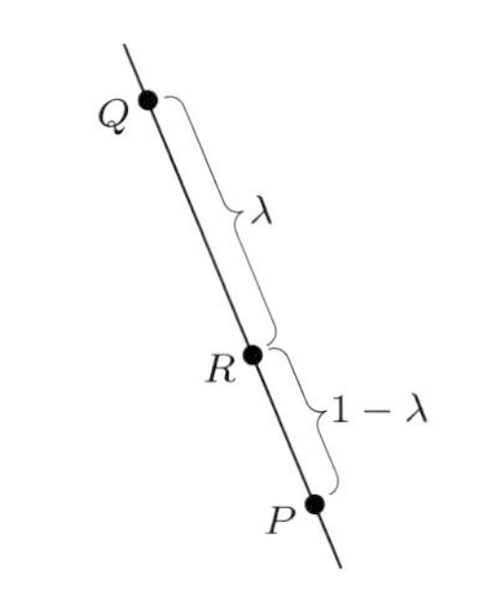


Comparing these expressions for $\overrightarrow{RQ}$ and $\overrightarrow{PR}$, we conclude that $R$ is the point that divides the line $PQ$ in the ratio $(1 - \lambda) : \lambda$.

For example, let $PR : RQ = 3 : 2$. Since the ratio $3 : 2$ is just the same as the ratio $\frac{3}{5} : \frac{2}{5}$, we write this equation in the form $PR : RQ = \frac{3}{5} : \frac{2}{5}$, so that $PR : RQ = (1 - \lambda) : \lambda$ with $\lambda = \frac{2}{5}$. (Here we divide each expression in the ratio by the sum $3 + 2 = 5$, in order to obtain the ratio in the standard form $(1 - \lambda) : \lambda$.)

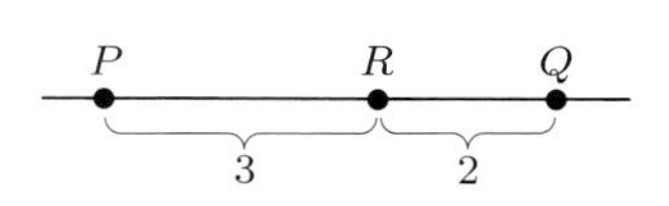


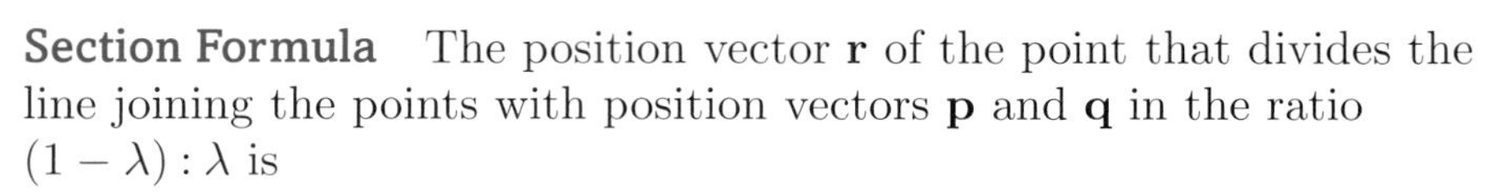

> **Section Formula** The position vector $\mathbf{r}$ of the point that divides the line joining the points with position vectors $\mathbf{p}$ and $\mathbf{q}$ in the ratio $(1 - \lambda) : \lambda$ is
>
> $$\mathbf{r} = \lambda\mathbf{p} + (1 - \lambda)\mathbf{q}.$$

When $\mathbf{q} = (0, 0)$, $\mathbf{r}$ has the simple form $\mathbf{r} = \lambda\mathbf{p}$; we shall find this fact useful later.

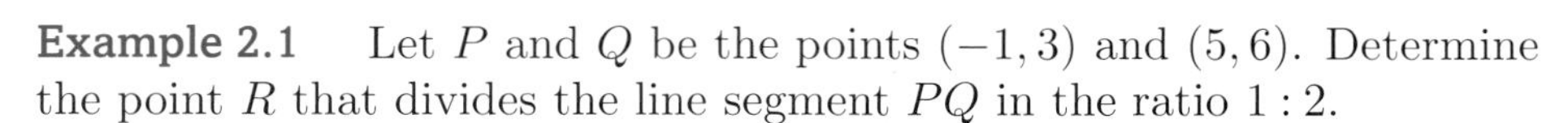

**Example 2.1** Let $P$ and $Q$ be the points $(-1, 3)$ and $(5, 6)$. Determine the point $R$ that divides the line segment $PQ$ in the ratio $1 : 2$.

Thus $R$ is one-third of the way from $P$ to $Q$.

**Solution** The position vectors of $P$ and $Q$ are $\mathbf{p} = (-1, 3)$ and $\mathbf{q} = (5, 6)$; let $R$ have position vector $\mathbf{r}$.

Since $PR : RQ = 1 : 2 = \frac{1}{3} : \frac{2}{3}$, we can apply the Section Formula with $\lambda = \frac{2}{3}$; hence

$$\begin{aligned}\mathbf{r} &= \tfrac{2}{3}\mathbf{p} + \tfrac{1}{3}\mathbf{q}\\ &= \tfrac{2}{3}(-1, 3) + \tfrac{1}{3}(5, 6) = (1, 4).\end{aligned}$$

Thus $R$ is the point with coordinates $(1, 4)$. ■

**Exercise 2.11** Let $P$ and $Q$ be the points $(-3, 1)$ and $(7, -4)$. Determine

(a) the point $R$ that divides $PQ$ in the ratio $3 : 2$;

(b) the midpoint $M$ of $PQ$.

We finish with an example that uses many of the ideas that you have met in this section.

**Example 2.2** The triangle $OAB$ has vertices at $O$ (the origin) and at points $A$ and $B$ with position vectors $\mathbf{a}$ and $\mathbf{b}$, respectively. $Q$ is the midpoint of $OB$, and the point $P$ is one-third of the way along $BA$ from the vertex $B$; $R$ is the point of intersection of the lines $OP$ and $AQ$. The points $P$, $Q$ and $R$ have position vectors $\mathbf{p}$, $\mathbf{q}$ and $\mathbf{r}$, respectively.

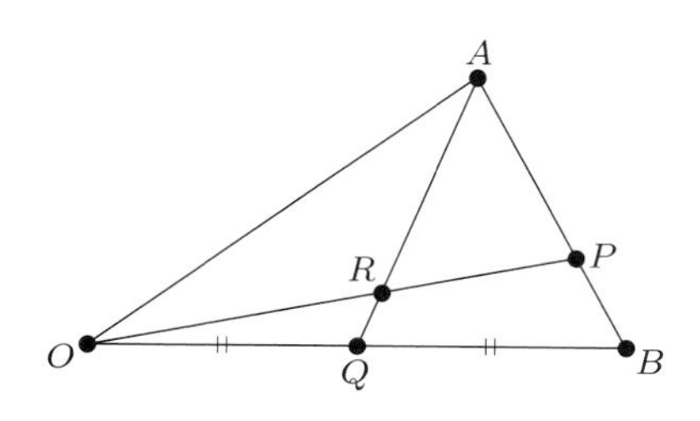


Determine $\mathbf{p}$, $\mathbf{q}$ and $\mathbf{r}$ in terms of $\mathbf{a}$ and $\mathbf{b}$.

**Solution** The point $P$ divides $BA$ in the ratio $1:2 = \frac{1}{3}:\frac{2}{3}$. It follows from the Section Formula with $\lambda = \frac{2}{3}$ that

$$\mathbf{p} = \tfrac{2}{3}\mathbf{b} + \tfrac{1}{3}\mathbf{a}. \tag{2.4}$$

Now $Q$ is the midpoint of $OB$, so

$$\mathbf{q} = \tfrac{1}{2}\mathbf{b}. \tag{2.5}$$

Here we use the fact that the position vector of $O$ is $\mathbf{0} = (0,0)$.

To find $\mathbf{r}$, we use the fact that $R$ is the point of intersection of $OP$ and $AQ$. First, since $R$ lies on $AQ$, its position vector $\mathbf{r}$ must be of the form

$$\mathbf{r} = \lambda\mathbf{q} + (1-\lambda)\mathbf{a},$$

for some real number $\lambda$. Substituting from equation (2.5), we can rewrite this formula as

$\mathbf{r}$ could also be written as $\lambda\mathbf{a} + (1-\lambda)\mathbf{q}$, but with a different value of $\lambda$.

$$\mathbf{r} = \tfrac{1}{2}\lambda\mathbf{b} + (1-\lambda)\mathbf{a}. \tag{2.6}$$

The point $R$ lies on the line $OP$ also, so we can express its position vector $\mathbf{r}$ as a scalar multiple of $\mathbf{p}$. Thus we can use equation (2.4) to write $\mathbf{r}$ in the form

$$\mathbf{r} = k\left(\tfrac{2}{3}\mathbf{b} + \tfrac{1}{3}\mathbf{a}\right), \tag{2.7}$$

for some real number $k$.

The expressions in equations (2.6) and (2.7) for $\mathbf{r}$ must be equal, so

$$\tfrac{1}{2}\lambda\mathbf{b} + (1-\lambda)\mathbf{a} = k\left(\tfrac{2}{3}\mathbf{b} + \tfrac{1}{3}\mathbf{a}\right),$$

which we can rewrite as

$$\left(1-\lambda-\tfrac{1}{3}k\right)\mathbf{a} = \left(\tfrac{2}{3}k - \tfrac{1}{2}\lambda\right)\mathbf{b}. \tag{2.8}$$

We know that the vectors $\mathbf{a}$ and $\mathbf{b}$ are not parallel. Hence non-zero multiples of $\mathbf{a}$ and $\mathbf{b}$ cannot be parallel. It follows that the only way in which equation (2.8) can hold is for the coefficients of $\mathbf{a}$ and $\mathbf{b}$ in equation (2.8) to be zero: that is, we must have $1-\lambda-\frac{1}{3}k = 0$ and $\frac{2}{3}k - \frac{1}{2}\lambda = 0$. Hence the following simultaneous equations for $\lambda$ and $k$ must hold:

This is a common technique in the application of vectors to the solution of geometric problems.

$$1-\lambda = \tfrac{1}{3}k \quad \text{and} \quad \tfrac{2}{3}k = \tfrac{1}{2}\lambda.$$

From the second equation we deduce that $k = \frac{3}{4}\lambda$. Then, substituting this value for $k$ into the first equation, we find that $1-\lambda = \frac{1}{4}\lambda$; hence $1 = \frac{5}{4}\lambda$, so $\lambda = \frac{4}{5}$.

Substituting the value $\frac{4}{5}$ for $\lambda$ into equation (2.6), we conclude that

$$\begin{aligned}\mathbf{r} &= \tfrac{1}{2}\times\tfrac{4}{5}\mathbf{b} + \left(1-\tfrac{4}{5}\right)\mathbf{a}\\ &= \tfrac{1}{5}\mathbf{a} + \tfrac{2}{5}\mathbf{b}. \quad \blacksquare\end{aligned}$$

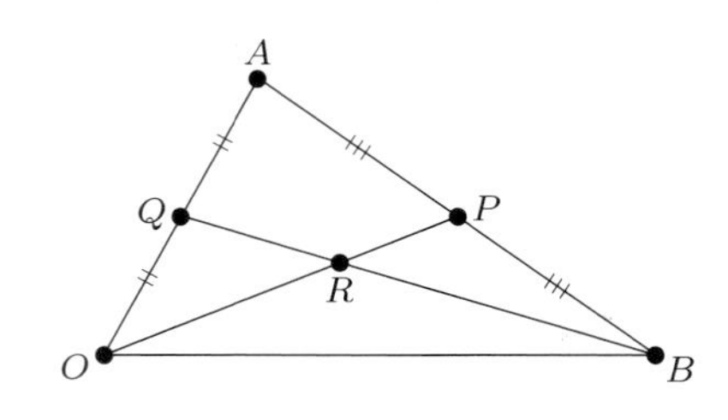


**Exercise 2.12** The triangle $OAB$ has vertices at $O$ (the origin) and at points $A$ and $B$ with position vectors $\mathbf{a}$ and $\mathbf{b}$, respectively. $P$ is the midpoint of $AB$, and $Q$ is the midpoint of $OA$; $R$ is the point of intersection of the lines $OP$ and $BQ$. The points $P$, $Q$ and $R$ have position vectors $\mathbf{p}$, $\mathbf{q}$ and $\mathbf{r}$, respectively.

(a) Determine $\mathbf{p}$, $\mathbf{q}$ and $\mathbf{r}$ in terms of $\mathbf{a}$ and $\mathbf{b}$.

(b) Determine the ratio $OR : RP$.

# Further exercises

**Exercise 2.13** Let $\mathbf{p} = 2\mathbf{i} - 3\mathbf{j} + \mathbf{k}$ and $\mathbf{q} = -\mathbf{i} - 2\mathbf{j} - 4\mathbf{k}$ be two vectors in $\mathbb{R}^3$. Determine $\mathbf{p} + \mathbf{q}$, $\mathbf{p} - \mathbf{q}$ and $2\mathbf{p} - 3\mathbf{q}$.

**Exercise 2.14** Let $\mathbf{u}$ and $\mathbf{v}$ be the position vectors $(1, 1)$ and $(2, 1)$, respectively.

(a) Determine the position vectors $\mathbf{u} + 2\mathbf{v}$, $-\mathbf{u}$, $-\mathbf{u} + 3\mathbf{v}$ and $\mathbf{u} - 3\mathbf{v}$.

(b) On a single diagram, sketch $\mathbf{u}$, $\mathbf{v}$ and the position vectors that you found in part (a).

**Exercise 2.15** Let $\mathbf{u} = (2, 6)$ and $\mathbf{v} = (4, 2)$.

(a) Determine numbers $\alpha$ and $\beta$ such that

$$(3, 4) = \alpha\mathbf{u} + \beta\mathbf{v}. \tag{2.9}$$

Hint: Obtain simultaneous equations involving $\alpha$ and $\beta$ by equating the first and second components of the vectors on each side of equation (2.9).

(b) Sketch the position vectors $\mathbf{u}$, $\mathbf{v}$ and $(3, 4)$ on a single diagram.

**Exercise 2.16** Let $A$ and $B$ be the points $(5, 4)$ and $(-2, -3)$.

Determine the point $R$ that divides $AB$ in the ratio $2 : 5$, and the midpoint $M$ of $AB$.

**Exercise 2.17**

(a) Determine the vector form of the equation of the line $\ell$ through the points $(2, 3)$ and $(5, -1)$.

(b) Hence determine whether the points $(7, 2)$ and $(-1, 7)$ lie on $\ell$.

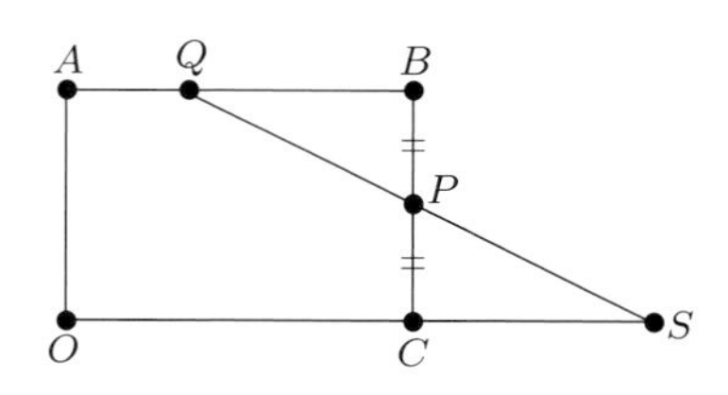


**Exercise 2.18** The rectangle $OABC$ has vertex $O$ at the origin, and the position vectors of the vertices $A$, $B$ and $C$ are $\mathbf{a}$, $\mathbf{b}$ and $\mathbf{c}$, respectively. $P$ is the midpoint of $BC$, and the point $Q$ is one-third of the way along $AB$ from $A$. $S$ is the point of intersection of the lines $OC$ and $QP$.

(a) Determine the position vectors of $P$ and $Q$, in terms of $\mathbf{a}$ and $\mathbf{c}$.

(b) Determine the vector form of the equation of the line that passes through $P$ and $Q$, in terms of $\mathbf{a}$ and $\mathbf{c}$.

(c) Use the equation that you obtained in part (b), and the fact that $S$ lies on the line $OC$, to find the position vector of $S$, in terms of $\mathbf{a}$ and $\mathbf{c}$.

# 3 Dot product

After working through this section, you should be able to:

(a) explain what is meant by the *dot product* of two vectors;

(b) use the dot product to find the angle between two vectors and the *projection* of one vector onto another;

(c) determine the *equation of a plane* in $\mathbb{R}^3$, given a point in the plane and the direction of a *normal* to the plane.

## 3.1 Definition, properties and some applications

In the previous section we saw how to add two vectors and how to multiply a vector by a scalar, but we did not consider how to multiply two vectors. There are two different ways in which we can multiply two vectors, known as the *dot product* (or *scalar product*) and the *vector product*. They are given these names because the result of the first is a scalar and the result of the second is a vector.

We shall not consider vector products in this course.

In the audio section we explain the definition of the dot product and investigate some of its basic properties. In addition, we see how the dot product can be used to find the angle between two vectors, to give a condition for two vectors to be orthogonal (that is, at right angles) and to find the projection of one vector onto another vector.

**Listen to the audio as you work through the frames.**

Audio

## 1. Dot product in $\mathbb{R}^2$

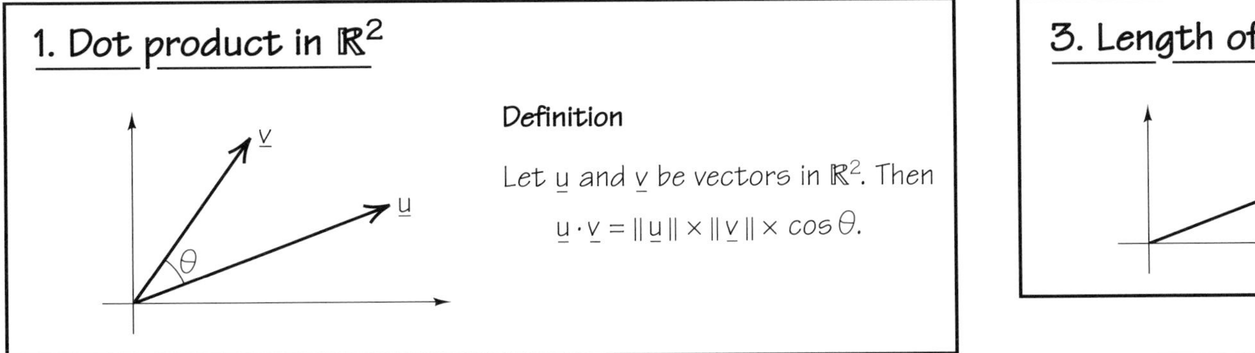


**Definition**

Let $\underline{u}$ and $\underline{v}$ be vectors in $\mathbb{R}^2$. Then

$$\underline{u}\cdot\underline{v} = \|\underline{u}\| \times \|\underline{v}\| \times \cos\theta.$$

## 2. Examples

$$\|\underline{u}\| = 2,$$
$$\|\underline{v}\| = \sqrt{3^2 + 3^2} = 3\sqrt{2},$$
$$\theta = \frac{\pi}{4},$$
$$\underline{u}\cdot\underline{v} = 2 \times 3\sqrt{2} \times \frac{1}{\sqrt{2}} = 6.$$

$\cos\frac{\pi}{4} = \frac{1}{\sqrt{2}}$

$$\|\underline{u}\| = \sqrt{(\sqrt{3})^2 + 3^2} = \sqrt{12},$$
$$\|\underline{v}\| = \sqrt{(\sqrt{3})^2 + (-3)^2} = \sqrt{12},$$
$$\theta = \pi - \frac{\pi}{6} - \frac{\pi}{6} = \frac{2\pi}{3},$$
$$\underline{u}\cdot\underline{v} = \sqrt{12} \times \sqrt{12} \times \left(-\frac{1}{2}\right) = -6.$$

$\cos\frac{2\pi}{3} = -\frac{1}{2}$

## 3. Length of a vector in terms of dot product

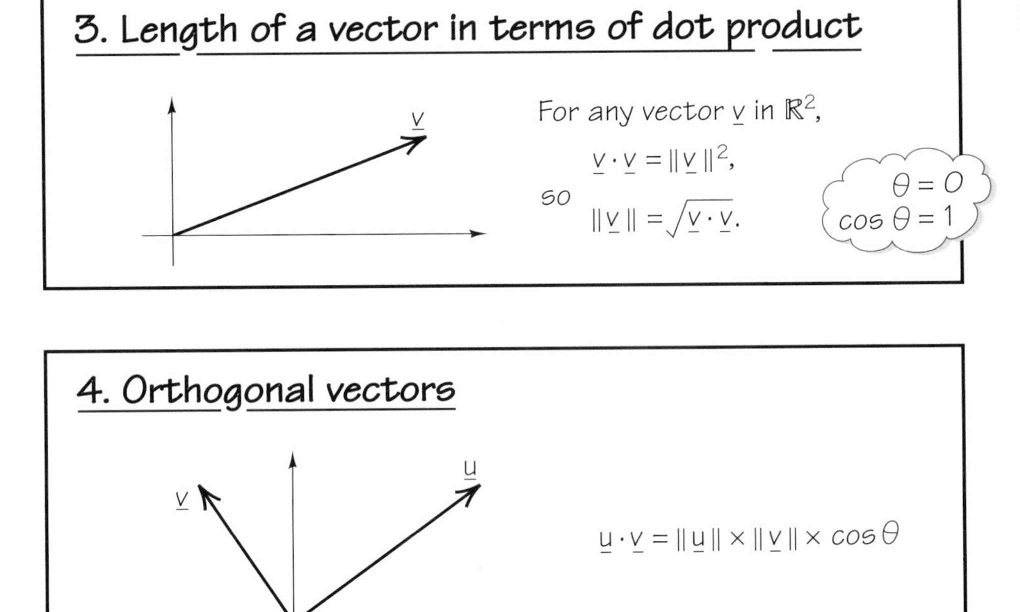


For any vector $\underline{v}$ in $\mathbb{R}^2$,

$$\underline{v}\cdot\underline{v} = \|\underline{v}\|^2,$$

so

$$\|\underline{v}\| = \sqrt{\underline{v}\cdot\underline{v}}.$$

$\theta = 0$, $\cos\theta = 1$

## 4. Orthogonal vectors

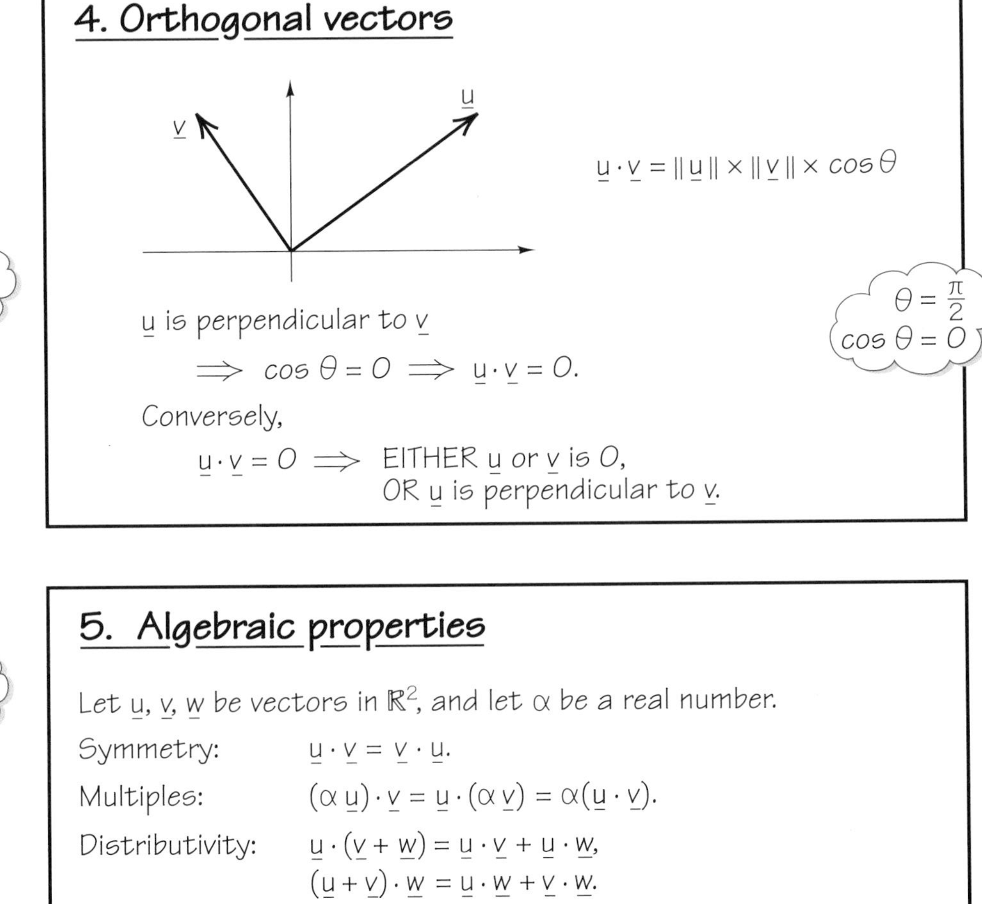


$$\underline{u}\cdot\underline{v} = \|\underline{u}\| \times \|\underline{v}\| \times \cos\theta$$

$\theta = \frac{\pi}{2}$, $\cos\theta = 0$

$\underline{u}$ is perpendicular to $\underline{v}$

$\Longrightarrow \cos\theta = 0 \Longrightarrow \underline{u}\cdot\underline{v} = 0.$

Conversely,

$\underline{u}\cdot\underline{v} = 0 \Longrightarrow$ EITHER $\underline{u}$ or $\underline{v}$ is $0$,
OR $\underline{u}$ is perpendicular to $\underline{v}$.

## 5. Algebraic properties

Let $\underline{u}$, $\underline{v}$, $\underline{w}$ be vectors in $\mathbb{R}^2$, and let $\alpha$ be a real number.

Symmetry: $\underline{u}\cdot\underline{v} = \underline{v}\cdot\underline{u}$.

Multiples: $(\alpha\underline{u})\cdot\underline{v} = \underline{u}\cdot(\alpha\underline{v}) = \alpha(\underline{u}\cdot\underline{v})$.

Distributivity: $\underline{u}\cdot(\underline{v}+\underline{w}) = \underline{u}\cdot\underline{v} + \underline{u}\cdot\underline{w}$,
$(\underline{u}+\underline{v})\cdot\underline{w} = \underline{u}\cdot\underline{w} + \underline{v}\cdot\underline{w}$.

## 6. Calculating dot products in $\mathbb{R}^2$

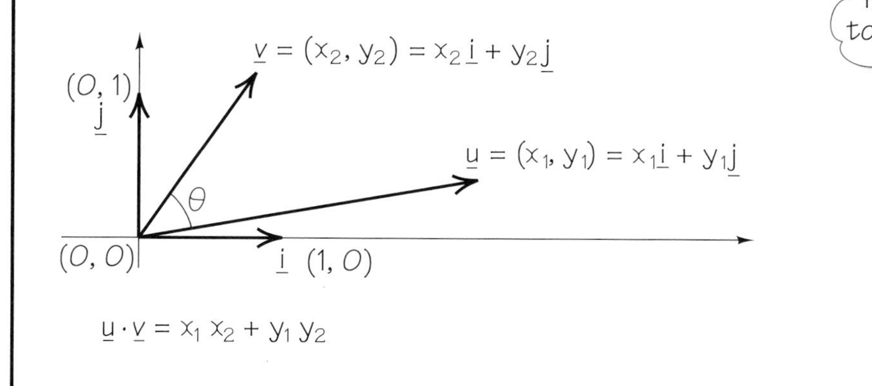
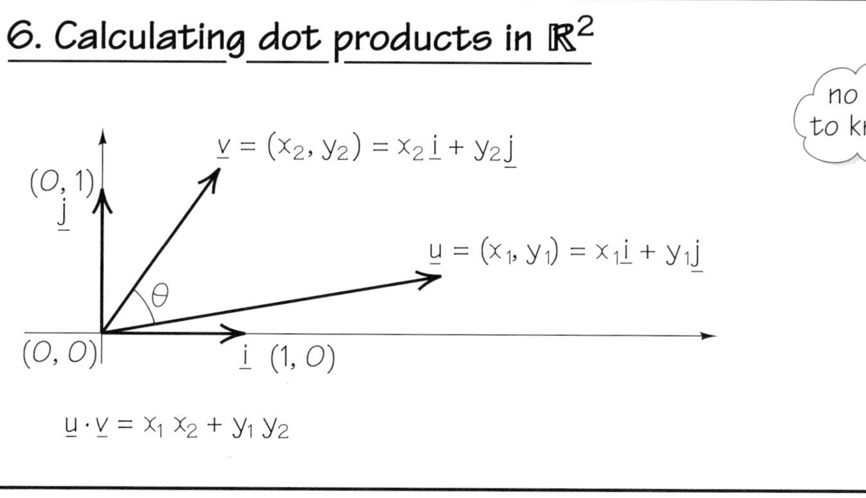


$\underline{u} \cdot \underline{v} = x_1 x_2 + y_1 y_2$

## 7. Proof of formula

$$\begin{aligned}\underline{u} \cdot \underline{v} &= (x_1\underline{i} + y_1\underline{j}) \cdot (x_2\underline{i} + y_2\underline{j}) \\ &= (x_1\underline{i} + y_1\underline{j}) \cdot x_2\underline{i} + (x_1\underline{i} + y_1\underline{j}) \cdot y_2\underline{j} \\ &= x_1\underline{i} \cdot x_2\underline{i} + y_1\underline{j} \cdot x_2\underline{i} + x_1\underline{i} \cdot y_2\underline{j} + y_1\underline{j} \cdot y_2\underline{j} \\ &= x_1 x_2\, \underline{i} \cdot \underline{i} + y_1 x_2\, \underline{j} \cdot \underline{i} + x_1 y_2\, \underline{i} \cdot \underline{j} + y_1 y_2\, \underline{j} \cdot \underline{j}\end{aligned}$$

Distributivity

Multiples

Now simplify, using

$\underline{i} \cdot \underline{i} = \|\underline{i}\|^2 = 1$ (Frame 3),

$\underline{j} \cdot \underline{j} = \|\underline{j}\|^2 = 1$ (Frame 3),

$\underline{i} \cdot \underline{j} = \underline{j} \cdot \underline{i} = 0$ (Frame 4).

$\underline{i}$ and $\underline{j}$ are perpendicular

So

$\underline{u} \cdot \underline{v} = x_1 x_2 + y_1 y_2.$

## 8. Examples

Frame 2

(a) $(\sqrt{3}, 3) \cdot (\sqrt{3}, -3) = \sqrt{3} \times \sqrt{3} + 3 \times (-3) = 3 - 9 = -6$

(b) $(2\underline{i} + 3\underline{j}) \cdot (2\underline{i} - \underline{j}) = 2 \times 2 + 3 \times (-1) = 4 - 3 = 1$

(c) $(\sqrt{2}, -4) \cdot (2\sqrt{2}, 1) = \sqrt{2} \times 2\sqrt{2} - 4 \times 1 = 0$

vectors are perpendicular

**Exercise 3.1**

Calculate the following dot products.

(a) $(2, 3) \cdot \left(\frac{5}{2}, -4\right)$ (b) $(1, 4) \cdot \left(2, -\frac{1}{2}\right)$ (c) $(-2\underline{i} + \underline{j}) \cdot (3\underline{i} - 2\underline{j})$

## 9. Unit vectors

Let $\underline{u} = (x, y)$. Then $\|\underline{u}\| = \sqrt{x^2 + y^2}$.

Unit vector in same direction as $\underline{u}$ is

$$\hat{\underline{u}} = \frac{\underline{u}}{\|\underline{u}\|}.$$

unit length

**Example**

Let $\underline{u} = (3, 4)$. Then

$$\|\underline{u}\| = \sqrt{3^2 + 4^2} = \sqrt{25} = 5,$$

so

$$\hat{\underline{u}} = \frac{1}{5}(3, 4) = \left(\frac{3}{5}, \frac{4}{5}\right).$$

**Exercise 3.2**

Find $\hat{\underline{u}}$ when $\underline{u}$ is (a) $(2, -3)$, (b) $5\underline{i} + 12\underline{j}$.

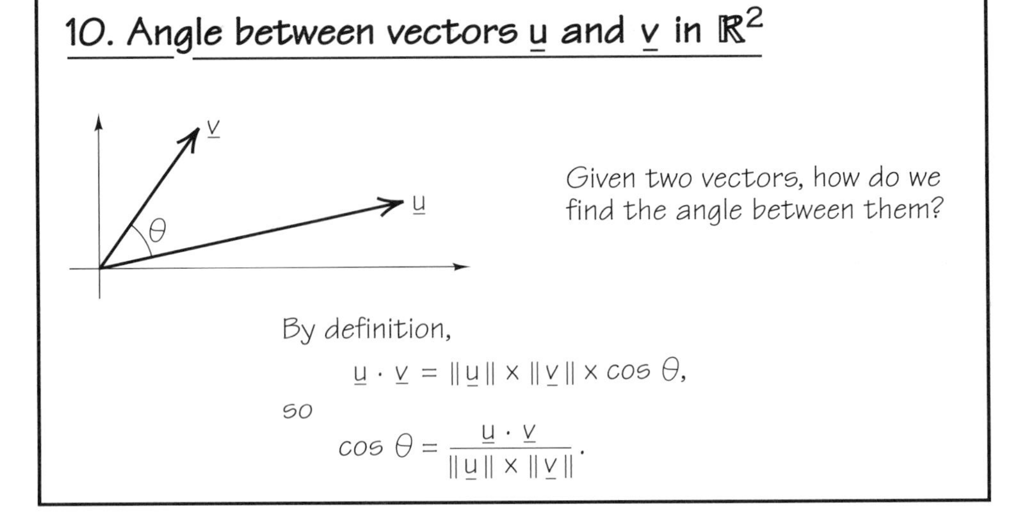


## 11. Example

Let $\underline{u} = (4, -2)$ and $\underline{v} = (9, 3)$.

Then

$$\underline{u} \cdot \underline{v} = 4 \times 9 + (-2) \times 3 = 30,$$

$$\|\underline{u}\| = \sqrt{4^2 + (-2)^2} = \sqrt{20},$$

$$\|\underline{v}\| = \sqrt{9^2 + 3^2} = \sqrt{90}.$$

So

$$\cos\theta = \frac{30}{\sqrt{20} \times \sqrt{90}} = \frac{30}{\sqrt{2 \times 900}} = \frac{1}{\sqrt{2}},$$

which gives

$$\theta = \frac{\pi}{4}.$$

**Exercise 3.3**

Find the angle between each of the following pairs of vectors.

(a) (1, 4), (5, 2) (b) (−2, 2), (1, −1) (c) $9\underline{i} - 2\underline{j}$, $\underline{i} + 2\underline{j}$

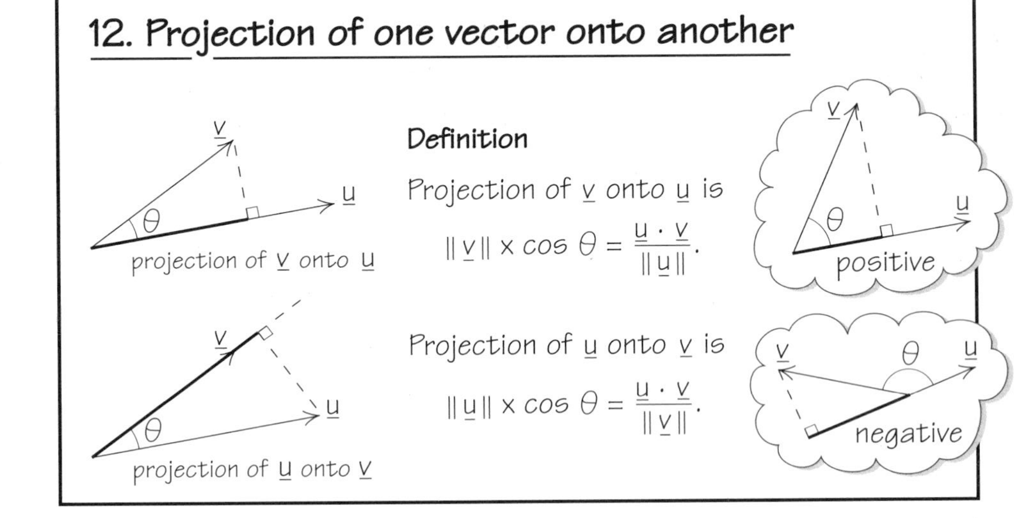


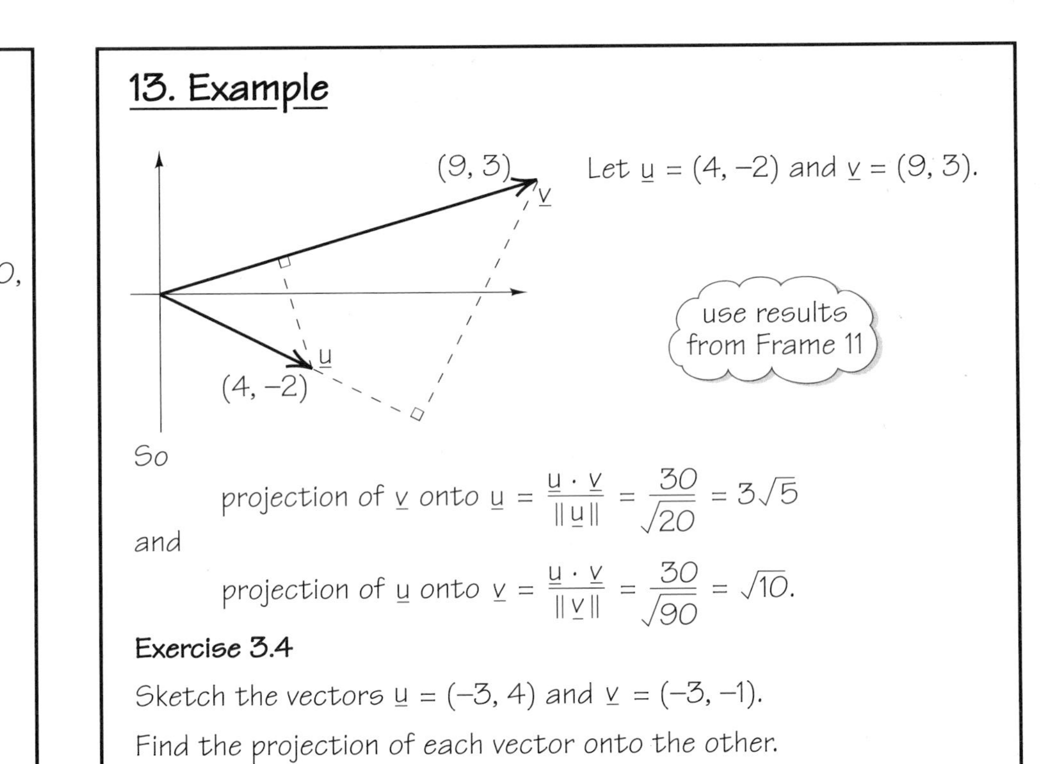

## 14. Dot product in $\mathbb{R}^3$

SAME definition as for $\mathbb{R}^2$

$$\underline{u} \cdot \underline{v} = \|\underline{u}\| \times \|\underline{v}\| \times \cos\theta$$

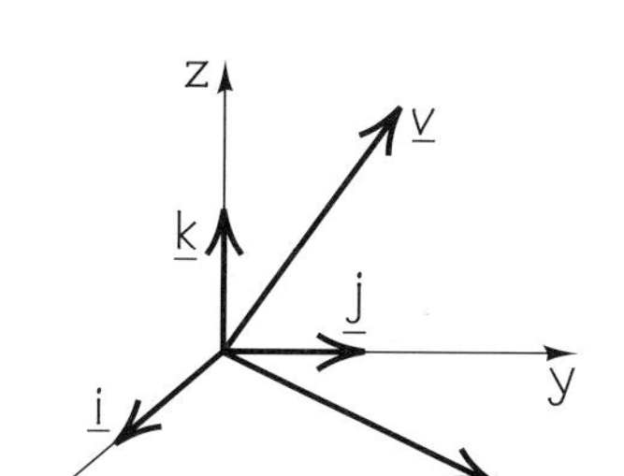


Let $\underline{u} = (x_1, y_1, z_1)$ and $\underline{v} = (x_2, y_2, z_2)$.

Then

$$\underline{u} \cdot \underline{v} = x_1x_2 + y_1y_2 + z_1z_2.$$

SAME properties:

orthogonality, (Frame 4)

symmetry, multiples, distributivity. (Frame 5)

## 15. Angle between vectors $\underline{u}$ and $\underline{v}$ in $\mathbb{R}^3$

In general, $\cos\theta = \dfrac{\underline{u} \cdot \underline{v}}{\|\underline{u}\| \times \|\underline{v}\|}$. (Frame 10)

**Example**

Let $\underline{u} = (3, 1, -1)$ and $\underline{v} = (1, 2, 3)$. Then

$$\underline{u} \cdot \underline{v} = 3 \times 1 + 1 \times 2 + (-1) \times 3 = 2,$$

$$\|\underline{u}\| = \sqrt{3^2 + 1^2 + (-1)^2} = \sqrt{11},$$

$$\|\underline{v}\| = \sqrt{1^2 + 2^2 + 3^2} = \sqrt{14}.$$

So

$$\cos\theta = \frac{2}{\sqrt{11} \times \sqrt{14}} = 0.1612 \quad \text{(to 4 decimal places)}$$

which gives

$$\theta = 1.41 \text{ radians} \quad \text{(to 2 decimal places)}.$$

1.41 radians ≃ 81 degrees

**Exercise 3.5**

Find the angle between each of the following pairs of vectors.

(a) (1, 2, 0), (3, −1, 2) (b) $2\underline{j} - 3\underline{k}$, $-\underline{i} - \underline{j} - 2\underline{k}$

## 16. Example

Find a unit vector $\underline{u}$ perpendicular to both of the vectors $\underline{v} = (0, 1, -1)$ and $\underline{w} = (2, 2, -1)$.

Solution

Let $\underline{u} = (x, y, z)$.

$\|\underline{u}\| = 1 \implies \|\underline{u}\|^2 = 1$

$\implies x^2 + y^2 + z^2 = 1$ (1)

$\underline{u} \cdot \underline{v} = 0 \implies x \times 0 + y \times 1 + z \times (-1) = 0$

$\implies y - z = 0$

$\implies y = z$ (2)

$\underline{u} \cdot \underline{w} = 0 \implies x \times 2 + y \times 2 + z \times (-1) = 0$

$\implies 2x + 2y - z = 0$ (3)

## 17. Example continued

solve (1), (2), (3)

Substitute y for z in (1) and (3).

$x^2 + y^2 + y^2 = 1 \implies x^2 + 2y^2 = 1$ (1′)

$2x + 2y - y = 0 \implies 2x + y = 0$ (3′)

Substitute $-2x$ for y in (1′).

$$x^2 + 2(-2x)^2 = 1 \implies 9x^2 = 1 \implies x = \pm\tfrac{1}{3}$$

When $x = \frac{1}{3}$, $y = -\frac{2}{3}$ and $z = -\frac{2}{3}$, so $\underline{u} = \left(\frac{1}{3}, -\frac{2}{3}, -\frac{2}{3}\right)$.

When $x = -\frac{1}{3}$, $y = \frac{2}{3}$ and $z = \frac{2}{3}$, so $\underline{u} = \left(-\frac{1}{3}, \frac{2}{3}, \frac{2}{3}\right)$.

using (2) and (3′)

Hence there are two possible vectors:

$$\left(\tfrac{1}{3}, -\tfrac{2}{3}, -\tfrac{2}{3}\right) \quad \text{and} \quad \left(-\tfrac{1}{3}, \tfrac{2}{3}, \tfrac{2}{3}\right)$$

same line, opposite directions

## Post-audio exercises

**Exercise 3.6** Let $\mathbf{u}$ and $\mathbf{v}$ be the position vectors $(6, 8)$ and $(-12, 5)$, respectively.

(a) Sketch $\mathbf{u}$ and $\mathbf{v}$ on a single diagram. On the same diagram, sketch the projection of $\mathbf{u}$ onto $\mathbf{v}$, and the projection of $\mathbf{v}$ onto $\mathbf{u}$.

(b) Determine the angle between $\mathbf{u}$ and $\mathbf{v}$.

(c) Determine the projection of $\mathbf{u}$ onto $\mathbf{v}$, and the projection of $\mathbf{v}$ onto $\mathbf{u}$.

**Exercise 3.7** Determine the angle between the vectors $\mathbf{u} = (3, 4, 5)$ and $\mathbf{v} = (1, 0, -1)$ in $\mathbb{R}^3$.

**Exercise 3.8** Find a vector of length 2 that is perpendicular to both of the vectors $\mathbf{a} = (2, 1, 0)$ and $\mathbf{b} = (1, 0, -1)$.

## 3.2 Equation of a plane in $\mathbb{R}^3$

We stated earlier that the general form of the equation of a plane in $\mathbb{R}^3$ is

Subsection 1.2

$$ax + by + cz = d, \tag{3.1}$$

where $a$, $b$ and $c$ are not all zero. We can prove this now, using the dot product.

How can we specify a plane uniquely in $\mathbb{R}^3$? One possibility is to specify three points that lie in the plane. However, this does not enable us to prove equation (3.1) without a significant amount of algebra; so we adopt a different approach.

For a given plane in $\mathbb{R}^3$, there is a particular direction that can be used to specify the plane—the direction perpendicular to all the vectors in that plane.

> **Definition** A vector that is perpendicular to all the vectors in a given plane is called a **normal vector** to the plane.

A normal vector to a plane is also called a *normal* to the plane, and its direction is said to be *normal to* the plane.

If $\mathbf{n}$ is a normal vector to a given plane, then so is $k\mathbf{n}$, for any non-zero real number $k$. If $k > 0$, then $k\mathbf{n}$ is in the same direction as $\mathbf{n}$, whereas if $k < 0$, then $k\mathbf{n}$ is in the opposite direction to $\mathbf{n}$.

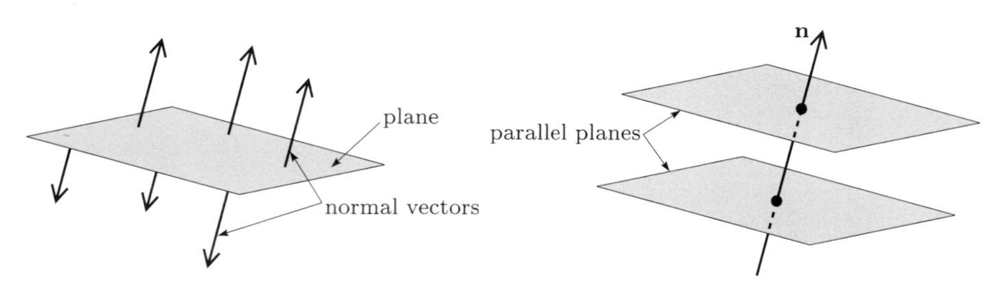


A normal vector $\mathbf{n}$ does not determine a plane uniquely, as there are infinitely many planes that have $\mathbf{n}$ as a normal; these planes are parallel to one another. However, if we specify both a normal vector and a point that lies in the plane, then the plane is determined uniquely.

**Example 3.1** Determine the equation of the plane in $\mathbb{R}^3$ that contains the point $P(2,3,4)$ and has $\mathbf{n} = (1,2,-1)$ as a normal.

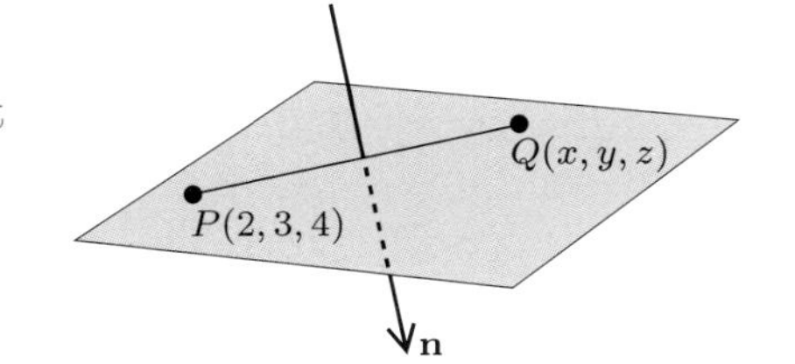


**Solution** If the point $Q(x,y,z)$ lies in the plane, then the vector $\overrightarrow{PQ}$ must be perpendicular to the normal vector $\mathbf{n}$; it follows that $\overrightarrow{PQ} \cdot \mathbf{n}$ must be zero. Hence

$$(x-2, y-3, z-4) \cdot (1,2,-1) = 0,$$

so

$$(x-2) \times 1 + (y-3) \times 2 + (z-4) \times (-1) = 0.$$

This equation can be rearranged in the form

$$x + 2y - z = 4;$$

this is the equation of the plane. ■

In general, let $\mathbf{n} = (a,b,c)$ be normal to a given plane that contains the point $P(x_1, y_1, z_1)$. Then an arbitrary point $Q(x,y,z)$ lies in the plane if and only if the vectors $\overrightarrow{PQ}$ and $\mathbf{n}$ are orthogonal; that is, if and only if $\overrightarrow{PQ} \cdot \mathbf{n} = 0$.

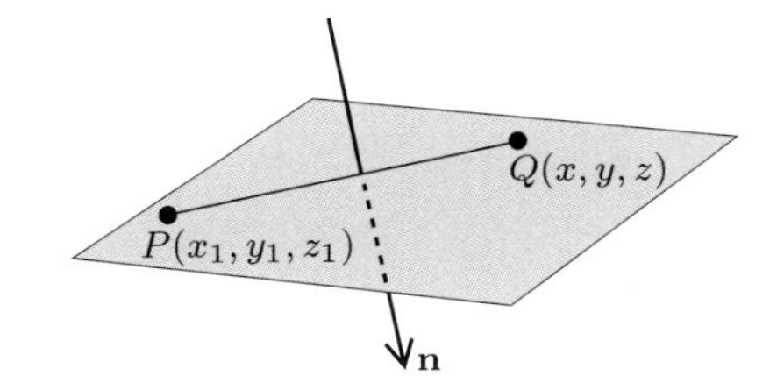


Since $\overrightarrow{PQ} = (x - x_1, y - y_1, z - z_1)$, this condition can be written in the form

$$(x - x_1, y - y_1, z - z_1) \cdot (a,b,c) = 0,$$

so

$$(x - x_1) \times a + (y - y_1) \times b + (z - z_1) \times c = 0.$$

This equation can be rearranged in the form

$$ax + by + cz = ax_1 + by_1 + cz_1,$$

that is,

$$ax + by + cz = d,$$

where $d = ax_1 + by_1 + cz_1$.

**Theorem 3.1** The equation of the plane that contains the point $(x_1, y_1, z_1)$ and has $\mathbf{n} = (a,b,c)$ as a normal is

$$ax + by + cz = d,$$

where $d = ax_1 + by_1 + cz_1$.

Once we know the equation of a plane, we can 'read off' the components of a normal vector as they are the coefficients of $x$, $y$ and $z$ in the equation. For instance, one normal to the plane with equation $x - 2y + 3z = 7$ is $\mathbf{n} = (1,-2,3)$.

We shall not make use of the formula for $d$ given in the above theorem. In practice, it is simpler to use the following corollary.

**Corollary to Theorem 3.1**

The equation of the plane that contains the point $(x_1, y_1, z_1)$ and has $\mathbf{n} = (a, b, c)$ as a normal is

$$\mathbf{x} \cdot \mathbf{n} = \mathbf{p} \cdot \mathbf{n},$$

where $\mathbf{x} = (x, y, z)$ and $\mathbf{p} = (x_1, y_1, z_1)$.

**Proof**

$$\mathbf{x} \cdot \mathbf{n} = (x, y, z) \cdot (a, b, c) = ax + by + cz$$

and

$$\mathbf{p} \cdot \mathbf{n} = (x_1, y_1, z_1) \cdot (a, b, c) = ax_1 + by_1 + cz_1 = d.$$

Since $ax + by + cz = d$, from Theorem 3.1, it follows that $\mathbf{x} \cdot \mathbf{n} = \mathbf{p} \cdot \mathbf{n}$. ■

**Example 3.2** Determine the equation of the plane in $\mathbb{R}^3$ that contains the point $(1, -1, 4)$ and has $(2, -2, 3)$ as a normal.

**Solution** The equation of the plane is

$$\mathbf{x} \cdot \mathbf{n} = \mathbf{p} \cdot \mathbf{n},$$

where $\mathbf{x} = (x, y, z)$, $\mathbf{p} = (1, -1, 4)$ and $\mathbf{n} = (2, -2, 3)$; in other words, the equation of the plane is

$$(x, y, z) \cdot (2, -2, 3) = (1, -1, 4) \cdot (2, -2, 3),$$

that is,

$$2x - 2y + 3z = 1 \times 2 + (-1) \times (-2) + 4 \times 3,$$

or

$$2x - 2y + 3z = 16.$$ ■

**Exercise 3.9** Determine the equation of each of the following planes:

(a) the plane that contains the point $(1, 0, 2)$ and has $(2, 3, 1)$ as a normal;

(b) the plane that contains the point $(-1, 1, 5)$ and has $(4, -2, 1)$ as a normal.

We can use the general form of the equation of a plane to find the *equation of a plane that contains three given points*, as follows. We assume that the equation of the plane is $ax + by + cz = d$, and then substitute the coordinates of the three points in turn into this equation; this gives three simultaneous equations for $a$, $b$ and $c$, which we solve.

Sometimes this method involves rather cumbersome arithmetic. We shall return to the solution of simultaneous equations in Unit LA2.

**Exercise 3.10** Determine the equation of the plane that contains the points $(3, 0, 0)$, $(0, 4, 0)$ and $(3, 4, 5)$.

Write down a vector that is normal to this plane.

## Further exercises

**Exercise 3.11**

(a) Find the angle between each of the pairs of vectors:

$$(3,1) \quad \text{and} \quad (1,-2); \quad \mathbf{i}+2\mathbf{j} \quad \text{and} \quad -3\mathbf{i}+\mathbf{j}-2\mathbf{k}.$$

(b) Determine the projection of $(3,1)$ onto $(1,-2)$, and the projection of $\mathbf{i}+2\mathbf{j}$ onto $-3\mathbf{i}+\mathbf{j}-2\mathbf{k}$.

**Exercise 3.12** Determine the two vectors of length 2 which make an angle of $\pi/4$ with the vector $\mathbf{p}=(2,-2)$. Verify that the two vectors that you have found are perpendicular to each other.

**Exercise 3.13** Determine the equation of the plane that contains the point $(-1,3,2)$ with $(1,2,-1)$ as a normal.

**Exercise 3.14** Determine the equation of the plane through $(1,0,2)$, $(0,3,4)$ and $(0,-1,0)$.

# 4 Conics

After working through this section, you should be able to:

(a) explain the term *conic section*;

(b) determine the *equation of a circle*, given its centre and radius, and the centre and radius of a circle, given its equation;

(c) explain the *focus–directrix definitions* of the non-degenerate conics.

## 4.1 Conic sections

*Conic section* is the collective name given to the shapes that we obtain by taking different plane slices through a double cone. The shapes that we obtain from these cross-sections are drawn overleaf.

It is thought that the Greek mathematician Menaechmus discovered the conic sections around 350 BC.

The circle in slice 7 can be regarded as a special case of an ellipse.

We use the term *non-degenerate conic sections* to describe those conic sections that are parabolas, ellipses or hyperbolas; and the term *degenerate conic sections* to describe the single point, single line and pair of lines.

There are some interesting features of the parabola, ellipse and hyperbola that we note for use later. The ellipse and the hyperbola both have a *centre*; that is, there is a point about which rotation through an angle $\pi$ is a symmetry of the conic. For example, for the ellipse and hyperbola illustrated below, the centre is the origin. On the other hand, the parabola does not have a centre. The hyperbola has two lines, called *asymptotes*, which it approaches.

We usually use 'conic' rather than 'conic section' once we have described how conics arise.

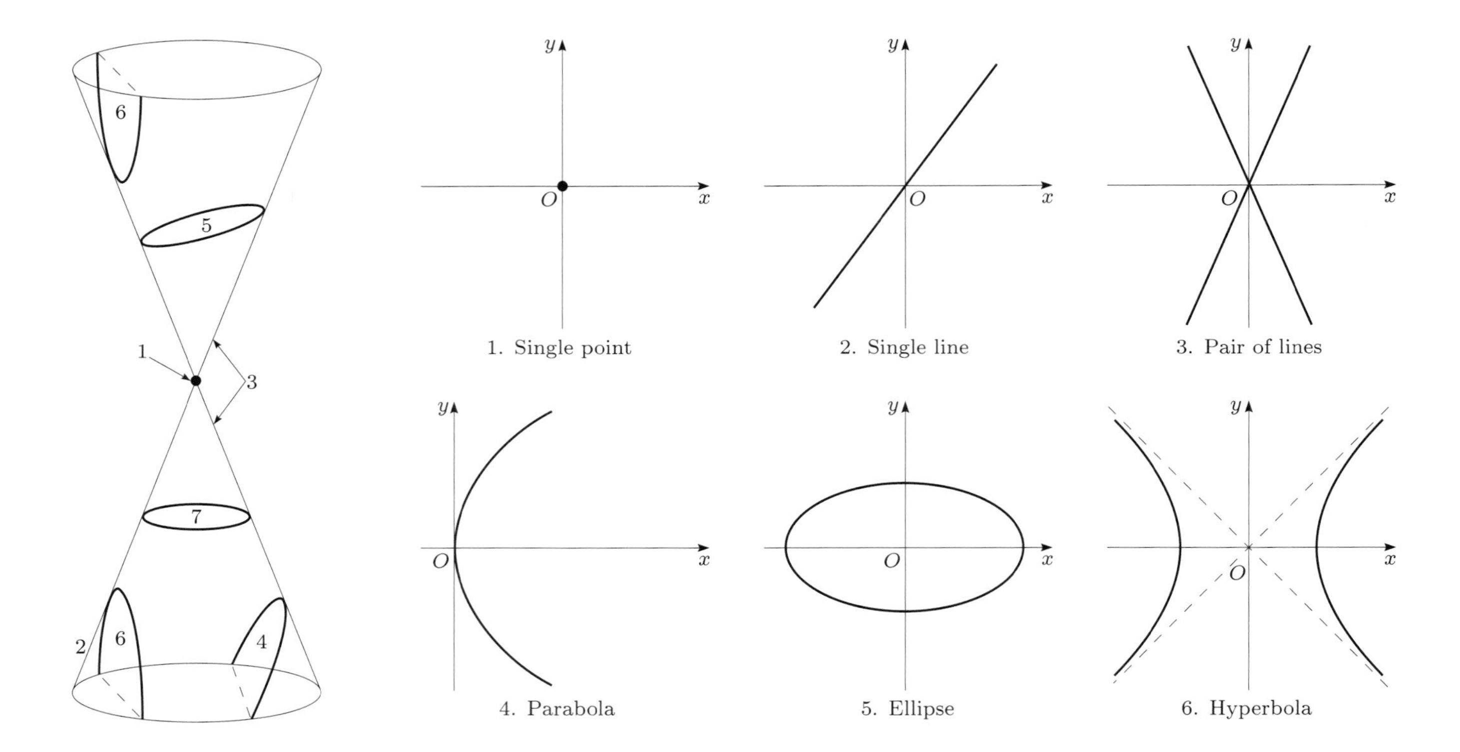


## 4.2 Circles

Recall that a *circle* in $\mathbb{R}^2$ is the set of points $(x, y)$ that lie at a fixed distance, called the *radius*, from a fixed point, called the *centre* of the circle. We can use the techniques of coordinate geometry to find the equation of a circle with a given centre and radius.

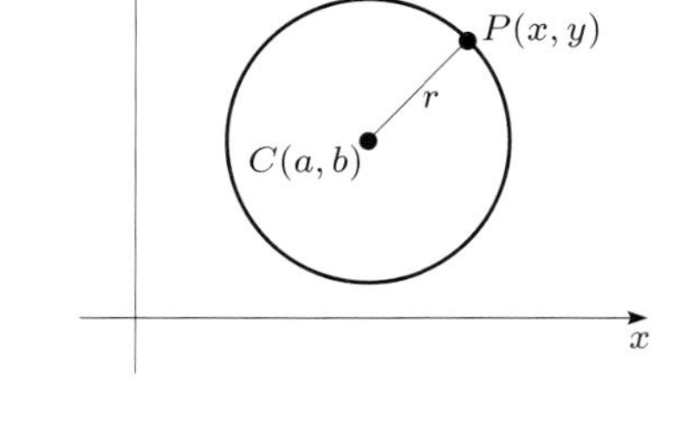


Let a circle have centre $C(a, b)$ and radius $r$. Then, if $P(x, y)$ is an arbitrary point on the circumference of the circle, the distance $CP$ equals $r$. It follows from the formula for the distance between two points in the plane that

Subsection 1.1

$$r^2 = (x - a)^2 + (y - b)^2. \tag{4.1}$$

**Theorem 4.1** The equation of a circle in $\mathbb{R}^2$ with centre $(a, b)$ and radius $r$ is

$$(x - a)^2 + (y - b)^2 = r^2.$$

For example, it follows from this formula that the circle with centre $(-1, 2)$ and radius $\sqrt{3}$ has equation

$$(x - (-1))^2 + (y - 2)^2 = (\sqrt{3})^2,$$

which can be simplified to give

$$x^2 + 2x + 1 + y^2 - 4y + 4 = 3,$$

or

$$x^2 + y^2 + 2x - 4y + 2 = 0.$$

**Exercise 4.1** Determine the equation of each of the following circles, given the centre and radius:

(a) centre the origin, radius 1;

(b) centre the origin, radius 4;

(c) centre $(3, 4)$, radius 2.

If we expand the brackets in equation (4.1) and collect the corresponding terms, we can rewrite equation (4.1) in the form

$$x^2 + y^2 - 2ax - 2by + (a^2 + b^2 - r^2) = 0.$$

Then, if we write $f$ for $-2a$, $g$ for $-2b$ and $h$ for $a^2 + b^2 - r^2$, this equation takes the form

$$x^2 + y^2 + fx + gy + h = 0. \quad (4.2)$$

The coefficients of $x^2$ and $y^2$ are equal.

In many situations, equation (4.1) is more useful than equation (4.2) for determining the equation of a particular circle.

We have seen that the equation of a circle can be written in the form

$$x^2 + y^2 + fx + gy + h = 0. \quad (4.2)$$

On the other hand, given an equation of the form (4.2), can we determine whether it represents a circle? If it does represent a circle, can we determine its centre and radius?

For example, consider the set of points $(x, y)$ in the plane that satisfy the equation

$$x^2 + y^2 - 4x + 6y + 9 = 0. \quad (4.3)$$

In equation (4.3) the coefficients of $x^2$ and $y^2$ are both 1.

In order to transform equation (4.3) into an equation of the form (4.1), we use a technique called 'completing the square'. We rewrite the terms that involve only $x$ and the terms that involve only $y$, as follows:

$$x^2 - 4x = (x - 2)^2 - 4,$$
$$y^2 + 6y = (y + 3)^2 - 9.$$

$-2$ is half the coefficient of $x$ and $+3$ is half the coefficient of $y$ in equation (4.3).

Substituting these expressions into equation (4.3), we obtain

$$((x - 2)^2 - 4) + ((y + 3)^2 - 9) + 9 = 0,$$

that is,

$$(x - 2)^2 + (y + 3)^2 = 4.$$

We can 'read off' the centre and radius of the circle from this equation.

It follows that equation (4.3) represents a circle with centre $(2, -3)$ and radius 2.

In general, we can use the same method, 'completing the square', to rewrite the equation

$$x^2 + y^2 + fx + gy + h = 0$$

Again, the coefficients of $x^2$ and $y^2$ are both 1.

in the form

$$\left(x + \tfrac{1}{2}f\right)^2 + \left(y + \tfrac{1}{2}g\right)^2 = \tfrac{1}{4}f^2 + \tfrac{1}{4}g^2 - h, \quad (4.4)$$

from which we can 'read off' the centre and radius.

The constant in the first bracket is half the coefficient of $x$ in the previous equation, and the constant in the second bracket is half the coefficient of $y$.

**Theorem 4.2** An equation of the form

$$x^2 + y^2 + fx + gy + h = 0$$

represents a circle with

$$\text{centre } \left(-\tfrac{1}{2}f, -\tfrac{1}{2}g\right) \quad \text{and} \quad \text{radius } \sqrt{\tfrac{1}{4}f^2 + \tfrac{1}{4}g^2 - h}$$

if and only if $\frac{1}{4}f^2 + \frac{1}{4}g^2 - h > 0$.

*Remark* It follows from equation (4.4) that if $\frac{1}{4}f^2 + \frac{1}{4}g^2 - h < 0$, then there are no points $(x, y)$ that satisfy the equation $x^2 + y^2 + fx + gy + h = 0$; and if $\frac{1}{4}f^2 + \frac{1}{4}g^2 - h = 0$, then the given equation simply represents the single point $\left(-\frac{1}{2}f, -\frac{1}{2}g\right)$.

**Exercise 4.2** Determine the condition on the numbers $f$, $g$ and $h$ in the equation

$$x^2 + y^2 + fx + gy + h = 0$$

for the circle with this equation to pass through the origin.

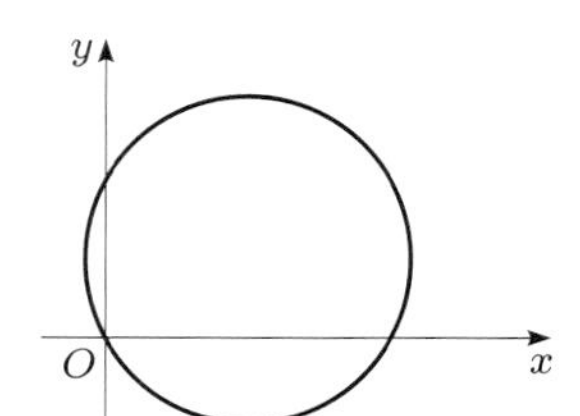


**Exercise 4.3** Determine the centre and radius of each of the circles given by the following equations.

(a) $x^2 + y^2 - 2x - 6y + 1 = 0$

(b) $3x^2 + 3y^2 - 12x - 48y = 0$

**Exercise 4.4** Determine the set of points $(x, y)$ in $\mathbb{R}^2$ that satisfy each of the following equations.

(a) $x^2 + y^2 + x + y + 1 = 0$

(b) $x^2 + y^2 - 2x + 4y + 5 = 0$

(c) $2x^2 + 2y^2 + x - 3y - 5 = 0$

## 4.3 Focus–directrix definitions of the non-degenerate conics

Earlier, we defined the conic sections as the curves of intersection of planes with a double cone. One of these conic sections, the circle, can be defined as the set of points a fixed distance from a fixed point.

We met these conics briefly in Unit I1.

Here we define the other non-degenerate conics, the parabola, ellipse and hyperbola, as sets of points that satisfy a somewhat similar condition.

These three *non-degenerate conics* (the parabola, ellipse and hyperbola) can be defined as the set of points $P$ in the plane that satisfy the following condition: the distance of $P$ from a fixed point is a constant multiple $e$ of the distance of $P$ from a fixed line. The fixed point is called the *focus* of the conic, the fixed line is called its *directrix*, and the constant multiple $e$ is called its *eccentricity*.

The different conics arise according to the value $e$ of the eccentricity, as follows.

> **Eccentricity** A non-degenerate conic is
>
> an ellipse if $0 \leq e < 1$,
> a parabola if $e = 1$,
> a hyperbola if $e > 1$.

When $e = 0$, the ellipse is a circle; the focus is the centre of the circle, and the directrix is 'at infinity'.

## Parabola ($e = 1$)

A *parabola* is defined to be the set of points $P$ in the plane whose distances from a fixed point $F$ are equal to their distances from a fixed line $d$. We obtain a parabola *in standard form* if

1. the focus $F$ lies on the $x$-axis, and has coordinates $(a, 0)$, where $a > 0$;
2. the directrix $d$ is the line with equation $x = -a$.

Thus the origin lies on the parabola, since it is equidistant from $F$ and $d$.

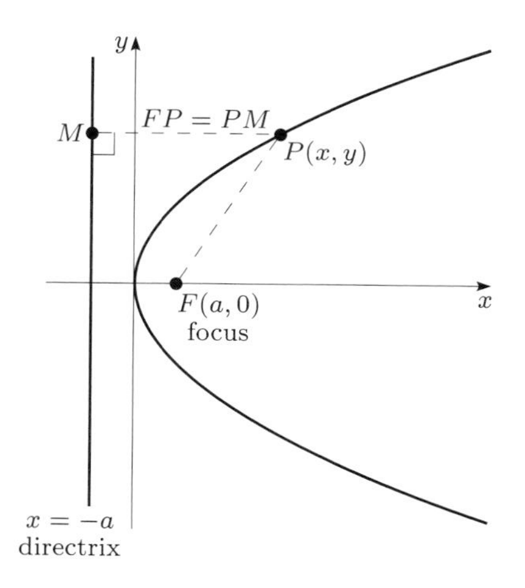


Let $P(x, y)$ be an arbitrary point on the parabola, and let $M$ be the foot of the perpendicular from $P$ to the directrix. Since $FP = PM$, by the definition of the parabola, it follows that $FP^2 = PM^2$; that is,

$$(x - a)^2 + (y - 0)^2 = (x + a)^2.$$

Multiplying out the brackets, we obtain

$$x^2 - 2ax + a^2 + y^2 = x^2 + 2ax + a^2,$$

which simplifies to the equation

$$y^2 = 4ax.$$

Each point with coordinates of the form $(at^2, 2at)$, where $t \in \mathbb{R}$, lies on the parabola, since $(2at)^2 = 4a \times at^2$. Conversely, we can write the coordinates of each point on the parabola in the form $(at^2, 2at)$. If we choose $t = y/(2a)$, then $y = 2at$ and

$$x = \frac{y^2}{4a} \quad \text{(from the equation } y^2 = 4ax\text{)}$$
$$= \frac{(2at)^2}{4a} = at^2,$$

as required. Thus there is a one-one correspondence between the real numbers $t$ and the points of the parabola.

We call the $x$-axis the *axis* of a parabola in standard form, since the parabola is symmetric with respect to this line, and we call the origin the *vertex* of a parabola in standard form, since it is the point of intersection of the axis with the parabola. A parabola has no centre.

We summarise these facts as follows.

> **Parabola in standard form** A parabola in standard form has equation
>
> $$y^2 = 4ax, \quad \text{where } a > 0.$$
>
> It can also be described by the parametric equations
>
> $$x = at^2, \quad y = 2at \quad (t \in \mathbb{R}).$$
>
> It has focus $(a, 0)$ and directrix $x = -a$; its axis is the $x$-axis and its vertex is the origin.

**Example 4.1** Consider the parabola with equation $y^2 = 2x$ and parametric equations $x = \frac{1}{2}t^2$, $y = t$ $(t \in \mathbb{R})$.

(a) Write down the focus, vertex, axis and directrix of the parabola.

(b) Determine the equation of the chord that joins the two distinct points $P$ and $Q$ with parameters $t_1$ and $t_2$, respectively. Determine the condition on $t_1$ and $t_2$ such that the chord $PQ$ passes through the focus of the parabola.

Such a chord is called a *focal chord*.

**Solution**

(a) The parabola is in standard form, where $4a = 2$, that is, $a = \frac{1}{2}$. It follows that its focus is $\left(\frac{1}{2}, 0\right)$, its vertex is $(0, 0)$, its axis is the $x$-axis and the equation of its directrix is $x = -\frac{1}{2}$.

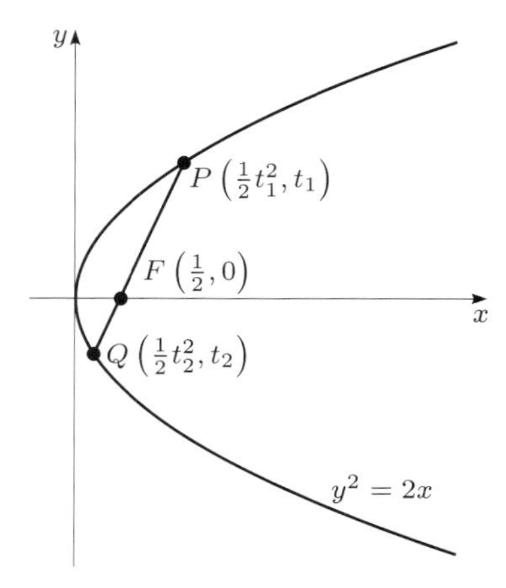


(b) The coordinates of $P$ and $Q$ are $\left(\frac{1}{2}t_1^2, t_1\right)$ and $\left(\frac{1}{2}t_2^2, t_2\right)$, respectively. We must consider the cases $t_1^2 \neq t_2^2$ and $t_1^2 = t_2^2$ separately.

We suppose first that $t_1^2 \neq t_2^2$. Then the gradient of $PQ$ is

$$\frac{t_1 - t_2}{\frac{1}{2}t_1^2 - \frac{1}{2}t_2^2} = \frac{t_1 - t_2}{\frac{1}{2}(t_1^2 - t_2^2)} = \frac{2}{t_1 + t_2}.$$

Since $\left(\frac{1}{2}t_1^2, t_1\right)$ lies on the line $PQ$, the equation of $PQ$ is

$$y - t_1 = \frac{2}{t_1 + t_2}\left(x - \frac{1}{2}t_1^2\right).$$

Multiplying both sides by $t_1 + t_2$, we obtain

$$(t_1 + t_2)(y - t_1) = 2x - t_1^2,$$

so

$$(t_1 + t_2)y - t_1^2 - t_1t_2 = 2x - t_1^2,$$

and hence

$$(t_1 + t_2)y = 2x + t_1t_2. \tag{4.5}$$

If $t_1^2 = t_2^2$, then $t_1 = -t_2$ (as $t_1 \neq t_2$, since $P$ and $Q$ are distinct). When $t_1 = -t_2$, $PQ$ is parallel to the $y$-axis and the equation of $PQ$ is $x = \frac{1}{2}t_1^2 = -\frac{1}{2}t_1t_2$, that is,

$$0 = 2x + t_1t_2.$$

Thus equation (4.5) is the equation of $PQ$ in the case $t_1 = -t_2$ also, for then $t_1 + t_2 = 0$.

Thus $PQ$ passes through the focus $\left(\frac{1}{2}, 0\right)$ if and only if $\left(\frac{1}{2}, 0\right)$ satisfies equation (4.5), which is the case if and only if

$$(t_1 + t_2)\,0 = 1 + t_1t_2;$$

that is, if and only if $t_1t_2 = -1$. ■

**Exercise 4.5** Consider the parabola with equation $y^2 = x$ and parametric equations $x = \frac{1}{4}t^2$, $y = \frac{1}{2}t$ $(t \in \mathbb{R})$.

(a) Write down the focus, vertex, axis and directrix.

(b) Determine the equation of the chord that joins the two distinct points $P$ and $Q$ with parameters $t_1$ and $t_2$, respectively.

(c) Determine the condition on $t_1$ and $t_2$, and so on $P$ and $Q$, such that the focus of the parabola is the midpoint of the chord $PQ$.

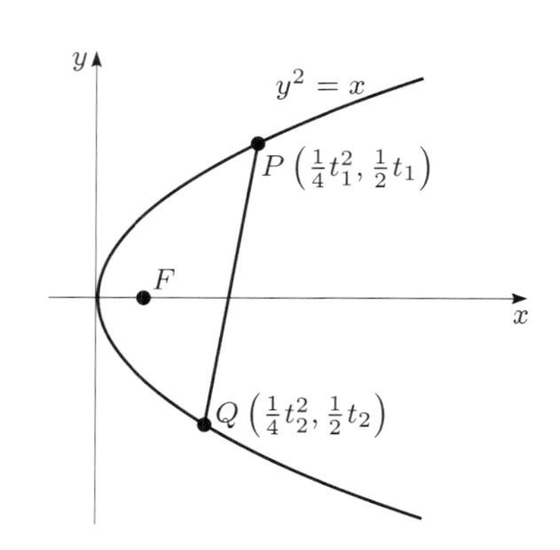

## Ellipse ($0 < e < 1$)

An *ellipse* with eccentricity $e$ (where $0 < e < 1$) is the set of points $P$ in the plane whose distances from a fixed point $F$ are $e$ times their distances from a fixed line $d$. We obtain such an ellipse *in standard form* if

1. the focus $F$ lies on the $x$-axis, and has coordinates $(ae, 0)$, where $a > 0$;
2. the directrix $d$ is the line with equation $x = a/e$.

Let $P(x, y)$ be an arbitrary point on the ellipse, and let $M$ be the foot of the perpendicular from $P$ to the directrix. Since $FP = e \times PM$, by the definition of the ellipse, it follows that $FP^2 = e^2 \times PM^2$; that is,

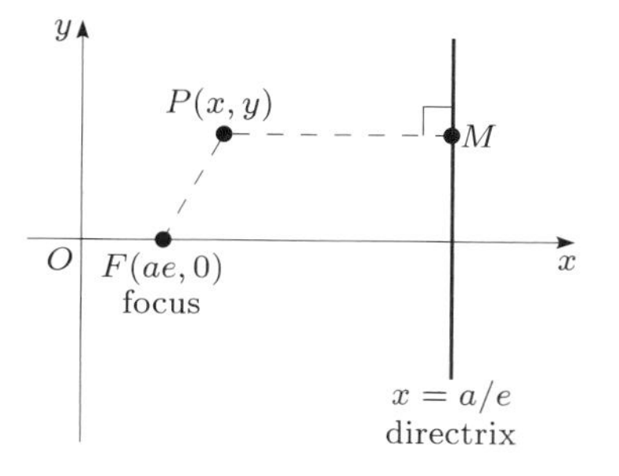


$$\begin{aligned}(x - ae)^2 + y^2 &= e^2\left(x - \frac{a}{e}\right)^2 \\ &= (ex - a)^2.\end{aligned}$$

Multiplying out the brackets, we obtain

$$x^2 - 2aex + a^2e^2 + y^2 = e^2x^2 - 2aex + a^2,$$

which simplifies to the equation

$$x^2(1 - e^2) + y^2 = a^2(1 - e^2),$$

that is,

$$\frac{x^2}{a^2} + \frac{y^2}{a^2(1 - e^2)} = 1.$$

Substituting $b$ for $a\sqrt{1 - e^2}$, so that $b^2 = a^2(1 - e^2)$, we obtain the standard form of the equation of the ellipse

$$\frac{x^2}{a^2} + \frac{y^2}{b^2} = 1.$$

This equation is symmetric in $x$ and in $y$, so that the ellipse also has a second focus $F'$ at $(-ae, 0)$, and a second directrix $d'$ with equation $x = -a/e$.

The ellipse intersects the axes at the points $(\pm a, 0)$ and $(0, \pm b)$. We call the line segment joining the points $(\pm a, 0)$ the *major axis* of the ellipse, and the line segment joining the points $(0, \pm b)$ the *minor axis* of the ellipse. Since $b < a$, the minor axis is shorter than the major axis. The origin is the centre of this ellipse.

Since $0 < e < 1$, we have $0 < b < a$.

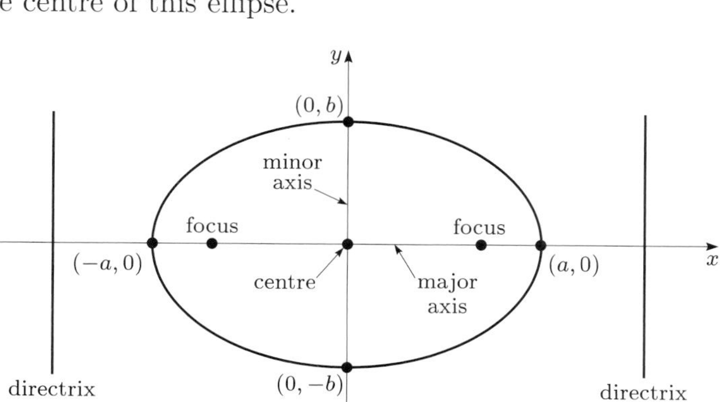


Each point with coordinates $(a\cos t, b\sin t)$ lies on the ellipse, since

$$\frac{(a\cos t)^2}{a^2} + \frac{(b\sin t)^2}{b^2} = \cos^2 t + \sin^2 t = 1.$$

Then, just as for the parabola, we can check that

$$x = a\cos t, \quad y = b\sin t \quad (t \in \mathbb{R})$$

gives a parametric representation of the ellipse.

An ellipse with eccentricity $e = 0$ is a circle. In this case, $a = b$ and the circle $x^2 + y^2 = a^2$ can be parametrised by

$$x = a\cos t, \quad y = a\sin t \quad (t \in \mathbb{R}).$$

We summarise these facts about ellipses (including circles) as follows.

**Ellipse in standard form** An ellipse in standard form has equation

$$\frac{x^2}{a^2} + \frac{y^2}{b^2} = 1, \quad \text{where } a \geq b > 0,\ b^2 = a^2(1 - e^2),\ 0 \leq e < 1.$$

It can also be described by the parametric equations

$$x = a\cos t, \quad y = b\sin t \quad (t \in \mathbb{R}).$$

If $e > 0$, it has foci $(\pm ae, 0)$ and directrices $x = \pm a/e$; its major axis is the line segment joining the points $(\pm a, 0)$, and its minor axis is the line segment joining the points $(0, \pm b)$.

If $e = 0$, the ellipse is a circle.

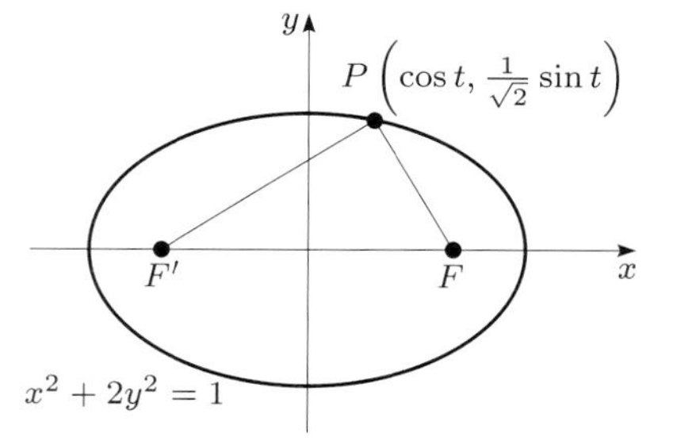


**Exercise 4.6** Let $P$ be a point $\left(\cos t, \frac{1}{\sqrt{2}}\sin t\right)$, $t \in \mathbb{R}$, on the ellipse with equation $x^2 + 2y^2 = 1$.

(a) Determine the foci $F$ and $F'$ of the ellipse.

(b) Determine the gradients of $FP$ and $F'P$, when these lines are not parallel to the $y$-axis.

(c) Find those points $P$ on the ellipse for which $FP$ is perpendicular to $F'P$.

## Hyperbola ($e > 1$)

A *hyperbola* is the set of points $P$ in the plane whose distances from a fixed point $F$ are $e$ times their distances from a fixed line $d$, where $e > 1$. We obtain a hyperbola *in standard form* if

1. the focus $F$ lies on the $x$-axis, and has coordinates $(ae, 0)$, where $a > 0$;
2. the directrix $d$ is the line with equation $x = a/e$.

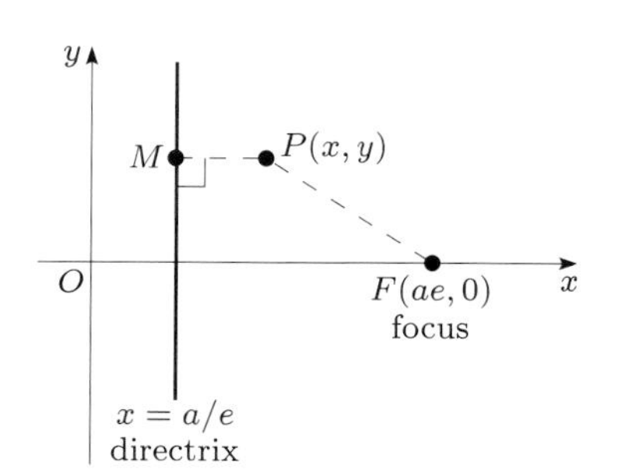


Let $P(x, y)$ be an arbitrary point on the hyperbola, and let $M$ be the foot of the perpendicular from $P$ to the directrix. Since $FP = e \times PM$, by the definition of the hyperbola, it follows that $FP^2 = e^2 \times PM^2$; that is,

$$\begin{aligned}(x - ae)^2 + y^2 &= e^2\left(x - \frac{a}{e}\right)^2 \\ &= (ex - a)^2.\end{aligned}$$

Multiplying out the brackets, we obtain

$$x^2 - 2aex + a^2e^2 + y^2 = e^2x^2 - 2aex + a^2,$$

which simplifies to the equation

$$x^2(e^2 - 1) - y^2 = a^2(e^2 - 1),$$

that is,

$$\frac{x^2}{a^2} - \frac{y^2}{a^2(e^2 - 1)} = 1.$$

Substituting $b$ for $a\sqrt{e^2 - 1}$, so that $b^2 = a^2(e^2 - 1)$, we obtain the standard form of the equation of the hyperbola

$$\frac{x^2}{a^2} - \frac{y^2}{b^2} = 1.$$

This equation is symmetric in $x$ and in $y$, so that the hyperbola also has a second focus $F'$ at $(-ae, 0)$, and a second directrix $d'$ with equation $x = -a/e$.

The hyperbola intersects the $x$-axis at the points $(\pm a, 0)$. We call the line segment joining the points $(\pm a, 0)$ the *major axis* or *transverse axis* of the hyperbola, and the line segment joining the points $(0, \pm b)$ the *minor axis* or *conjugate axis* of the hyperbola (this is NOT a chord of the hyperbola). The origin is the centre of this hyperbola.

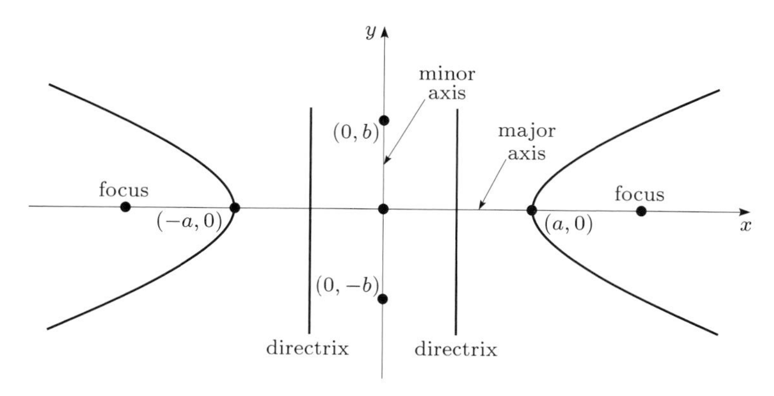


Each point with coordinates $(a \sec t, b \tan t)$ lies on the hyperbola, since

$$\frac{a^2 \sec^2 t}{a^2} - \frac{b^2 \tan^2 t}{b^2} = 1.$$

In general,
$$\sec^2 t = 1 + \tan^2 t.$$

Then, just as for the parabola, we can check that

$$x = a \sec t, \quad y = b \tan t \quad \left(t \in [-\pi, \pi] \text{ excluding } -\frac{\pi}{2} \text{ and } \frac{\pi}{2}\right)$$

gives a parametric representation of the hyperbola.

An alternative parametrisation, using hyperbolic functions, is $x = a \cosh t$, $y = b \sinh t$ $(t \in \mathbb{R})$.

Two other features of the shape of the hyperbola stand out.

First, the hyperbola consists of two separate curves or *branches*.

Secondly, the lines with equations $y = \pm bx/a$ divide the plane into two pairs of opposite sectors; the branches of the hyperbola lie in one pair. As $x \to \pm\infty$, the branches of the hyperbola get closer and closer to these two lines. We call the lines $y = \pm bx/a$ the *asymptotes* of the hyperbola.

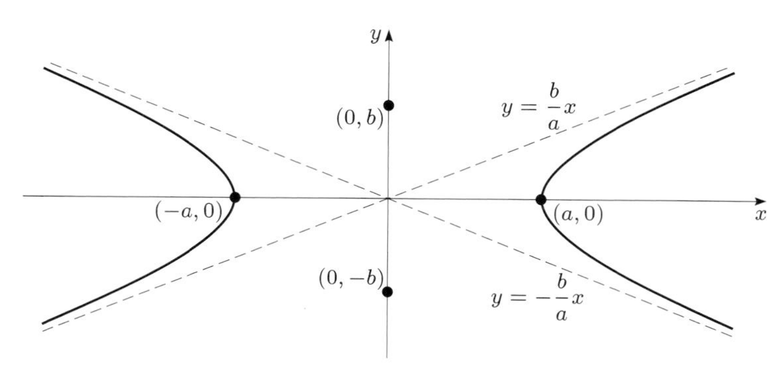


We summarise these facts as follows.

**Hyperbola in standard form** A hyperbola in standard form has equation

$$\frac{x^2}{a^2} - \frac{y^2}{b^2} = 1, \quad \text{where } b^2 = a^2(e^2 - 1),\ e > 1.$$

It can also be described by the parametric equations

$$x = a\sec t, \quad y = b\tan t \quad \left(t \in [-\pi, \pi] \text{ excluding } -\frac{\pi}{2} \text{ and } \frac{\pi}{2}\right).$$

It has foci $(\pm ae, 0)$ and directrices $x = \pm a/e$; its major axis is the line segment joining the points $(\pm a, 0)$, and its minor axis is the line segment joining the points $(0, \pm b)$.

**Exercise 4.7** Let $P$ be a point $\left(\sec t, \frac{1}{\sqrt{2}}\tan t\right)$, $t \in \mathbb{R}$, on the hyperbola with equation $x^2 - 2y^2 = 1$.

(a) Determine the foci $F$ and $F'$ of the hyperbola.

(b) Determine the gradients of $FP$ and $F'P$, when these lines are not parallel to the $y$-axis.

(c) Find the point $P$ on the hyperbola, in the first quadrant, for which $FP$ is perpendicular to $F'P$.

### Rectangular hyperbola ($e = \sqrt{2}$)

If the eccentricity $e$ of a hyperbola is equal to $\sqrt{2}$, then $e^2 = 2$ and $b = a$. Then the asymptotes of the hyperbola have equations $y = \pm x$, so they are at right angles. A hyperbola whose asymptotes are at right angles is called a *rectangular hyperbola*.

Then, if we use the asymptotes as new $x$- and $y$-axes (instead of the original $x$- and $y$-axes), the equation of the hyperbola can be written in the form $xy = c^2$, for some positive number $c$. (We omit the details.)

The rectangular hyperbola with equation $xy = c^2$ has the origin as its centre, and the $x$- and $y$-axes as its asymptotes. It can be described by the parametric equations

$$x = ct, \quad y = \frac{c}{t}, \quad \text{where } t \neq 0.$$

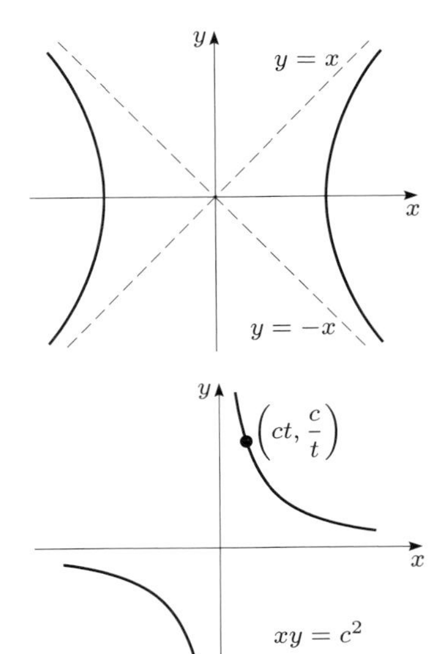


## 4.4 General equation of a conic

You have already met the parabola, ellipse and hyperbola. So far, you have considered the equation of a conic only when it is in standard form; that is, when the centre of the conic (if it has a centre) is at the origin, and the axes of the conic are parallel to the $x$- and $y$-axes. However, most of the conics that arise in calculations are not in standard form.

We have seen that any circle can be described by an equation of the form

$$x^2 + y^2 + fx + gy + h = 0. \tag{4.6}$$

More generally, it can be shown that any conic can be described by an equation of the form

$$Ax^2 + Bxy + Cy^2 + Fx + Gy + H = 0, \tag{4.7}$$

where $A$, $B$ and $C$ are not all zero.

Equation (4.6) is of the form (4.7) with $A = C = 1$ and $B = 0$.

We know that the equations of the non-degenerate conics in standard form are

$$y^2 = 4ax, \quad \frac{x^2}{a^2} + \frac{y^2}{b^2} = 1 \quad \text{and} \quad \frac{x^2}{a^2} - \frac{y^2}{b^2} = 1.$$

Each of these equations is of the form (4.7).

The equations of degenerate conics can also be expressed in the form (4.7). For example:

$x^2 + y^2 = 0$ represents the single point $(0,0)$;

$y^2 - 2xy + x^2 = 0$ represents the single line $y = x$, since $y^2 - 2xy + x^2 = (y-x)^2$;

$y^2 - x^2 = 0$ represents the pair of lines $y = \pm x$, since $y^2 - x^2 = (y+x)(y-x)$.

However, an equation of the form (4.7) can also describe the empty set; an example of this is the equation $x^2 + y^2 + 1 = 0$, as there is no point $(x, y)$ in $\mathbb{R}^2$ for which $x^2 + y^2 = -1$. For simplicity in the statement of the theorem below, therefore, we add the empty set to our existing list of degenerate conics.

This is an unexpected possibility!

**Theorem 4.3** Any conic has an equation of the form

$$Ax^2 + Bxy + Cy^2 + Fx + Gy + H = 0, \tag{4.7}$$

where $A$, $B$, $C$, $F$, $G$ and $H$ are real numbers, and $A$, $B$ and $C$ are not all zero. Conversely, the set of all points in $\mathbb{R}^2$ whose coordinates $(x, y)$ satisfy an equation of the form (4.7) is a conic.

We omit a proof of this result.

Given the general equation (4.7) of a non-degenerate conic, we should like to be able to decide whether it represents an ellipse, hyperbola or parabola. A method of classifying a non-degenerate conic, given its equation, will be established in Unit LA5.

## Further exercises

**Exercise 4.8** Determine the equation of the circle with centre $(2, 1)$ and radius 3.

**Exercise 4.9** Determine the points of intersection of the line with equation $y = x + 2$ and the circle in Exercise 4.8.

**Exercise 4.10** This question concerns the parabola $y^2 = 4ax$ $(a > 0)$ with parametric equations $x = at^2$, $y = 2at$ and focus $F$. Let $P$ and $Q$ be points on the parabola with parameters $t_1$ and $t_2$, respectively. Prove that:

(a) if $PQ$ subtends a right angle at the vertex $O$ of the parabola, then $t_1t_2 = -4$;

(b) if $t_1 = 2$ and $PQ$ is perpendicular to $FP$, then $t_2 = -\frac{14}{3}$.

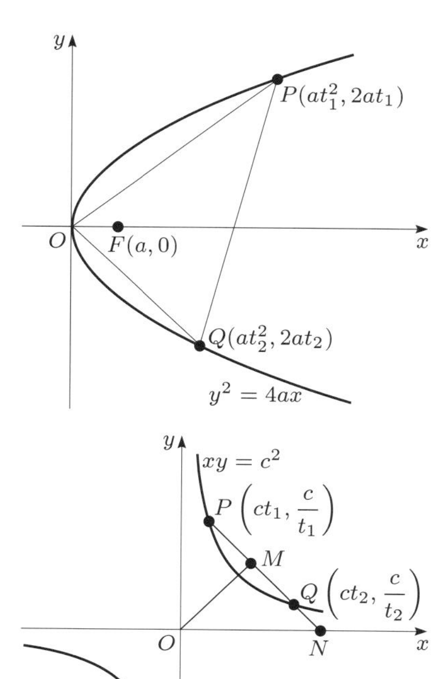


**Exercise 4.11** This question concerns the rectangular hyperbola $xy = c^2$ $(c > 0)$ with parametric equations $x = ct$, $y = c/t$. Let $P$ and $Q$ be points on the hyperbola with parameters $t_1$ and $t_2$, respectively.

(a) Determine the equation of the chord $PQ$.

(b) Determine the coordinates of the point $N$ where $PQ$ meets the $x$-axis.

(c) Determine the midpoint $M$ of $PQ$.

(d) Prove that $OM = MN$, where $O$ is the origin.

# Solutions to the exercises

**1.1** Using the formula for the equation of a line when given its gradient and one point on it, we find that the equation of this line is

$$y - (-1) = -3(x - 2).$$

We can rearrange this in the form

$$y = -3x + 5.$$

**1.2 (a)** Since $(1, 1)$ and $(3, 5)$ lie on the line, its gradient is

$$m = \frac{1-5}{1-3} = 2.$$

Then, since the point $(1, 1)$ lies on the line, its equation must be

$$y - 1 = 2(x - 1),$$

or

$$y = 2x - 1.$$

**(b)** Both these points have $x$-coordinate 0, so they lie on the line with equation $x = 0$, the $y$-axis.

**(c)** Since the origin lies on the line, its equation must be of the form $y = mx$, where $m$ is its gradient. Since $(4, 2)$ lies on the line, its coordinates must satisfy the equation of the line. Thus $2 = 4m$, so $m = \frac{1}{2}$.

Hence the equation of this line is $y = \frac{1}{2}x$.

**(d)** Both these points have $y$-coordinate $-1$, so they lie on the line with equation $y = -1$.

**1.3** Since the gradient of a line whose equation is in the form $y = mx + c$ is $m$, the gradients of the given lines are $-2$, $2$, $-\frac{1}{2}$, $\frac{1}{2}$, $\frac{1}{2}$ and $-2$, respectively. Thus $\ell_1$ and $\ell_6$ are parallel, and $\ell_4$ and $\ell_5$ are parallel; $\ell_1$ and $\ell_4$ are perpendicular, $\ell_1$ and $\ell_5$ are perpendicular, $\ell_2$ and $\ell_3$ are perpendicular, $\ell_4$ and $\ell_6$ are perpendicular, and $\ell_5$ and $\ell_6$ are perpendicular.

**1.4 (a)** These lines have gradients $\frac{1}{2}$ and 2, and $y$-intercepts 1 and $-1$, respectively. This enables us to sketch the lines. They intersect at a single point, in the right half-plane.

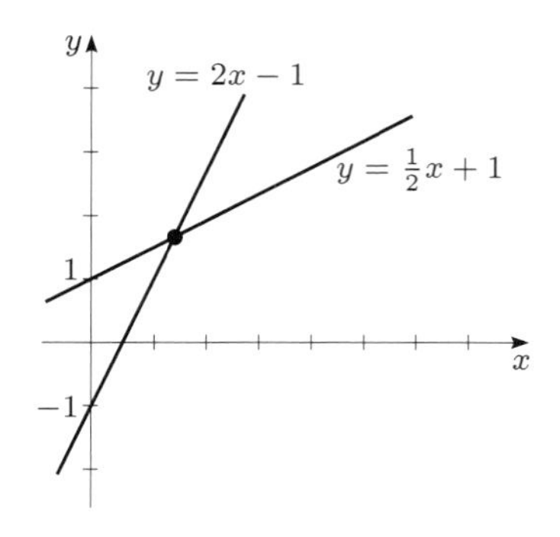


At the point of intersection,

$$\tfrac{1}{2}x + 1 = 2x - 1,$$

so

$$\tfrac{3}{2}x = 2, \quad \text{that is,} \quad x = \tfrac{4}{3}.$$

Substituting for $x$ in the equation of the second line, we obtain

$$y = 2 \times \tfrac{4}{3} - 1 = \tfrac{5}{3}.$$

Thus the point of intersection of the lines is $\left(\frac{4}{3}, \frac{5}{3}\right)$.

**(b)** These lines both have gradient 2. However, since they have different $y$-intercepts, $-1$ and $\frac{1}{2}$, they do not coincide and so they are parallel.

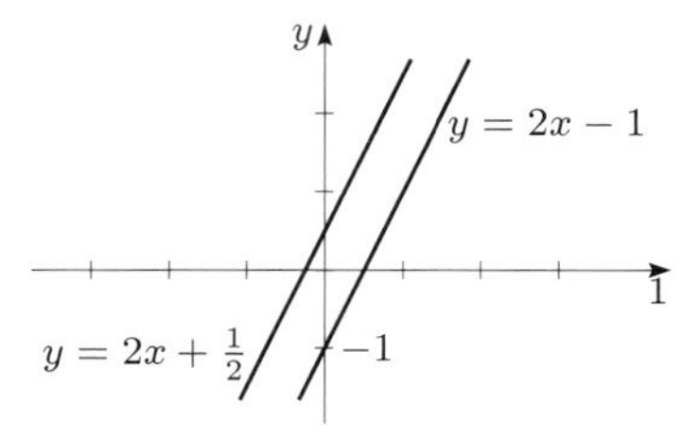


**(c)** These two lines coincide, since the equation of the second line is the equation of the first multiplied by $\frac{3}{2}$.

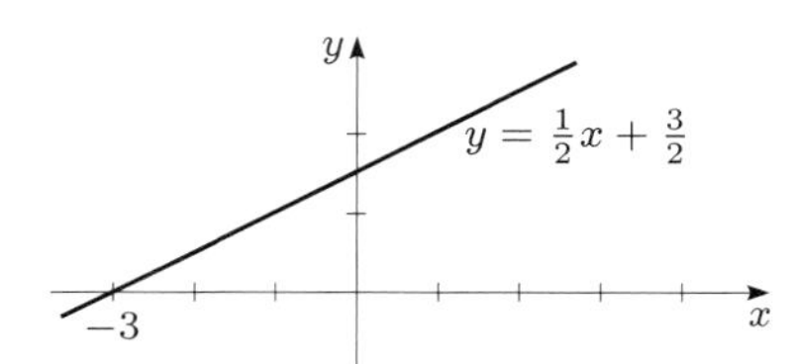


**(d)** These lines have gradients 7 and $-1$, and $y$-intercepts $-1$ and 0, respectively. This enables us to sketch the lines. They intersect at a single point, in the right half-plane.

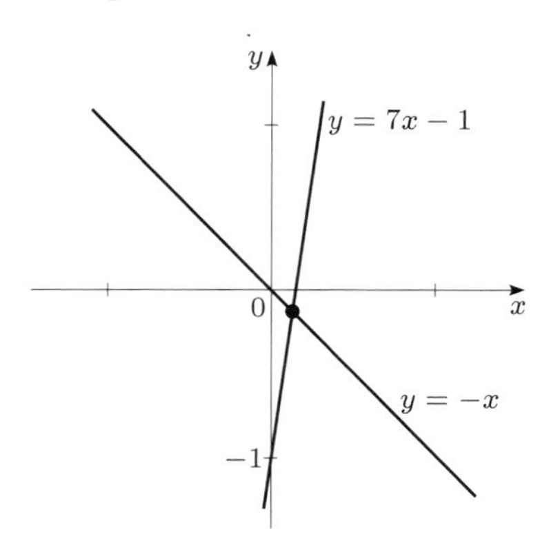


At the point of intersection,

$$7x - 1 = -x,$$

so

$$8x = 1, \quad \text{that is,} \quad x = \tfrac{1}{8}.$$

Substituting for $x$ in the equation of the second line,

$$y = -\tfrac{1}{8}.$$

Thus the point of intersection of the lines is $\left(\frac{1}{8}, -\frac{1}{8}\right)$.

**1.5** We use the formula for the distance between two points in the plane. This gives the following distances.

(a) $\sqrt{(5-0)^2 + (0-0)^2} = 5$

(b) $\sqrt{(3-0)^2 + (4-0)^2} = 5$

(c) $\sqrt{(5-1)^2 + (1-2)^2} = \sqrt{17}$

(d) $\sqrt{(-1-3)^2 + (4+8)^2} = 4\sqrt{10}$

**1.6**

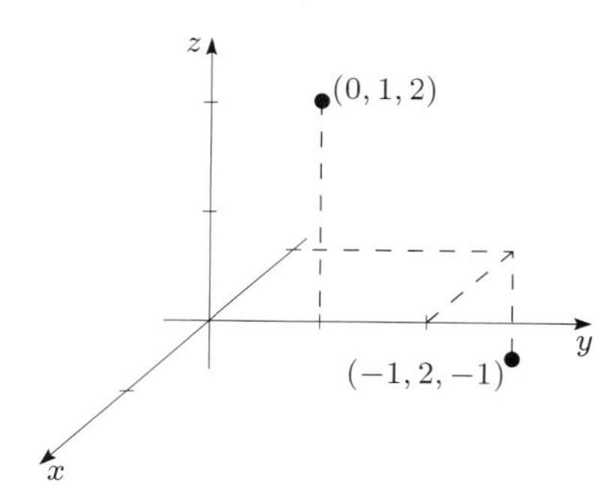


**1.7** Points $(x, y, z)$ that lie in the $(y, z)$-plane all have $x = 0$; so $x = 0$ is the equation of this plane.

Similarly, points $(x, y, z)$ that lie in the $(x, z)$-plane all have $y = 0$; so $y = 0$ is the equation of this plane.

**1.8** (a)

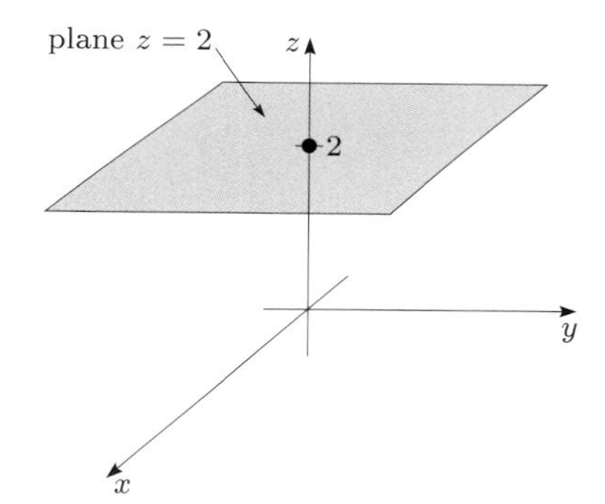


(b)

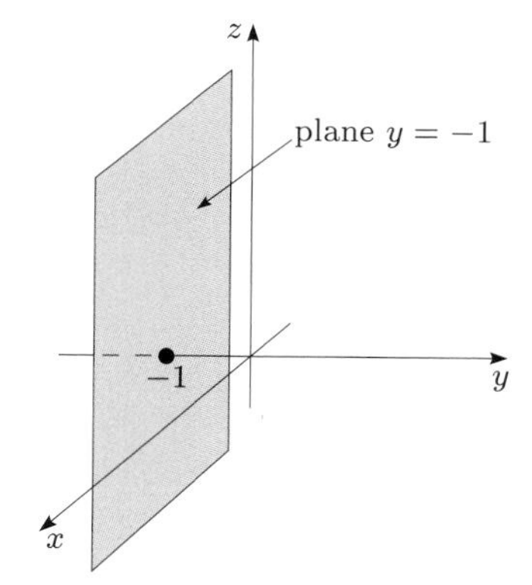


**1.9** (a) Let the equation of the plane be of the form

$$ax + by + cz = d.$$

Since $(1, 2, 3)$ lies in the plane, its coordinates must satisfy the equation of the plane; thus

$$a \times 1 + b \times 2 + c \times 3 = d,$$

so

$$d = a + 2b + 3c.$$

Thus the general form of the equation of a plane through $(1, 2, 3)$ is

$$ax + by + cz = a + 2b + 3c.$$

(b) Let the equation of the plane be of the form

$$ax + by + cz = d.$$

Since $(-1, -4, 2)$ lies in the plane, its coordinates must satisfy the equation of the plane; thus

$$a \times (-1) + b \times (-4) + c \times 2 = d,$$

so

$$d = -a - 4b + 2c.$$

Thus the general form of the equation of a plane through $(-1, -4, 2)$ is

$$ax + by + cz = -a - 4b + 2c.$$

**1.10** From the sketches in Exercise 1.8, the two planes are clearly not parallel or coincident; hence they must intersect in a line that lies in both planes.

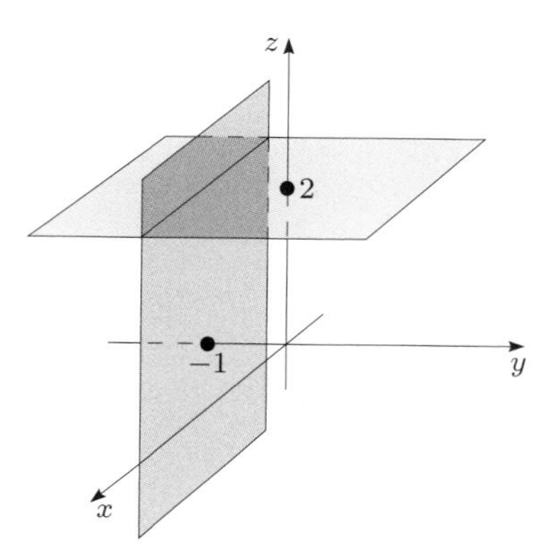


**1.11** We use the formula for the distance between two points in $\mathbb{R}^3$. This gives the following distances.

(a) $\sqrt{(4-1)^2 + (1-1)^2 + (-3-1)^2}$
$= \sqrt{9 + 0 + 16} = 5$

(b) $\sqrt{(3-1)^2 + (0-2)^2 + (3-3)^2}$
$= \sqrt{4 + 4 + 0} = 2\sqrt{2}$

**1.12** (a) Since $(-2, -4)$ and $(1, 6)$ lie on the line, its gradient is

$$m = \frac{(-4) - 6}{(-2) - 1} = \frac{10}{3}.$$

It follows that the equation of the line is

$$y - 6 = \tfrac{10}{3}(x - 1),$$

which can be simplified to

$$3y - 18 = 10x - 10,$$

that is,

$$10x - 3y = -8.$$

This equation is of the desired form, with $a = 10$, $b = -3$ and $c = -8$. (Any multiple of these numbers is also a valid answer.)

**(b)** Since the line passes through the origin and the point $(7,3)$, it has an equation of the form $y = mx$, for some $m$. The coordinates of $(7,3)$ must satisfy the equation $y = mx$. Thus $3 = 7m$, so $m = \frac{3}{7}$.

Hence the equation of the line is

$$y = \tfrac{3}{7}x.$$

This can be written as

$$3x - 7y = 0,$$

which is of the desired form, with $a = 3$, $b = -7$ and $c = 0$.

**1.13** The gradients of the lines $3x + 4y + 7 = 0$ and $2x + ky = 3$ are $-\frac{3}{4}$ and $-\dfrac{2}{k}$ $(k \neq 0)$, respectively. Thus the lines are

**(a)** parallel if $-\dfrac{3}{4} = -\dfrac{2}{k}$, that is, $k = \frac{8}{3}$;

**(b)** perpendicular if $\left(-\dfrac{3}{4}\right) \times \left(-\dfrac{2}{k}\right) = -1$, that is, $k = -\frac{3}{2}$.

**1.14**

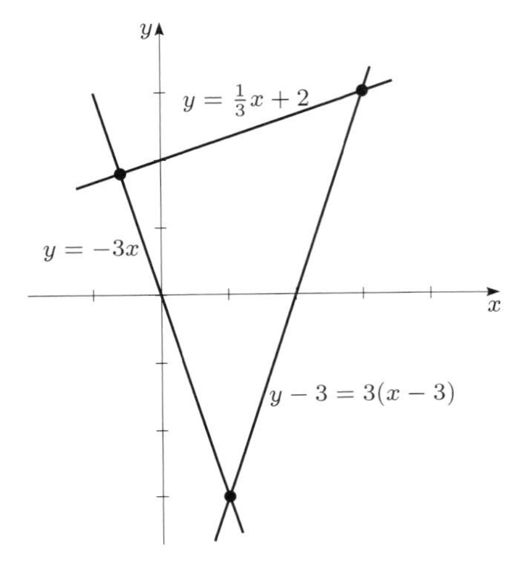


**1.15** Let $A$ be the point of intersection of the lines $y = -3x$ and $y = \frac{1}{3}x + 2$. We equate the two expressions for $y$ to obtain

$$-3x = \tfrac{1}{3}x + 2.$$

Multiplying through by 3 gives

$$-9x = x + 6,$$

so

$$-10x = 6, \quad \text{or} \quad x = -\tfrac{3}{5}.$$

Since $A$ lies on the line $y = -3x$, it follows that $y = \frac{9}{5}$. So the point $A$ has coordinates $\left(-\frac{3}{5}, \frac{9}{5}\right)$.

Next, let $B$ be the point of intersection of the lines $y = \frac{1}{3}x + 2$ and $y - 3 = 3(x - 3)$. We rewrite the second equation, and equate the two expressions for $y$ to obtain

$$\tfrac{1}{3}x + 2 = 3(x - 3) + 3.$$

Multiplying through by 3 and collecting terms gives

$$8x = 24,$$

so

$$x = 3.$$

Since $B$ lies on the line $y = \frac{1}{3}x + 2$, it follows that $y = 3$. So the point $B$ has coordinates $(3,3)$.

Finally, let $C$ be the point of intersection of the lines $y = -3x$ and $y - 3 = 3(x - 3)$. We rewrite the second equation, and equate the two expressions for $y$ to obtain

$$-3x = 3(x - 3) + 3.$$

Collecting terms gives

$$6x = 6,$$

so

$$x = 1.$$

Since $C$ lies on the line $y = -3x$, it follows that $y = -3$. So the point $C$ has coordinates $(1, -3)$.

**1.16** We use the Distance Formula given on page 10. Since $A = \left(-\frac{3}{5}, \frac{9}{5}\right)$, $B = (3,3)$ and $C = (1,-3)$,

$$\begin{aligned}
AB &= \sqrt{\left(3 + \tfrac{3}{5}\right)^2 + \left(3 - \tfrac{9}{5}\right)^2} \\
&= \sqrt{\left(\tfrac{18}{5}\right)^2 + \left(\tfrac{6}{5}\right)^2} \\
&= \sqrt{\tfrac{360}{25}} = 6\sqrt{\tfrac{2}{5}}, \\
AC &= \sqrt{\left(1 + \tfrac{3}{5}\right)^2 + \left(-3 - \tfrac{9}{5}\right)^2} \\
&= \sqrt{\left(\tfrac{8}{5}\right)^2 + \left(-\tfrac{24}{5}\right)^2} \\
&= \sqrt{\tfrac{640}{25}} = 8\sqrt{\tfrac{2}{5}}, \\
BC &= \sqrt{(1-3)^2 + (-3-3)^2} \\
&= \sqrt{(-2)^2 + (-6)^2} \\
&= \sqrt{40} = 2\sqrt{10}.
\end{aligned}$$

*Remark* In the triangle $ABC$,

$$AB^2 + AC^2 = BC^2,$$

so $\angle BAC$ is a right angle.

**1.17** **(a)** The planes with equations $x = 1$ and $y = 2$ are parallel to the $(y,z)$-plane and the $(x,z)$-plane, respectively. They intersect in a line, as shown.

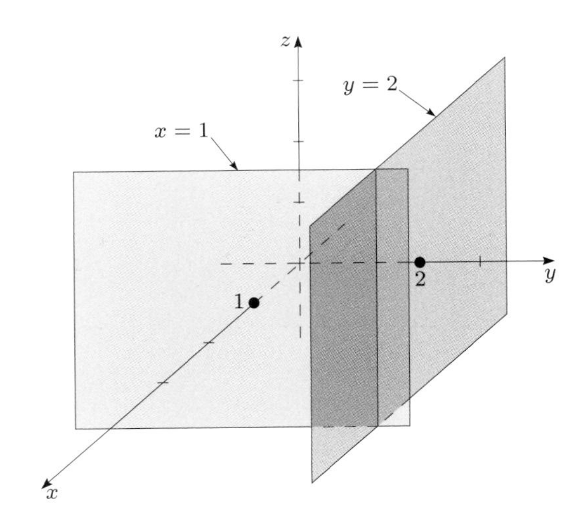

(b) The planes with equations $z = 1$ and $z = 3$ are both parallel to the $(x, y)$-plane. They are parallel to each other, as shown.

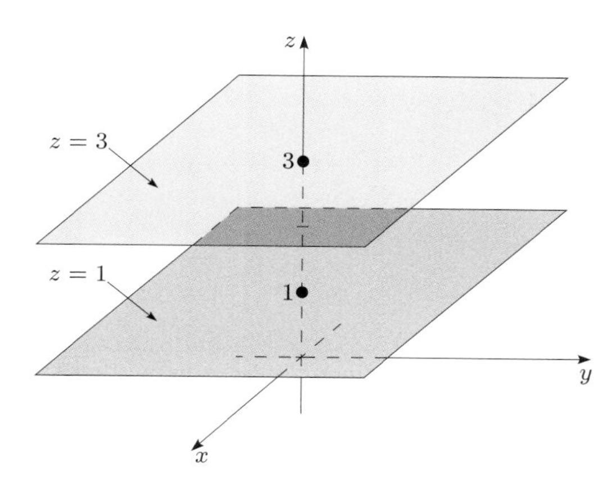


**1.18** We use the Distance Formula given at the end of Subsection 1.2. The required distance is thus

$$\sqrt{(-2-1)^2 + (3+2)^2 + (-1-3)^2}$$
$$= \sqrt{9 + 25 + 16}$$
$$= \sqrt{50} = 5\sqrt{2}.$$

**2.1** The vector $\mathbf{d}$ is in the same direction as $\mathbf{a}$, but none of the other vectors is; also, the length of $\mathbf{d}$ is two-thirds that of $\mathbf{a}$. Hence

$$\mathbf{d} = \tfrac{2}{3}\mathbf{a} \quad \text{and} \quad \mathbf{a} = \tfrac{3}{2}\mathbf{d}.$$

Next, $\mathbf{e}$ is along the same line as $\mathbf{b}$ but in the opposite direction; none of the others is along the same line. Also, the length of $\mathbf{e}$ is three times that of $\mathbf{b}$. Hence

$$\mathbf{e} = -3\mathbf{b} \quad \text{and} \quad \mathbf{b} = -\tfrac{1}{3}\mathbf{e}.$$

Finally, $\mathbf{c}$ and $\mathbf{f}$ are not multiples of any of the other vectors.

**2.2** The vector $3\mathbf{d}$ is in the same direction as $\mathbf{d}$, but its magnitude is three times that of $\mathbf{d}$; the vector $-2\mathbf{d}$ is in the direction opposite to that of $\mathbf{d}$, and its magnitude is twice that of $\mathbf{d}$.

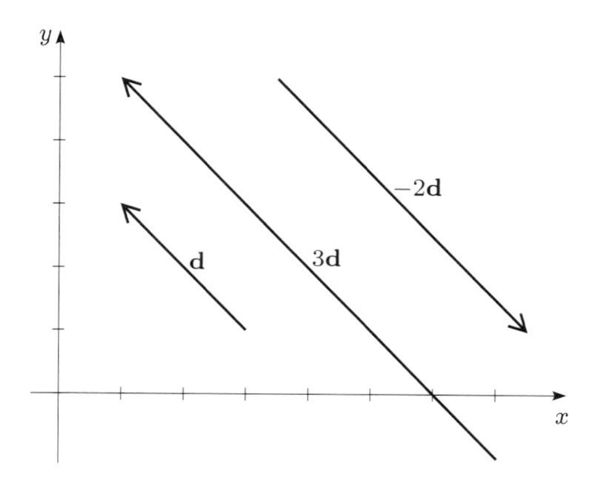


**2.3** First we sketch the vectors $\mathbf{p}$, $\mathbf{q}$, $-\mathbf{q}$, $2\mathbf{p}$ and $\frac{1}{2}\mathbf{q}$.

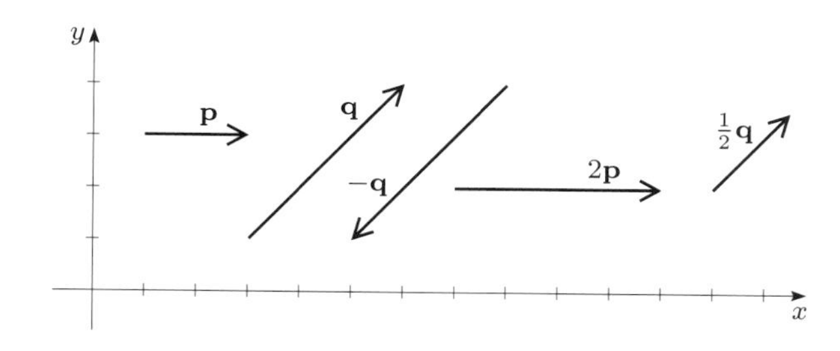


We use the Triangle Law for the addition of vectors to sketch $\mathbf{p} + \mathbf{q}$, $\mathbf{p} - \mathbf{q}$ and $2\mathbf{p} + \frac{1}{2}\mathbf{q}$.

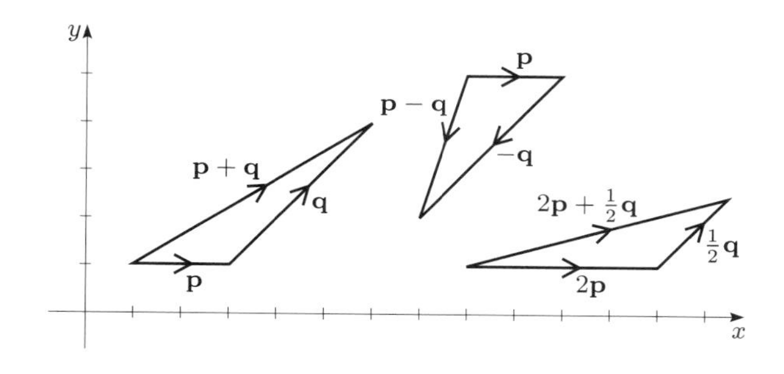


**2.4**

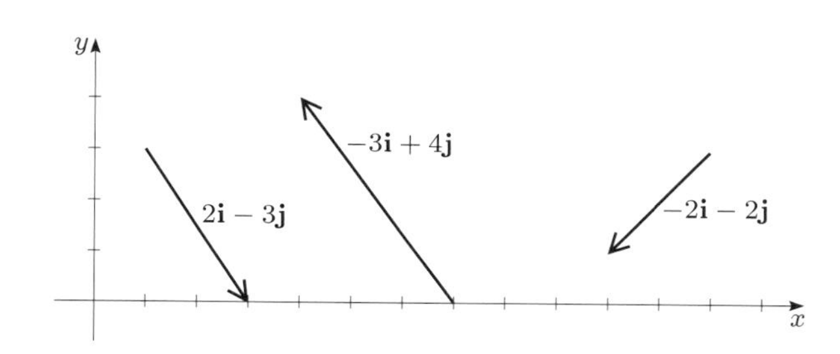


**2.5** We add vectors by adding their corresponding components. Hence

$$(3, 2) + (1, -5) = (4, -3),$$
$$(5, -2) + (-5, 2) = (0, 0),$$
$$(4, 1) + (0, 0) = (4, 1),$$
$$((1, 3) + (4, 2)) + (-3, 1) = (5, 5) + (-3, 1) = (2, 6),$$
$$(1, 3) + ((4, 2) + (-3, 1)) = (1, 3) + (1, 3) = (2, 6).$$

**2.6** (a) Here $\mathbf{p} = (3, -1)$ and $\mathbf{q} = (-1, -2)$, so

$$-\mathbf{p} = (-3, 1),$$
$$-\mathbf{q} = (1, 2),$$
$$\mathbf{p} - \mathbf{q} = (3 + 1, -1 + 2) = (4, 1).$$

(b) Here $\mathbf{p} = -\mathbf{i} - 2\mathbf{j}$ and $\mathbf{q} = 2\mathbf{i} - \mathbf{j}$, so

$$-\mathbf{p} = \mathbf{i} + 2\mathbf{j},$$
$$-\mathbf{q} = -2\mathbf{i} + \mathbf{j},$$
$$\mathbf{p} - \mathbf{q} = (-1 - 2)\mathbf{i} + (-2 + 1)\mathbf{j} = -3\mathbf{i} - \mathbf{j}.$$

(c) Here $\mathbf{p} = -\mathbf{i} + 2\mathbf{k}$ and $\mathbf{q} = \mathbf{i} - 2\mathbf{j} - \mathbf{k}$, so

$$-\mathbf{p} = \mathbf{i} - 2\mathbf{k},$$
$$-\mathbf{q} = -\mathbf{i} + 2\mathbf{j} + \mathbf{k},$$
$$\mathbf{p} - \mathbf{q} = -2\mathbf{i} + 2\mathbf{j} + 3\mathbf{k}.$$

**2.7** (a) Since $\mathbf{p} = (3, -1)$ and $\mathbf{q} = (-1, -2)$,

$$2\mathbf{p} = (6, -2),$$
$$3\mathbf{q} = (-3, -6),$$
$$2\mathbf{p} + 3\mathbf{q} = (3, -8),$$
$$2\mathbf{p} - 3\mathbf{q} = (9, 4).$$

(b) Since $\mathbf{p} = -\mathbf{i} + 2\mathbf{k}$ and $\mathbf{q} = \mathbf{i} - 2\mathbf{j} - \mathbf{k}$,

$$2\mathbf{p} = -2\mathbf{i} + 4\mathbf{k},$$
$$3\mathbf{q} = 3\mathbf{i} - 6\mathbf{j} - 3\mathbf{k},$$
$$2\mathbf{p} + 3\mathbf{q} = \mathbf{i} - 6\mathbf{j} + \mathbf{k},$$
$$2\mathbf{p} - 3\mathbf{q} = -5\mathbf{i} + 6\mathbf{j} + 7\mathbf{k}.$$

**2.8** (a) Since $\mathbf{p} = (5, 3)$ and $\mathbf{q} = (1, 4)$,

$$\mathbf{p} - \mathbf{q} = (4, -1),$$
$$\mathbf{p} + \mathbf{q} = (6, 7),$$
$$\tfrac{1}{2}\mathbf{p} + \tfrac{1}{2}\mathbf{q} = \left(\tfrac{5}{2}, \tfrac{3}{2}\right) + \left(\tfrac{1}{2}, 2\right) = \left(3, \tfrac{7}{2}\right).$$

(b)

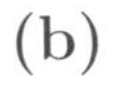

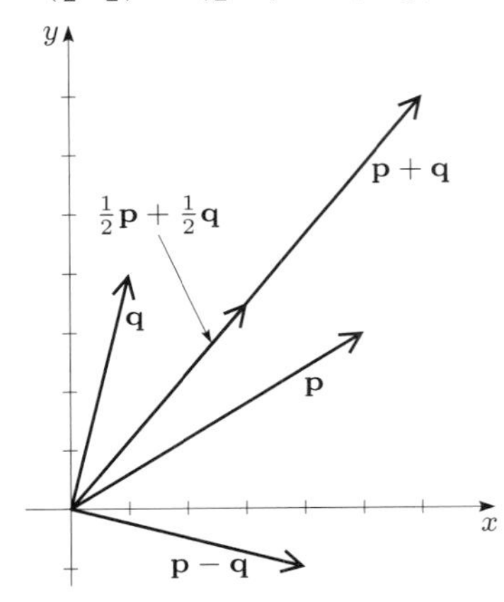


**2.9** (a) We use equation (2.3) to obtain the vector form of the equation of $\ell$ as

$$\mathbf{r} = \lambda(3, 1) + (1 - \lambda)(2, 3).$$

(b) Using the above formula with $\lambda = \frac{1}{3}$, $\frac{3}{2}$ and $-\frac{1}{2}$ in turn, we obtain the following position vectors:

$$\mathbf{r}_1 = \tfrac{1}{3}(3, 1) + \tfrac{2}{3}(2, 3) = \left(\tfrac{7}{3}, \tfrac{7}{3}\right),$$
$$\mathbf{r}_2 = \tfrac{3}{2}(3, 1) - \tfrac{1}{2}(2, 3) = \left(\tfrac{7}{2}, 0\right),$$
$$\mathbf{r}_3 = -\tfrac{1}{2}(3, 1) + \tfrac{3}{2}(2, 3) = \left(\tfrac{3}{2}, 4\right).$$

Thus the three points have Cartesian coordinates $\left(\frac{7}{3}, \frac{7}{3}\right)$, $\left(\frac{7}{2}, 0\right)$ and $\left(\frac{3}{2}, 4\right)$, respectively.

(c)

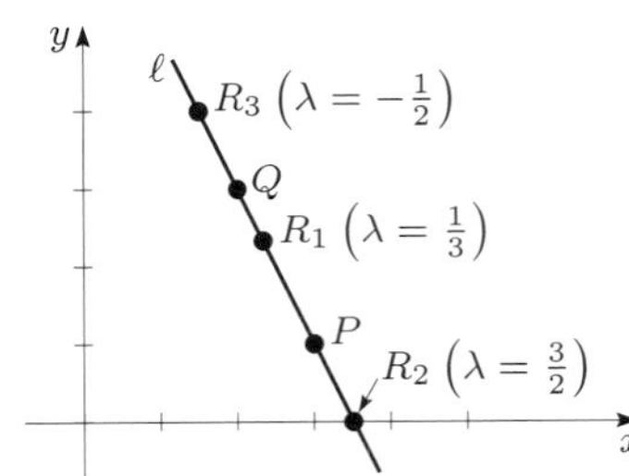


**2.10** (a) The vector form of the equation of $\ell$ is

$$\mathbf{r} = \lambda(3, 1) + (1 - \lambda)(2, 3).$$

Hence at the point $(4, -1)$ on $\ell$, we have

$$(4, -1) = \lambda(3, 1) + (1 - \lambda)(2, 3)$$
$$= (2 + \lambda, 3 - 2\lambda).$$

Equating corresponding components, we obtain the following pair of simultaneous equations that must be satisfied by the number $\lambda$:

$$2 + \lambda = 4 \quad \text{and} \quad 3 - 2\lambda = -1.$$

These have the solution $\lambda = 2$.

(b) Since the vector equation of $\ell$ is $\mathbf{r} = \lambda(3, 1) + (1 - \lambda)(2, 3)$, the point $\left(\frac{1}{2}, \frac{1}{2}\right)$ lies on $\ell$ if and only if there is some real number $\lambda$ for which

$$\left(\tfrac{1}{2}, \tfrac{1}{2}\right) = \lambda(3, 1) + (1 - \lambda)(2, 3)$$
$$= (2 + \lambda, 3 - 2\lambda). \qquad \text{(S.1)}$$

Equating corresponding components, we obtain the following pair of simultaneous equations that must be satisfied by such a number $\lambda$:

$$2 + \lambda = \tfrac{1}{2} \quad \text{and} \quad 3 - 2\lambda = \tfrac{1}{2}.$$

The first of these equations has solution $\lambda = -\frac{3}{2}$, and the second has solution $\lambda = \frac{5}{4}$.

It follows that there is no real number $\lambda$ that satisfies equation (S.1), so the point $\left(\frac{1}{2}, \frac{1}{2}\right)$ does not lie on $\ell$.

**2.11** (a) The point $R$ divides $PQ$ in the ratio $3 : 2 = \frac{3}{5} : \frac{2}{5}$. Applying the Section Formula with $\lambda = \frac{2}{5}$, we find that the position vector of $R$ is

$$\mathbf{r} = \tfrac{2}{5}(-3, 1) + \tfrac{3}{5}(7, -4) = (3, -2).$$

Thus $R$ is the point $(3, -2)$.

(b) The midpoint $M$ divides $PQ$ in the ratio $1 : 1 = \frac{1}{2} : \frac{1}{2}$. Applying the Section Formula with $\lambda = \frac{1}{2}$, we find that the position vector of $M$ is

$$\mathbf{r} = \tfrac{1}{2}(-3, 1) + \tfrac{1}{2}(7, -4) = \left(2, -\tfrac{3}{2}\right).$$

Thus $M$ is the point $\left(2, -\frac{3}{2}\right)$.

**2.12**

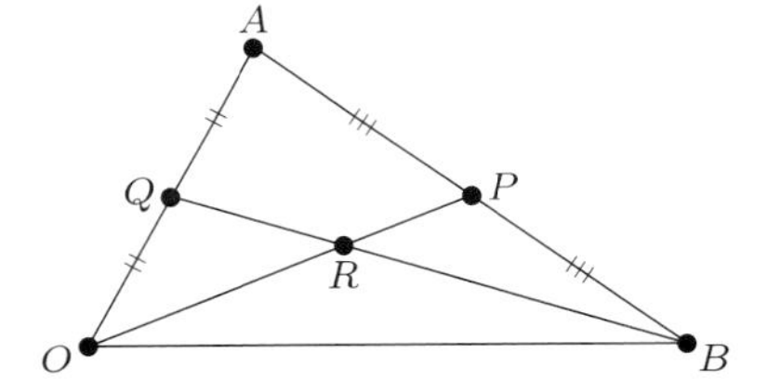


(a) Since $P$ is the midpoint of $AB$, its position vector is

$$\mathbf{p} = \tfrac{1}{2}(\mathbf{a} + \mathbf{b}).$$

Since $Q$ is the midpoint of $OA$, its position vector is

$$\mathbf{q} = \tfrac{1}{2}\mathbf{a}.$$

The point $R$ lies on the two lines $OP$ and $BQ$, so we can express its position vector $\mathbf{r}$ in two different ways. Since $R$ lies on $OP$,

$$\mathbf{r} = k \times \tfrac{1}{2}(\mathbf{a} + \mathbf{b}), \quad \text{for some number } k;$$

and since $R$ lies on $BQ$,

$$\mathbf{r} = \lambda\mathbf{b} + (1 - \lambda)\mathbf{q}$$
$$= \lambda\mathbf{b} + (1 - \lambda) \times \tfrac{1}{2}\mathbf{a}, \quad \text{for some number } \lambda.$$

These two expressions for $\mathbf{r}$ must be equal; thus

$$\lambda\mathbf{b} + \tfrac{1}{2}(1-\lambda)\mathbf{a} = \tfrac{1}{2}k\mathbf{a} + \tfrac{1}{2}k\mathbf{b},$$

so

$$\left(\lambda - \tfrac{1}{2}k\right)\mathbf{b} = \tfrac{1}{2}(k - 1 + \lambda)\mathbf{a}.$$

Since $\mathbf{a}$ and $\mathbf{b}$ are not parallel, their coefficients in this last equation must both be zero. This gives two equations for $k$ and $\lambda$:

$$\lambda - \tfrac{1}{2}k = 0 \quad \text{and} \quad k - 1 + \lambda = 0.$$

Thus $k = 2\lambda$, so $2\lambda - 1 + \lambda = 0$, and hence $\lambda = \frac{1}{3}$.

Hence

$$\mathbf{r} = \tfrac{1}{3}\mathbf{a} + \tfrac{1}{3}\mathbf{b}.$$

**(b)** The position vectors of $O$, $R$ and $P$ are $\mathbf{0}$, $\mathbf{r} = \frac{1}{3}\mathbf{a} + \frac{1}{3}\mathbf{b}$ and $\mathbf{p} = \frac{1}{2}(\mathbf{a}+\mathbf{b})$, respectively. Thus

$$\mathbf{r} = \tfrac{2}{3}\mathbf{p} = \tfrac{1}{3}\mathbf{0} + \tfrac{2}{3}\mathbf{p}.$$

It follows from the Section Formula (with $\lambda = \frac{1}{3}$) that

$$\begin{aligned} OR : RP &= \left(1 - \tfrac{1}{3}\right) : \tfrac{1}{3} \\ &= \tfrac{2}{3} : \tfrac{1}{3} \\ &= 2 : 1. \end{aligned}$$

Thus $R$ is two-thirds of the way along $OP$ from $O$.

**2.13** Since $\mathbf{p} = 2\mathbf{i} - 3\mathbf{j} + \mathbf{k}$ and $\mathbf{q} = -\mathbf{i} - 2\mathbf{j} - 4\mathbf{k}$, we have

$$\mathbf{p} + \mathbf{q} = \mathbf{i} - 5\mathbf{j} - 3\mathbf{k},$$
$$\mathbf{p} - \mathbf{q} = 3\mathbf{i} - \mathbf{j} + 5\mathbf{k}$$

and

$$\begin{aligned} 2\mathbf{p} - 3\mathbf{q} &= (4\mathbf{i} - 6\mathbf{j} + 2\mathbf{k}) - (-3\mathbf{i} - 6\mathbf{j} - 12\mathbf{k}) \\ &= 7\mathbf{i} + 14\mathbf{k}. \end{aligned}$$

**2.14** **(a)** Here,

$$\begin{aligned} \mathbf{u} + 2\mathbf{v} &= (1,1) + 2(2,1) \\ &= (1,1) + (4,2) \\ &= (5,3), \end{aligned}$$

$$-\mathbf{u} = (-1,-1),$$

$$\begin{aligned} -\mathbf{u} + 3\mathbf{v} &= (-1,-1) + 3(2,1) \\ &= (-1,-1) + (6,3) \\ &= (5,2) \end{aligned}$$

and

$$\begin{aligned} \mathbf{u} - 3\mathbf{v} &= (1,1) + (-3)(2,1) \\ &= (1,1) + (-6,-3) \\ &= (-5,-2). \end{aligned}$$

**(b)**

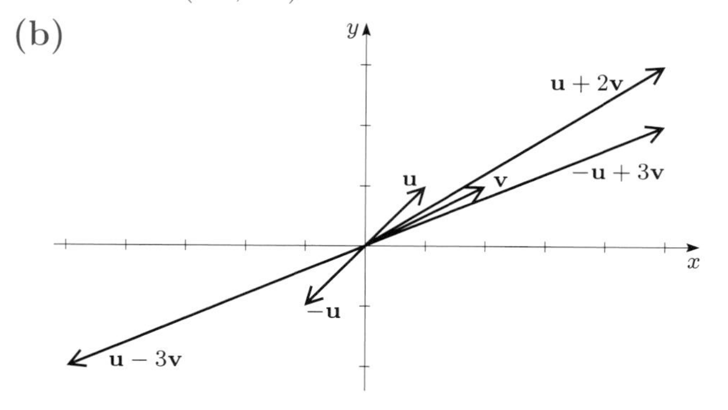


**2.15** **(a)** First we write

$$\begin{aligned} \alpha\mathbf{u} + \beta\mathbf{v} &= \alpha(2,6) + \beta(4,2) \\ &= (2\alpha, 6\alpha) + (4\beta, 2\beta) \\ &= (2\alpha + 4\beta, 6\alpha + 2\beta). \end{aligned}$$

Thus

$$(3,4) = (2\alpha + 4\beta, 6\alpha + 2\beta).$$

Then, following the hint, we equate the first and second components of these vectors; this gives two simultaneous equations:

$$2\alpha + 4\beta = 3,$$
$$6\alpha + 2\beta = 4.$$

These two equations can be solved to give

$$\alpha = \tfrac{1}{2} \quad \text{and} \quad \beta = \tfrac{1}{2}.$$

Thus we can write

$$(3,4) = \tfrac{1}{2}\mathbf{u} + \tfrac{1}{2}\mathbf{v}.$$

**(b)**

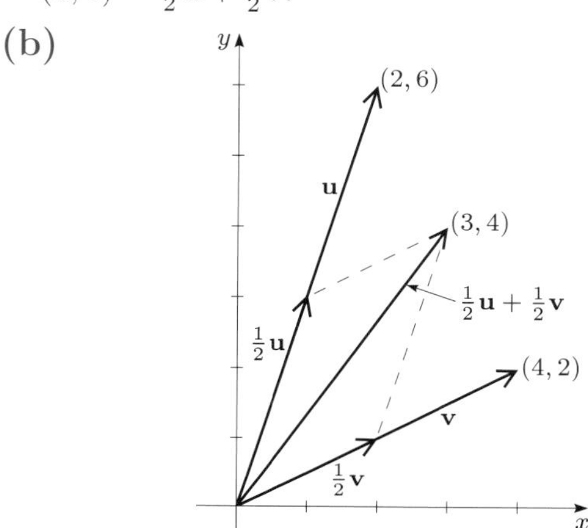


**2.16** The point $R$ divides $AB$ in the ratio $2:5 = \frac{2}{7} : \frac{5}{7}$. It follows from the Section Formula, with $\lambda = \frac{5}{7}$, that the position vector $\mathbf{r}$ of $R$ is

$$\mathbf{r} = \tfrac{5}{7}(5,4) + \tfrac{2}{7}(-2,-3) = (3,2).$$

Hence the coordinates of $R$ are $(3,2)$.

The midpoint $M$ of $AB$ has position vector $\mathbf{m}$, where

$$\mathbf{m} = \tfrac{1}{2}((5,4) + (-2,-3)) = \left(\tfrac{3}{2}, \tfrac{1}{2}\right).$$

Hence the coordinates of $M$ are $\left(\frac{3}{2}, \frac{1}{2}\right)$.

**2.17** **(a)** Let $\mathbf{p} = (2,3)$ and $\mathbf{q} = (5,-1)$. Then the vector form of the equation of the line $\ell$ is

$$\begin{aligned} \mathbf{r} &= \lambda\mathbf{p} + (1-\lambda)\mathbf{q} \\ &= \lambda(2,3) + (1-\lambda)(5,-1) \\ &= (2\lambda + 5(1-\lambda), 3\lambda - (1-\lambda)), \end{aligned}$$

that is,

$$\mathbf{r} = (-3\lambda + 5, 4\lambda - 1),$$

where $\lambda \in \mathbb{R}$.

**(b)** The point $(7,2)$ lies on the line $\ell$ if there is a value of $\lambda$ such that

$$(7,2) = (-3\lambda + 5, 4\lambda - 1).$$

Equating components in turn, we obtain

$$7 = -3\lambda + 5 \quad \text{and} \quad 2 = 4\lambda - 1.$$

The second equation gives $\lambda = \frac{3}{4}$, but this value of $\lambda$ does not satisfy the first equation. It follows that $(7, 2)$ does not lie on the line $\ell$.

The point $(-1, 7)$ lies on the line $\ell$ if there is a value of $\lambda$ such that

$$(-1, 7) = (-3\lambda + 5, 4\lambda - 1).$$

Equating components in turn, we obtain

$$-1 = -3\lambda + 5 \quad \text{and} \quad 7 = 4\lambda - 1.$$

The second equation gives $\lambda = 2$, and this value also satisfies the first equation. It follows that the point $(-1, 7)$ lies on the line $\ell$.

**2.18**

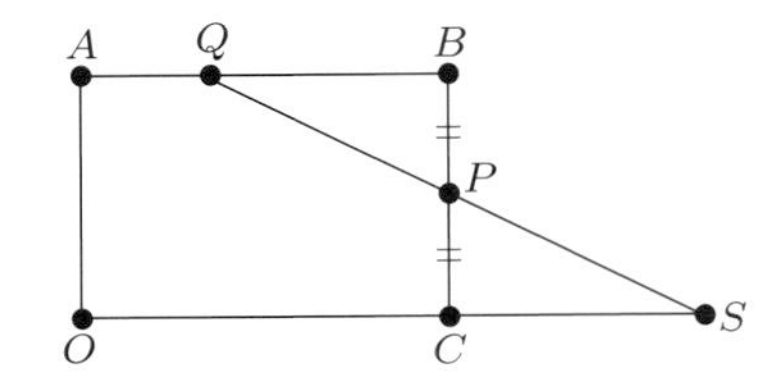


(a) $P$ is the midpoint of $BC$, so its position vector $\mathbf{p}$ can be written as

$$\mathbf{p} = \tfrac{1}{2}(\mathbf{b} + \mathbf{c}).$$

Now $\mathbf{b} = \mathbf{a} + \mathbf{c}$ by the Parallelogram Law, since $OB$ is the diagonal of the parallelogram with adjacent sides $\mathbf{a}$ and $\mathbf{c}$. Thus

$$\begin{aligned}\mathbf{p} &= \tfrac{1}{2}(\mathbf{a} + \mathbf{c} + \mathbf{c}) \\ &= \tfrac{1}{2}\mathbf{a} + \mathbf{c}.\end{aligned}$$

Next, the position vector $\mathbf{q}$ of the point $Q$ is given by $\mathbf{q} = \overrightarrow{OA} + \overrightarrow{AQ}$. Here $\overrightarrow{OA} = \mathbf{a}$; also $\overrightarrow{AQ} = \frac{1}{3}\overrightarrow{AB} = \frac{1}{3}\mathbf{c}$, since $\overrightarrow{OC} = \overrightarrow{AB}$ (as they have the same magnitude and direction). Hence

$$\mathbf{q} = \mathbf{a} + \tfrac{1}{3}\mathbf{c}.$$

(b) The vector form of the line through $P$ and $Q$ is

$$\begin{aligned}\mathbf{r} &= \lambda\mathbf{p} + (1 - \lambda)\mathbf{q} \\ &= \lambda\left(\tfrac{1}{2}\mathbf{a} + \mathbf{c}\right) + (1 - \lambda)\left(\mathbf{a} + \tfrac{1}{3}\mathbf{c}\right),\end{aligned}$$

where $\lambda \in \mathbb{R}$.

Multiplying out and collecting terms, we obtain

$$\mathbf{r} = \left(1 - \tfrac{1}{2}\lambda\right)\mathbf{a} + \left(\tfrac{1}{3} + \tfrac{2}{3}\lambda\right)\mathbf{c},$$

where $\lambda \in \mathbb{R}$.

(c) The point $S$ lies on $QP$, so its position vector $\mathbf{s}$ can be written in the form

$$\mathbf{s} = \left(1 - \tfrac{1}{2}\lambda\right)\mathbf{a} + \left(\tfrac{1}{3} + \tfrac{2}{3}\lambda\right)\mathbf{c}. \qquad \text{(S.2)}$$

But $\mathbf{s}$ can also be written solely as a multiple of $\mathbf{c}$, since $S$ is also on $OC$ and so $\mathbf{s}$ is in the same direction as $\mathbf{c}$. This means that the coefficient of $\mathbf{a}$ in equation (S.2) for $\mathbf{s}$ must be 0.

Thus $1 - \frac{1}{2}\lambda = 0$, so $\lambda = 2$.

It follows that

$$\mathbf{s} = \left(\tfrac{1}{3} + \tfrac{2}{3} \times 2\right)\mathbf{c} = \tfrac{5}{3}\mathbf{c}.$$

**3.1** We use the formula for the dot product given in Frame 6 on page 31.

(a) $$\begin{aligned}(2,3) \cdot \left(\tfrac{5}{2}, -4\right) &= 2 \times \left(\tfrac{5}{2}\right) + 3 \times (-4) \\ &= 5 - 12 = -7\end{aligned}$$

(b) $$\begin{aligned}(1,4) \cdot \left(2, -\tfrac{1}{2}\right) &= 1 \times 2 + 4 \times \left(-\tfrac{1}{2}\right) \\ &= 2 - 2 = 0\end{aligned}$$

(c) $$\begin{aligned}(-2\mathbf{i} + \mathbf{j}) \cdot (3\mathbf{i} - 2\mathbf{j}) &= (-2) \times 3 + 1 \times (-2) \\ &= -6 - 2 = -8\end{aligned}$$

**3.2** (a) When $\mathbf{u} = (2, -3)$, the length of $\mathbf{u}$ is

$$\|\mathbf{u}\| = \sqrt{2^2 + (-3)^2} = \sqrt{4 + 9} = \sqrt{13},$$

so

$$\begin{aligned}\widehat{\mathbf{u}} &= \mathbf{u}/\|\mathbf{u}\| \\ &= \left(\tfrac{2}{\sqrt{13}}, -\tfrac{3}{\sqrt{13}}\right).\end{aligned}$$

(b) When $\mathbf{u} = 5\mathbf{i} + 12\mathbf{j}$, the length of $\mathbf{u}$ is

$$\|\mathbf{u}\| = \sqrt{5^2 + 12^2} = \sqrt{25 + 144} = 13,$$

so

$$\widehat{\mathbf{u}} = \tfrac{5}{13}\mathbf{i} + \tfrac{12}{13}\mathbf{j}.$$

**3.3** In each case we use the formula for the angle between two vectors given in Frame 10 on page 32, letting $\mathbf{u}$ denote the first vector of the pair, $\mathbf{v}$ the second vector and $\theta$ the angle between the two vectors.

(a) Here $\mathbf{u} \cdot \mathbf{v} = (1,4) \cdot (5,2) = 5 + 8 = 13$,

$$\|\mathbf{u}\| = \sqrt{1^2 + 4^2} = \sqrt{1 + 16} = \sqrt{17}$$

and

$$\|\mathbf{v}\| = \sqrt{5^2 + 2^2} = \sqrt{25 + 4} = \sqrt{29}.$$

Then

$$\begin{aligned}\cos\theta &= \frac{13}{\sqrt{17}\sqrt{29}} \\ &= 0.5855 \quad \text{(to 4 d.p.)},\end{aligned}$$

so

$$\theta = 0.95 \text{ radians} \quad \text{(to 2 d.p.)}.$$

(b) Here $\mathbf{u} \cdot \mathbf{v} = (-2,2) \cdot (1,-1) = -2 - 2 = -4$,

$$\|\mathbf{u}\| = \sqrt{(-2)^2 + 2^2} = \sqrt{4 + 4} = \sqrt{8}$$

and

$$\|\mathbf{v}\| = \sqrt{1^2 + (-1)^2} = \sqrt{1 + 1} = \sqrt{2}.$$

Then

$$\cos\theta = \frac{-4}{\sqrt{8}\sqrt{2}} = -1,$$

so

$$\theta = \pi \text{ radians}.$$

(c) Here

$$\begin{aligned}\mathbf{u} \cdot \mathbf{v} &= (9\mathbf{i} - 2\mathbf{j}) \cdot (\mathbf{i} + 2\mathbf{j}) \\ &= 9 \times 1 + (-2) \times 2 \\ &= 9 - 4 = 5,\end{aligned}$$

$$\|\mathbf{u}\| = \sqrt{9^2 + (-2)^2} = \sqrt{81 + 4} = \sqrt{85}$$

and

$$\|\mathbf{v}\| = \sqrt{1^2 + 2^2} = \sqrt{5}.$$

Then

$$\cos\theta = \frac{5}{\sqrt{85}\sqrt{5}} = \frac{1}{\sqrt{17}} = 0.2425 \quad \text{(to 4 d.p.)},$$

so

$$\theta = 1.33 \text{ radians} \quad \text{(to 2 d.p.)}.$$

**3.4**

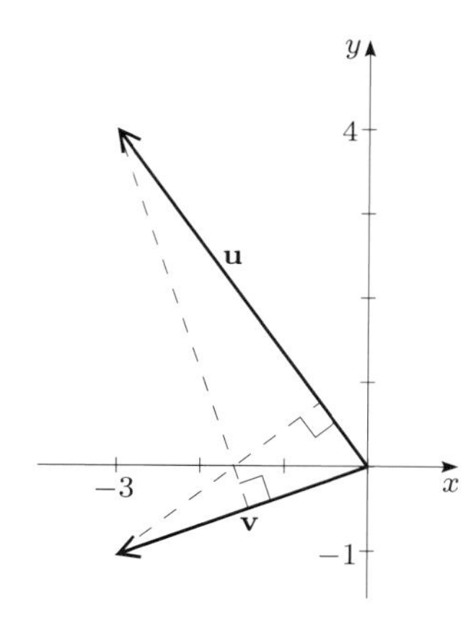


To calculate the projections of $\mathbf{u}$ onto $\mathbf{v}$ and $\mathbf{v}$ onto $\mathbf{u}$, we need the following:

$$\begin{aligned}\mathbf{u} \cdot \mathbf{v} &= (-3, 4) \cdot (-3, -1) \\ &= (-3) \times (-3) + 4 \times (-1) = 5,\end{aligned}$$

$$\|\mathbf{u}\| = \sqrt{(-3)^2 + 4^2} = \sqrt{25} = 5,$$

$$\|\mathbf{v}\| = \sqrt{(-3)^2 + (-1)^2} = \sqrt{9+1} = \sqrt{10}.$$

Then the projection of $\mathbf{v}$ onto $\mathbf{u}$ is

$$\frac{\mathbf{u} \cdot \mathbf{v}}{\|\mathbf{u}\|} = \frac{5}{5} = 1,$$

and the projection of $\mathbf{u}$ onto $\mathbf{v}$ is

$$\frac{\mathbf{u} \cdot \mathbf{v}}{\|\mathbf{v}\|} = \frac{5}{\sqrt{10}} = 1.58 \quad \text{(to 2 d.p.)}.$$

**3.5** In each case we use the formula for the angle between two vectors given in Frame 10 on page 32, letting $\mathbf{u}$ denote the first vector of the pair, $\mathbf{v}$ the second vector and $\theta$ the angle between the two vectors.

(a) Here $\mathbf{u} \cdot \mathbf{v} = (1, 2, 0) \cdot (3, -1, 2) = 3 - 2 + 0 = 1,$

$$\begin{aligned}\|\mathbf{u}\| &= \sqrt{1^2 + 2^2 + 0^2} \\ &= \sqrt{1 + 4 + 0} = \sqrt{5}\end{aligned}$$

and

$$\begin{aligned}\|\mathbf{v}\| &= \sqrt{3^2 + (-1)^2 + 2^2} \\ &= \sqrt{9 + 1 + 4} = \sqrt{14}.\end{aligned}$$

Then

$$\cos\theta = \frac{1}{\sqrt{5}\sqrt{14}} = 0.1195 \quad \text{(to 4 d.p.)},$$

so

$$\theta = 1.45 \text{ radians} \quad \text{(to 2 d.p.)}.$$

(b) Here

$$\begin{aligned}\mathbf{u} \cdot \mathbf{v} &= (2\mathbf{j} - 3\mathbf{k}) \cdot (-\mathbf{i} - \mathbf{j} - 2\mathbf{k}) \\ &= 0 \times (-1) + 2 \times (-1) + (-3) \times (-2) \\ &= -2 + 6 = 4,\end{aligned}$$

$$\begin{aligned}\|\mathbf{u}\| &= \sqrt{0^2 + 2^2 + (-3)^2} \\ &= \sqrt{4 + 9} = \sqrt{13}\end{aligned}$$

and

$$\begin{aligned}\|\mathbf{v}\| &= \sqrt{(-1)^2 + (-1)^2 + (-2)^2} \\ &= \sqrt{1 + 1 + 4} = \sqrt{6}.\end{aligned}$$

Then

$$\cos\theta = \frac{4}{\sqrt{13}\sqrt{6}} = 0.4529 \quad \text{(to 4 d.p.)},$$

so

$$\theta = 1.10 \text{ radians} \quad \text{(to 2 d.p.)}.$$

**3.6** (a)

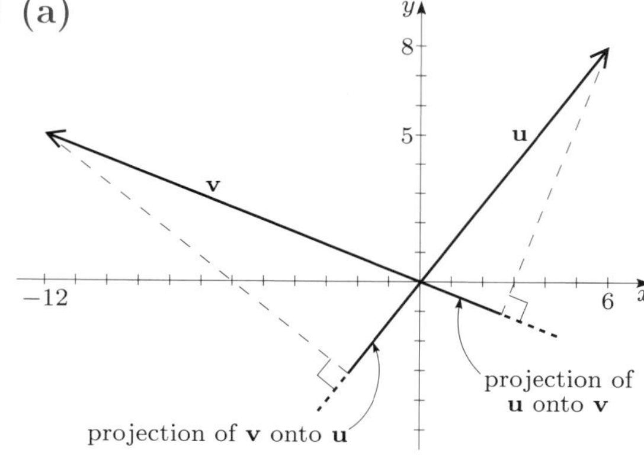


(b) Let $\theta$ denote the angle between $\mathbf{u}$ and $\mathbf{v}$. Now

$$\mathbf{u} \cdot \mathbf{v} = 6 \times (-12) + 8 \times 5 = -32,$$

$$\|\mathbf{u}\| = \sqrt{6^2 + 8^2} = 10$$

and

$$\|\mathbf{v}\| = \sqrt{(-12)^2 + 5^2} = 13.$$

Thus

$$\begin{aligned}\cos\theta &= \frac{\mathbf{u} \cdot \mathbf{v}}{\|\mathbf{u}\| \times \|\mathbf{v}\|} \\ &= \frac{-32}{10 \times 13} = -0.2462 \quad \text{(to 4 d.p.)},\end{aligned}$$

so

$$\theta = 1.82 \text{ radians} \quad \text{(to 2 d.p.)}.$$

(c) The projection of $\mathbf{u}$ onto $\mathbf{v}$ is

$$\frac{\mathbf{u} \cdot \mathbf{v}}{\|\mathbf{v}\|} = \frac{-32}{13} = -2.46 \quad \text{(to 2 d.p.)}.$$

The projection of $\mathbf{v}$ onto $\mathbf{u}$ is

$$\frac{\mathbf{u} \cdot \mathbf{v}}{\|\mathbf{u}\|} = \frac{-32}{10} = -3.2.$$

**3.7** Let $\theta$ denote the angle between $\mathbf{u}$ and $\mathbf{v}$. Now

$$\begin{aligned}\mathbf{u} \cdot \mathbf{v} &= (3, 4, 5) \cdot (1, 0, -1) \\ &= 3 \times 1 + 4 \times 0 + 5 \times (-1) = -2,\end{aligned}$$

$$\|\mathbf{u}\| = \sqrt{3^2 + 4^2 + 5^2} = 5\sqrt{2}$$

and

$$\|\mathbf{v}\| = \sqrt{1^2 + 0^2 + (-1)^2} = \sqrt{2}.$$

Thus

$$\cos\theta = \frac{\mathbf{u}\cdot\mathbf{v}}{\|\mathbf{u}\|\times\|\mathbf{v}\|} = \frac{-2}{5\sqrt{2}\times\sqrt{2}} = -0.2,$$

so

$$\theta = 1.77 \text{ radians} \quad \text{(to 2 d.p.)}.$$

**3.8** Let the vector we want be denoted by

$$\mathbf{v} = (x, y, z),$$

for some real numbers $x$, $y$ and $z$.

Since $\|\mathbf{v}\| = 2$,

$$x^2 + y^2 + z^2 = 4. \tag{S.3}$$

Since $\mathbf{v}$ is perpendicular to $\mathbf{a}$,

$$\mathbf{v}\cdot\mathbf{a} = 0;$$

thus

$$2x + y = 0,$$

that is,

$$y = -2x. \tag{S.4}$$

Since $\mathbf{v}$ is perpendicular to $\mathbf{b}$,

$$\mathbf{v}\cdot\mathbf{b} = 0;$$

thus

$$x - z = 0,$$

that is,

$$z = x. \tag{S.5}$$

Substituting the expressions for $y$ in equation (S.4) and for $z$ in equation (S.5) into equation (S.3), we obtain

$$x^2 + (-2x)^2 + x^2 = 4;$$

thus

$$6x^2 = 4,$$

so

$$x^2 = \tfrac{4}{6} = \tfrac{2}{3} \quad \text{and} \quad x = \pm\sqrt{\tfrac{2}{3}}.$$

It follows that the two possible vectors that satisfy the given conditions are

$$\left(\sqrt{\tfrac{2}{3}}, -2\sqrt{\tfrac{2}{3}}, \sqrt{\tfrac{2}{3}}\right) \quad \text{and} \quad \left(-\sqrt{\tfrac{2}{3}}, 2\sqrt{\tfrac{2}{3}}, -\sqrt{\tfrac{2}{3}}\right).$$

**3.9** We use the formula

$$\mathbf{x}\cdot\mathbf{n} = \mathbf{p}\cdot\mathbf{n}$$

for the equation of a plane, where $\mathbf{x} = (x, y, z)$, $\mathbf{n}$ is a normal to the plane and $\mathbf{p}$ is a point in the plane.

**(a)** Here $\mathbf{n} = (2, 3, 1)$ and $\mathbf{p} = (1, 0, 2)$, so the equation of the plane is

$$(x, y, z)\cdot(2, 3, 1) = (1, 0, 2)\cdot(2, 3, 1).$$

This can be expressed in the form

$$2x + 3y + z = 1\times 2 + 0\times 3 + 2\times 1,$$

that is,

$$2x + 3y + z = 4.$$

**(b)** Here $\mathbf{n} = (4, -2, 1)$ and $\mathbf{p} = (-1, 1, 5)$, so the equation of the plane is

$$(x, y, z)\cdot(4, -2, 1) = (-1, 1, 5)\cdot(4, -2, 1).$$

This can be expressed in the form

$$4x - 2y + z = (-1)\times 4 + 1\times(-2) + 5\times 1,$$

that is,

$$4x - 2y + z = -1.$$

**3.10** Let the equation of the plane be

$$ax + by + cz = d, \tag{S.6}$$

where $a$, $b$, $c$ and $d$ are real, and $a$, $b$ and $c$ are not all zero.

Substituting the coordinates of each of the points in turn into equation (S.6), we obtain

$$\begin{aligned} 3a \qquad\quad &= d, \\ 4b \quad\; &= d, \\ 3a + 4b + 5c &= d. \end{aligned}$$

From the first two equations we obtain

$$a = \tfrac{1}{3}d \quad \text{and} \quad b = \tfrac{1}{4}d.$$

Substituting these expressions into the third equation, we obtain

$$3\left(\tfrac{1}{3}d\right) + 4\left(\tfrac{1}{4}d\right) + 5c = d,$$

so

$$d + d + 5c = d,$$

hence

$$c = -\tfrac{1}{5}d.$$

Substituting these expressions for $a$, $b$ and $c$ into equation (S.6), we see that the equation of the plane can be written as

$$\tfrac{1}{3}dx + \tfrac{1}{4}dy - \tfrac{1}{5}dz = d.$$

Dividing by $d$, we obtain

$$\tfrac{1}{3}x + \tfrac{1}{4}y - \tfrac{1}{5}z = 1.$$

It follows that one possible normal vector is

$$\left(\tfrac{1}{3}, \tfrac{1}{4}, -\tfrac{1}{5}\right).$$

**3.11** Denote by $\mathbf{p}$ the first vector of each pair, by $\mathbf{q}$ the second vector and by $\theta$ the angle between the vectors.

**(a)** When $\mathbf{p} = (3, 1)$ and $\mathbf{q} = (1, -2)$, we have

$$\|\mathbf{p}\| = \sqrt{3^2 + 1^2} = \sqrt{10},$$

$$\|\mathbf{q}\| = \sqrt{1^2 + (-2)^2} = \sqrt{5},$$

$$\mathbf{p}\cdot\mathbf{q} = 3\times 1 + 1\times(-2) = 1.$$

It follows that

$$\cos\theta = \frac{\mathbf{p}\cdot\mathbf{q}}{\|\mathbf{p}\|\times\|\mathbf{q}\|} = \frac{1}{\sqrt{50}} = 0.1414 \quad \text{(to 4 d.p.)},$$

so

$$\theta = 1.43 \text{ radians} \quad \text{(to 2 d.p.)}.$$

When $\mathbf{p} = \mathbf{i} + 2\mathbf{j}$ and $\mathbf{q} = -3\mathbf{i} + \mathbf{j} - 2\mathbf{k}$, we have

$$\|\mathbf{p}\| = \sqrt{1^2 + 2^2} = \sqrt{5},$$
$$\|\mathbf{q}\| = \sqrt{(-3)^2 + 1^2 + (-2)^2} = \sqrt{14},$$
$$\mathbf{p} \cdot \mathbf{q} = 1 \times (-3) + 2 \times 1 + 0 \times (-2) = -1.$$

It follows that

$$\cos\theta = \frac{\mathbf{p} \cdot \mathbf{q}}{\|\mathbf{p}\| \times \|\mathbf{q}\|} = \frac{-1}{\sqrt{70}} = -0.1195 \quad \text{(to 4 d.p.)},$$

so

$$\theta = 1.69 \text{ radians} \quad \text{(to 2 d.p.)}.$$

**(b)** When $\mathbf{p} = (3, 1)$ and $\mathbf{q} = (1, -2)$, the projection of $\mathbf{p}$ onto $\mathbf{q}$ is

$$\frac{\mathbf{p} \cdot \mathbf{q}}{\|\mathbf{q}\|} = \frac{1}{\sqrt{5}} = 0.4472 \quad \text{(to 4 d.p.)}.$$

When $\mathbf{p} = \mathbf{i} + 2\mathbf{j}$ and $\mathbf{q} = -3\mathbf{i} + \mathbf{j} - 2\mathbf{k}$, the projection of $\mathbf{p}$ onto $\mathbf{q}$ is

$$\frac{\mathbf{p} \cdot \mathbf{q}}{\|\mathbf{q}\|} = \frac{-1}{\sqrt{14}} = -0.2673 \quad \text{(to 4 d.p.)}.$$

**3.12** Let such a vector be $\mathbf{r} = (x, y)$. Since $\mathbf{r}$ has length 2 and makes an angle $\pi/4$ with $\mathbf{p} = (2, -2)$,

$$\mathbf{p} \cdot \mathbf{r} = \|\mathbf{p}\| \times \|\mathbf{r}\| \cos\pi/4 = 2\sqrt{2} \times 2 \times \tfrac{1}{\sqrt{2}} = 4.$$

In component form we have

$$\mathbf{p} \cdot \mathbf{r} = 2x - 2y,$$

so

$$2x - 2y = 4,$$

that is,

$$x = y + 2.$$

Also, $\mathbf{r}$ has length 2, so

$$x^2 + y^2 = 4. \qquad \text{(S.7)}$$

Substituting the expression for $x$ into equation (S.7), we obtain

$$(y + 2)^2 + y^2 = 4,$$

thus

$$y^2 + 4y + 4 + y^2 = 4,$$

that is,

$$2y^2 + 4y = 0.$$

This has solutions

$$y = 0 \quad \text{and} \quad y = -2;$$

the corresponding values of $x$ are $x = 2$ and $x = 0$.

It follows that the two vectors of length 2 making an angle of $\pi/4$ with $(2, -2)$ are $(2, 0)$ and $(0, -2)$.

The dot product of these two vectors is

$$(2, 0) \cdot (0, -2) = 2 \times 0 + 0 \times (-2) = 0,$$

so the two vectors are perpendicular.

**3.13** We use the corollary to Theorem 3.1 on page 36. The equation of the plane is given by $\mathbf{x} \cdot \mathbf{n} = \mathbf{p} \cdot \mathbf{n}$, where $\mathbf{x} = (x, y, z)$, $\mathbf{p} = (-1, 3, 2)$ and $\mathbf{n} = (1, 2, -1)$.

Thus the equation of the plane is

$$x + 2y - z = (-1) \times 1 + 3 \times 2 + 2 \times (-1),$$

that is,

$$x + 2y - z = 3.$$

**3.14** Let the equation of the plane be

$$ax + by + cz = d, \qquad \text{(S.8)}$$

for some real numbers $a$, $b$, $c$ and $d$, where $a$, $b$ and $c$ are not all zero.

Substituting the coordinates of the three points in turn into equation (S.8), we obtain

$$a \quad + 2c = d, \qquad \text{(S.9)}$$
$$3b + 4c = d, \qquad \text{(S.10)}$$
$$-b \quad = d. \qquad \text{(S.11)}$$

Substituting $-b$ for $d$ in equations (S.9) and (S.10), we obtain

$$a + 2c = -b, \qquad \text{(S.12)}$$
$$3b + 4c = -b. \qquad \text{(S.13)}$$

Equation (S.13) gives $c = -b$; if we then substitute $-b$ for $c$ in equation (S.12), we obtain

$$a - 2b = -b,$$

that is,

$$a = b.$$

It follows that the equation of the plane is

$$bx + by - bz = -b,$$

that is,

$$x + y - z = -1.$$

**4.1** We use the standard formula for the equation of a circle of given centre and radius given in Theorem 4.1 on page 38.

**(a)** This circle has equation

$$(x - 0)^2 + (y - 0)^2 = 1^2,$$

which can be rewritten in the form

$$x^2 + y^2 = 1.$$

**(b)** This circle has equation

$$(x - 0)^2 + (y - 0)^2 = 4^2,$$

which can be rewritten in the form

$$x^2 + y^2 = 16.$$

**(c)** This circle has equation

$$(x - 3)^2 + (y - 4)^2 = 2^2,$$

which can be rewritten in the form

$$x^2 + y^2 - 6x - 8y + 21 = 0.$$

**4.2** Since the origin lies on the circle, its coordinates $(0,0)$ must satisfy the equation of the circle. Thus

$$0^2 + 0^2 + f \times 0 + g \times 0 + h = 0,$$

which reduces to the condition $h = 0$.

**4.3** **(a)** We can complete the square in the equation

$$x^2 + y^2 - 2x - 6y + 1 = 0$$

to obtain

$$(x-1)^2 - 1 + (y-3)^2 - 9 + 1 = 0,$$

or

$$(x-1)^2 + (y-3)^2 = 9.$$

So the circle has centre $(1,3)$ and radius $\sqrt{9} = 3$.

(Alternatively, use the general formula for centre and radius in Theorem 4.2 on page 40 with $f = -2$, $g = -6$ and $h = 1$.)

**(b)** Here the coefficients of $x^2$ and $y^2$ are both 3, so we divide the equation by 3 to obtain

$$x^2 + y^2 - 4x - 16y = 0. \qquad \text{(S.14)}$$

Completing the square gives

$$(x-2)^2 - 4 + (y-8)^2 - 64 = 0,$$

or

$$(x-2)^2 + (y-8)^2 = 68.$$

So the circle has centre $(2,8)$ and radius $\sqrt{68} = 2\sqrt{17}$.

(Alternatively, apply the general formula for centre and radius to the equation in the form of equation (S.14), with $f = -4$, $g = -16$ and $h = 0$.)

**4.4** **(a)** If we complete the square in the equation

$$x^2 + y^2 + x + y + 1 = 0, \qquad \text{(S.15)}$$

we obtain the equation

$$\left(x + \tfrac{1}{2}\right)^2 + \left(y + \tfrac{1}{2}\right)^2 = -\tfrac{1}{2}.$$

This equation represents the empty set, since its left-hand side is always non-negative whereas its right-hand side is negative.

(Alternatively, we can use information about the quantity $\frac{1}{4}f^2 + \frac{1}{4}g^2 - h$. In equation (S.15), we have $f = 1$, $g = 1$ and $h = 1$. Thus

$$\tfrac{1}{4}f^2 + \tfrac{1}{4}g^2 - h = \tfrac{1}{4} + \tfrac{1}{4} - 1 < 0,$$

so the set must be empty.)

**(b)** If we complete the square in the equation

$$x^2 + y^2 - 2x + 4y + 5 = 0, \qquad \text{(S.16)}$$

we obtain the equation

$$(x-1)^2 + (y+2)^2 = 0.$$

Thus the set in the plane represented by equation (S.16) is the single point $(1,-2)$.

(Alternatively, we can use information about the quantity $\frac{1}{4}f^2 + \frac{1}{4}g^2 - h$. In equation (S.16), we have $f = -2$, $g = 4$ and $h = 5$. Thus

$$\tfrac{1}{4}f^2 + \tfrac{1}{4}g^2 - h = 1 + 4 - 5 = 0,$$

so the set is the single point $\left(-\frac{1}{2}f, -\frac{1}{2}g\right) = (1,-2)$.)

**(c)** Here the coefficients of $x^2$ and $y^2$ are both 2, so we divide the equation by 2 to give

$$x^2 + y^2 + \tfrac{1}{2}x - \tfrac{3}{2}y - \tfrac{5}{2} = 0. \qquad \text{(S.17)}$$

If we complete the square in equation (S.17), we obtain the equation

$$\left(x + \tfrac{1}{4}\right)^2 - \tfrac{1}{16} + \left(y - \tfrac{3}{4}\right)^2 - \tfrac{9}{16} - \tfrac{5}{2} = 0,$$

that is,

$$\left(x + \tfrac{1}{4}\right)^2 + \left(y - \tfrac{3}{4}\right)^2 = \tfrac{25}{8}.$$

Thus the set in the plane represented by equation (S.17) is a circle with centre $\left(-\frac{1}{4}, \frac{3}{4}\right)$ and radius $\sqrt{\frac{25}{8}} = \frac{5}{4}\sqrt{2}$.

(Alternatively, we can use information about the quantity $\frac{1}{4}f^2 + \frac{1}{4}g^2 - h$. In equation (S.17), we have $f = \frac{1}{2}$, $g = -\frac{3}{2}$ and $h = -\frac{5}{2}$. Thus

$$\tfrac{1}{4}f^2 + \tfrac{1}{4}g^2 - h = \tfrac{1}{16} + \tfrac{9}{16} + \tfrac{5}{2} = \tfrac{25}{8},$$

so the set is the circle with centre $\left(-\frac{1}{4}, \frac{3}{4}\right)$ and radius $\sqrt{\frac{25}{8}} = \frac{5}{4}\sqrt{2}$.)

**4.5**

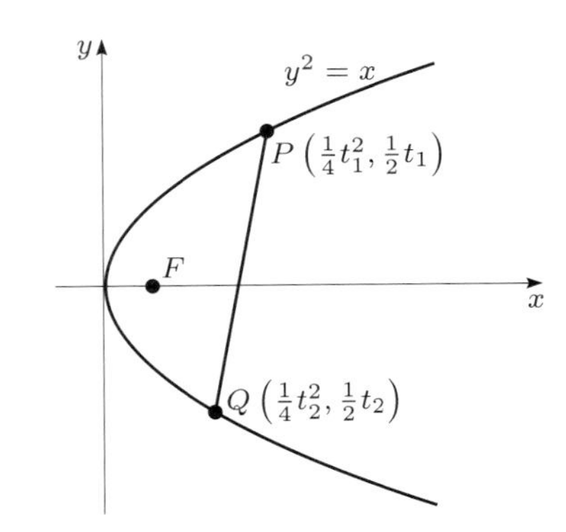


**(a)** The parabola is in standard form, where $4a = 1$, that is, $a = \frac{1}{4}$. It follows that the focus is $\left(\frac{1}{4}, 0\right)$, the vertex is $(0,0)$, the axis is the $x$-axis, and the equation of the directrix is $x = -\frac{1}{4}$.

**(b)** The coordinates of $P$ and $Q$ are $\left(\frac{1}{4}t_1^2, \frac{1}{2}t_1\right)$ and $\left(\frac{1}{4}t_2^2, \frac{1}{2}t_2\right)$, respectively. It follows that if $t_1^2 \neq t_2^2$, then the gradient of $PQ$ is

$$\frac{\frac{1}{2}t_1 - \frac{1}{2}t_2}{\frac{1}{4}t_1^2 - \frac{1}{4}t_2^2} = \frac{2(t_1 - t_2)}{t_1^2 - t_2^2} = \frac{2}{t_1 + t_2}.$$

Since $\left(\frac{1}{4}t_1^2, \frac{1}{2}t_1\right)$ lies on the line $PQ$, it follows that the equation of $PQ$ is

$$y - \tfrac{1}{2}t_1 = \frac{2}{t_1 + t_2}\left(x - \tfrac{1}{4}t_1^2\right).$$

Multiplying both sides by $2(t_1 + t_2)$, we obtain

$$2(t_1 + t_2)\left(y - \tfrac{1}{2}t_1\right) = 4\left(x - \tfrac{1}{4}t_1^2\right),$$

so

$$2(t_1 + t_2)y - t_1^2 - t_1 t_2 = 4x - t_1^2,$$

and hence

$$2(t_1 + t_2)y = 4x + t_1 t_2. \qquad \text{(S.18)}$$

If $t_1^2 = t_2^2$, then $t_1 = -t_2$ (as $t_1 \neq t_2$, since $P$ and $Q$ are distinct). If $t_1 = -t_2$, then $PQ$ is parallel to the $y$-axis and the equation of $PQ$ is $x = \frac{1}{4}t_1^2 = -\frac{1}{4}t_1 t_2$, that is,

$$0 = 4x + t_1 t_2.$$

Thus equation (S.18) is the equation of $PQ$ in the case $t_1 = -t_2$ also, for then $t_1 + t_2 = 0$.

**(c)** The midpoint of $PQ$ is

$$\left(\tfrac{1}{8}(t_1^2 + t_2^2), \tfrac{1}{4}(t_1 + t_2)\right).$$

This is the focus $\left(\frac{1}{4}, 0\right)$ if and only if

$$\tfrac{1}{8}(t_1^2 + t_2^2) = \tfrac{1}{4} \quad \text{and} \quad \tfrac{1}{4}(t_1 + t_2) = 0,$$

which is the case if and only if $t_2 = -t_1$ and $\frac{1}{8}(2t_1^2) = \frac{1}{4}$, that is, $t_1^2 = 1$ and so $t_1 = \pm 1$. Thus the midpoint of $PQ$ is the focus if and only if $P$ and $Q$ are the points $\left(\frac{1}{4}, \frac{1}{2}\right)$ and $\left(\frac{1}{4}, -\frac{1}{2}\right)$.

*Remark* The focus is the midpoint of $PQ$ if and only if $PQ$ is the chord through the focus parallel to the $y$-axis.

## 4.6

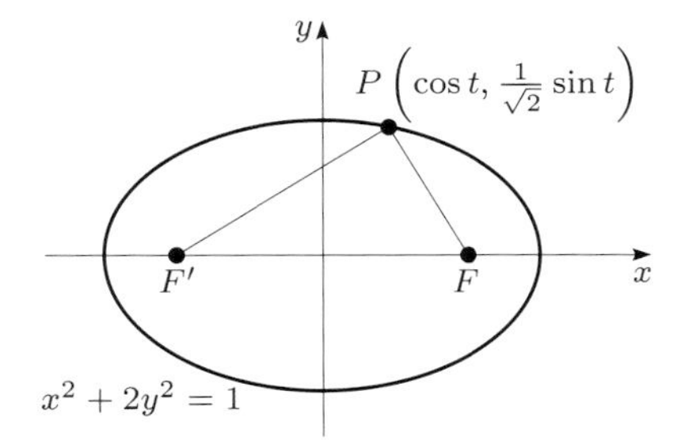


**(a)** This ellipse is of the form $\dfrac{x^2}{a^2} + \dfrac{y^2}{b^2} = 1$ with $a = 1$ and $b^2 = \frac{1}{2}$, so $b = \frac{1}{\sqrt{2}}$. If $e$ denotes the eccentricity of the ellipse, so that $b^2 = a^2(1 - e^2)$, then we have

$$\tfrac{1}{2} = 1 - e^2;$$

it follows that $e^2 = \frac{1}{2}$, so $e = \frac{1}{\sqrt{2}}$.

In the general case, the foci are $(\pm ae, 0)$; it follows that here the foci are $\left(\pm\frac{1}{\sqrt{2}}, 0\right)$.

**(b)** Let $F$ and $F'$ be $\left(\frac{1}{\sqrt{2}}, 0\right)$ and $\left(-\frac{1}{\sqrt{2}}, 0\right)$, respectively. (It does not matter which way round these are chosen.)

Then the gradient of $FP$ is

$$\frac{\frac{1}{\sqrt{2}}\sin t - 0}{\cos t - \frac{1}{\sqrt{2}}} = \frac{\sin t}{\sqrt{2}\cos t - 1},$$

where we know that $\cos t \neq \frac{1}{\sqrt{2}}$, since $FP$ is not parallel to the $y$-axis.

Similarly, the gradient of $F'P$ is

$$\frac{\frac{1}{\sqrt{2}}\sin t - 0}{\cos t + \frac{1}{\sqrt{2}}} = \frac{\sin t}{\sqrt{2}\cos t + 1},$$

where we know that $\cos t \neq -\frac{1}{\sqrt{2}}$, since $F'P$ is not parallel to the $y$-axis.

**(c)** When $FP$ is perpendicular to $F'P$, we have

$$\frac{\sin t}{\sqrt{2}\cos t - 1} \times \frac{\sin t}{\sqrt{2}\cos t + 1} = -1.$$

We may rewrite this in the form

$$\frac{\sin^2 t}{2\cos^2 t - 1} = -1,$$

so $2\cos^2 t - 1 + \sin^2 t = 0$.

Since $\cos^2 t + \sin^2 t = 1$, it follows that $\cos^2 t = 0$ and so $\cos t = 0$. This occurs only when $t = \pm\pi/2$; that is, at the points $\left(0, \pm\frac{1}{\sqrt{2}}\right)$.

## 4.7

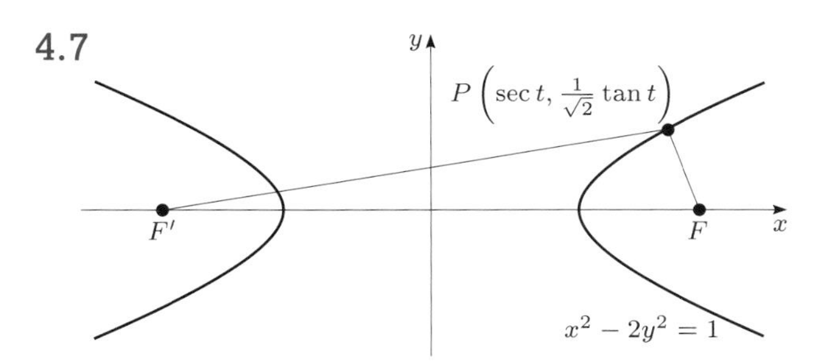


**(a)** This hyperbola is of the form $\dfrac{x^2}{a^2} - \dfrac{y^2}{b^2} = 1$ with $a = 1$ and $b^2 = \frac{1}{2}$, so $b = \frac{1}{\sqrt{2}}$. If $e$ denotes the eccentricity of the hyperbola, so that $b^2 = a^2(e^2 - 1)$, we have

$$\tfrac{1}{2} = e^2 - 1;$$

it follows that $e^2 = \frac{3}{2}$, so $e = \sqrt{\frac{3}{2}}$.

In the general case, the foci are $(\pm ae, 0)$; it follows that here the foci are $\left(\pm\sqrt{\frac{3}{2}}, 0\right)$.

**(b)** Let $F$ and $F'$ be $\left(\sqrt{\frac{3}{2}}, 0\right)$ and $\left(-\sqrt{\frac{3}{2}}, 0\right)$, respectively. (It does not matter which way round these are chosen.)

Then the gradient of $FP$ is

$$\frac{\frac{1}{\sqrt{2}}\tan t - 0}{\sec t - \sqrt{\frac{3}{2}}} = \frac{\tan t}{\sqrt{2}\sec t - \sqrt{3}},$$

where we know that $\sec t \neq \sqrt{\frac{3}{2}}$, since $FP$ is not parallel to the $y$-axis.

Similarly, the gradient of $F'P$ is

$$\frac{\frac{1}{\sqrt{2}}\tan t - 0}{\sec t + \sqrt{\frac{3}{2}}} = \frac{\tan t}{\sqrt{2}\sec t + \sqrt{3}},$$

where we know that $\sec t \neq -\sqrt{\frac{3}{2}}$, since $F'P$ is not parallel to the $y$-axis.

**(c)** When $FP$ is perpendicular to $F'P$, we have

$$\frac{\tan t}{\sqrt{2}\sec t - \sqrt{3}} \times \frac{\tan t}{\sqrt{2}\sec t + \sqrt{3}} = -1.$$

We may rewrite this in the form

$$\frac{\tan^2 t}{2\sec^2 t - 3} = -1,$$

so $2\sec^2 t - 3 + \tan^2 t = 0$.

Since $\sec^2 t = 1 + \tan^2 t$, it follows that $3\tan^2 t = 1$. Since we are looking for a point $P$ in the first quadrant, we choose $\tan t = \frac{1}{\sqrt{3}}$.

When $\tan t = \frac{1}{\sqrt{3}}$, we have $\sec^2 t = 1 + \frac{1}{3} = \frac{4}{3}$. Since we are looking for a point $P$ in the first quadrant, we choose $\sec t = \frac{2}{\sqrt{3}}$.

It follows that the required point $P$ has coordinates $\left(\frac{2}{\sqrt{3}}, \frac{1}{\sqrt{2}} \times \frac{1}{\sqrt{3}}\right) = \left(\frac{2}{\sqrt{3}}, \frac{1}{\sqrt{6}}\right)$.

**4.8** The equation of the circle is

$$(x-2)^2 + (y-1)^2 = 3^2,$$

which can be rewritten in the form

$$x^2 + y^2 - 4x - 2y - 4 = 0.$$

**4.9**

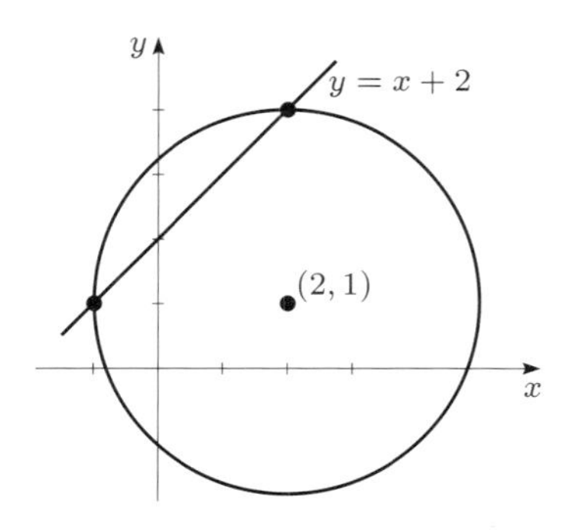


At the points of intersection of the line and the circle, the following equations must be satisfied:

$$y = x + 2$$

and

$$x^2 + y^2 - 4x - 2y - 4 = 0.$$

Substituting the expression for $y$ from the first equation into the second equation, we obtain

$$x^2 + (x+2)^2 - 4x - 2(x+2) - 4 = 0.$$

Multiplying this out and collecting terms, we obtain

$$2x^2 - 2x - 4 = 0,$$

or

$$x^2 - x - 2 = 0.$$

This can be factorised as

$$(x-2)(x+1) = 0,$$

so $x = 2$ or $x = -1$.

Substituting these values of $x$ into the equation $y = x + 2$ of the line, we find that the corresponding values of $y$ are $y = 4$ and $y = 1$.

Hence the points of intersection of the line and the circle are $(2, 4)$ and $(-1, 1)$.

**4.10**

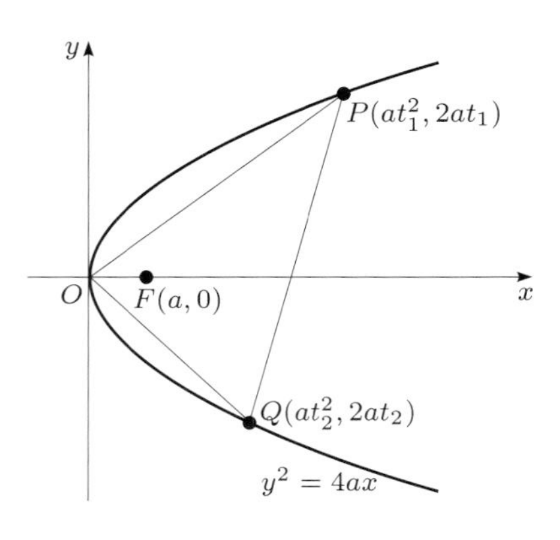


**(a)** The gradient of $OP$ is

$$m_1 = \frac{2at_1 - 0}{at_1^2 - 0} = \frac{2}{t_1},$$

and the gradient of $OQ$ is

$$m_2 = \frac{2at_2 - 0}{at_2^2 - 0} = \frac{2}{t_2}.$$

$OP$ and $OQ$ are perpendicular (in other words, $PQ$ subtends a right angle at $O$) if $m_1 m_2 = -1$, that is, if

$$\left(\frac{2}{t_1}\right) \times \left(\frac{2}{t_2}\right) = -1,$$

which reduces to $t_1 t_2 = -4$, as required.

**(b)** Here $P$ is the point $(4a, 4a)$. Also, $F$ is $(a, 0)$, so the gradient of $FP$ is

$$m_1 = \frac{4a - 0}{4a - a} = \frac{4}{3},$$

and the gradient of $PQ$ is

$$m_2 = \frac{2at_2 - 4a}{at_2^2 - 4a} = \frac{2}{2 + t_2}.$$

$FP$ and $PQ$ are perpendicular if $m_1 m_2 = -1$, that is, if

$$\left(\frac{4}{3}\right) \times \left(\frac{2}{2 + t_2}\right) = -1,$$

which reduces to $2 + t_2 = -\frac{8}{3}$, so $t_2 = -\frac{14}{3}$, as required.

**4.11**

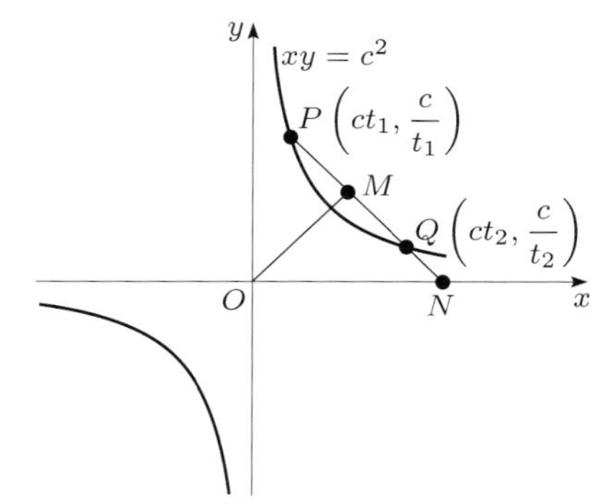


**(a)** The gradient of the chord $PQ$ is

$$\frac{c/t_2 - c/t_1}{ct_2 - ct_1} = -\frac{1}{t_1 t_2},$$

so the equation of $PQ$ is

$$y - \frac{c}{t_1} = -\frac{1}{t_1 t_2}(x - ct_1),$$

that is,

$$x + t_1 t_2 y = c(t_1 + t_2). \qquad \text{(S.19)}$$

**(b)** At the point $N$ where $PQ$ meets the $x$-axis, $y = 0$ and equation (S.19) also holds, so $x = c(t_1 + t_2)$. Hence $N$ is the point with coordinates $(c(t_1 + t_2), 0)$.

**(c)** The midpoint $M$ of $PQ$ is

$$\left(\frac{ct_1 + ct_2}{2}, \frac{c/t_1 + c/t_2}{2}\right)$$
$$= \left(\frac{c(t_1 + t_2)}{2}, \frac{c(t_1 + t_2)}{2t_1t_2}\right).$$

**(d)** By the Distance Formula, the distance $OM$ is

$$OM = \sqrt{\left(\frac{c(t_1 + t_2)}{2}\right)^2 + \left(\frac{c(t_1 + t_2)}{2t_1t_2}\right)^2}$$
$$= \frac{c|t_1 + t_2|}{2|t_1t_2|}\sqrt{(t_1t_2)^2 + 1}.$$

Also,

$$MN = \sqrt{\left(c(t_1 + t_2) - \frac{c(t_1 + t_2)}{2}\right)^2 + \left(\frac{c(t_1 + t_2)}{2t_1t_2}\right)^2}$$
$$= \sqrt{\left(\frac{c(t_1 + t_2)}{2}\right)^2 + \left(\frac{c(t_1 + t_2)}{2t_1t_2}\right)^2}$$
$$= \frac{c|t_1 + t_2|}{2|t_1t_2|}\sqrt{(t_1t_2)^2 + 1}.$$

Thus $OM = MN$.

*Remark* An alternative way of proving part (d) is as follows. Since the point $M$ is vertically above the midpoint $\left(\frac{c(t_1 + t_2)}{2}, 0\right)$ of $ON$, the triangle $OMN$ must be an isosceles triangle, so $OM = MN$.

# Index

The Open University

M208 Pure

# AB2

## Differentiation

This publication forms part of an Open University course. Details of this and other Open University courses can be obtained from the Student Registration and Enquiry Service, The Open University, PO Box 197, Milton Keynes, MK7 6BJ, United Kingdom: tel. +44 (0)870 333 4340, e-mail general-enquiries@open.ac.uk

Alternatively, you may visit the Open University website at http://www.open.ac.uk where you can learn more about the wide range of courses and packs offered at all levels by The Open University.

To purchase a selection of Open University course materials, visit the webshop at www.ouw.co.uk, or contact Open University Worldwide, Michael Young Building, Walton Hall, Milton Keynes, MK7 6AA, United Kingdom, for a brochure: tel. +44 (0)1908 858785, fax +44 (0)1908 858787, e-mail ouwenq@open.ac.uk

The Open University, Walton Hall, Milton Keynes, MK7 6AA.

First published 2006.



Edited, designed and typeset by The Open University, using the Open University TEX System.

Printed and bound in the United Kingdom by Hobbs the Printers Limited, Brunel Road, Totton, Hampshire SO40 3WX.

ISBN 0 7492 0212 2

1.1

# Contents

# Introduction

In Analysis Block A we considered *continuous* functions, and we found that they share some important properties; for example, they all satisfy the Intermediate Value Theorem, the Extreme Value Theorem and the Boundedness Theorem. However, many of the most interesting properties of functions are obtained only when we further restrict our attention to *differentiable* functions.

See Unit AA4, Section 3.

You have already met the idea of *differentiating* a given function $f$; that is, finding the slope of the tangent to the graph $y = f(x)$ at those points of the graph where a tangent exists. The slope of the tangent at the point $(c, f(c))$ is called the *derivative* of $f$ at $c$, and is written as $f'(c)$. In this unit we investigate which functions are differentiable, and we discuss some of the important properties that all differentiable functions possess.

In Section 1 we define what it means for a function $f$ to be differentiable at a point $c$, and we establish some of the basic differentiable functions. We also consider functions which possess higher derivatives, that is, functions which can be differentiated more than once. Finally, we show that differentiable functions are continuous, and also prove that the blancmange function, which was shown earlier to be continuous, is in fact nowhere differentiable.

See Unit AB1, Section 3.

In Section 2 we obtain further standard derivatives using several rules for differentiation.

In Sections 3 and 4 we study the properties of functions that are differentiable *on an interval*, and establish some useful results about derivatives which can also be described geometrically.

In Section 5 we give a result called l'Hôpital's Rule, which enables us to find limits of the form

$$\lim_{x \to c} \frac{f(x)}{g(x)}$$

in some of the awkward cases when $f(c) = g(c) = 0$.

In this situation, the Quotient Rule for limits of functions fails.

## Study guide

The sections should be read in the natural order.

Section 1 presents some key definitions and it makes essential use of several results about limits. The final part of Section 1 includes a rather technical proof, which is optional.

See Unit AB1, Section 1, for results about limits.

Section 2 contains many exercises and is the longest section of the unit. However, you should already be familiar with much of this material, and most of the exercises are included only in case you need to do some revision.

Sections 3 and 4 are particularly important, as they contain results and techniques needed in Section 5 and in later units.

Section 5 includes the video section. The video programme contains a review of the main ideas from Sections 3–5.

# 1 Differentiable functions

After working through this section, you should be able to:

(a) explain what is meant by a *differentiable function*, and understand its geometric significance;

(b) determine, using the definition, whether or not a function is differentiable at a point;

(c) explain what is meant by a *second derivative* and a higher-order derivative;

(d) explain what is meant by the *left derivative* and the *right derivative* of a function at a given point;

(e) state and use the Glue Rule for differentiation.

## 1.1 What is differentiability?

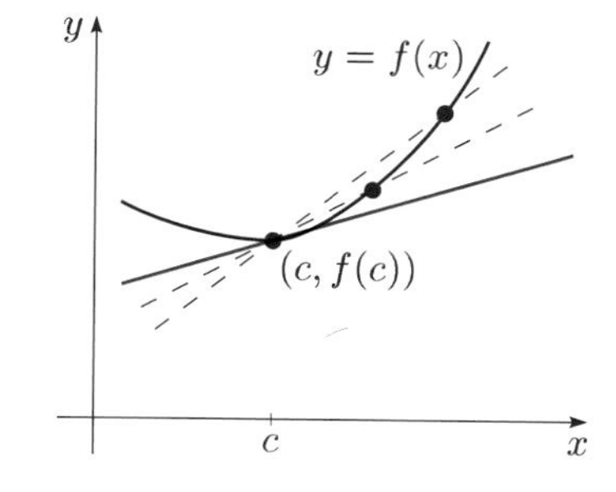


Differentiability arises from the geometric concept of the *tangent* to a graph. The tangent to the graph $y = f(x)$ at the point $(c, f(c))$ is the line through the point $(c, f(c))$ whose direction is the limiting direction of the chords joining the points $(c, f(c))$ and $(x, f(x))$ as $x$ tends to $c$.

The three examples below illustrate some of the possibilities that can occur when we try to find tangents in particular instances.

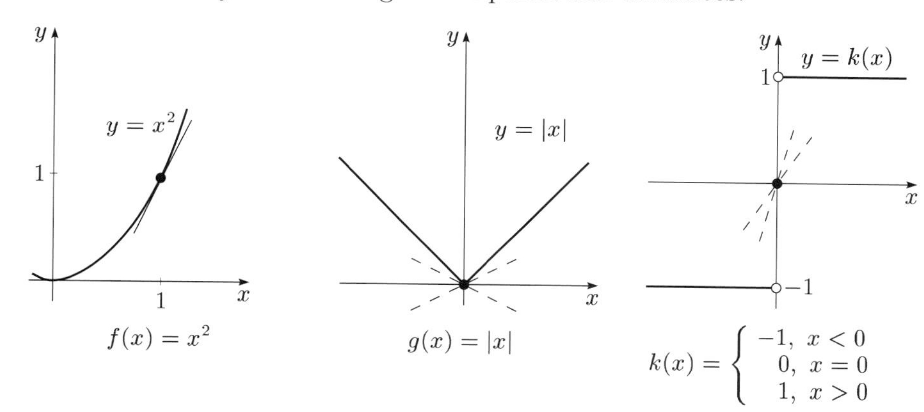


The function

$$f(x) = x^2 \quad (x \in \mathbb{R})$$

is continuous on $\mathbb{R}$, and its graph has a tangent at each point; for example, the line $y = 2x - 1$ is the tangent to the graph at the point $(1, 1)$.

The function

$$g(x) = |x| \quad (x \in \mathbb{R})$$

is also continuous on $\mathbb{R}$, but its graph does not have a tangent at the point $(0, 0)$; no line through the point $(0, 0)$ is a tangent to the graph. However, there is a tangent at every other point of the graph.

Finally, the function

$$k(x) = \begin{cases} -1, & x < 0, \\ 0, & x = 0, \\ 1, & x > 0, \end{cases}$$

is discontinuous at 0, and no line through the point $(0, 0)$ is a tangent to the graph. However, there is a tangent at every other point of the graph.

We now make these ideas precise, by using the concept of limit to pin down what we mean by 'limiting direction'. We define the **slope**, or **gradient**, of the graph at $(c, f(c))$ to be the limit, as $x$ tends to $c$, of the slope of the chord through the points $(c, f(c))$ and $(x, f(x))$. The slope of this chord is

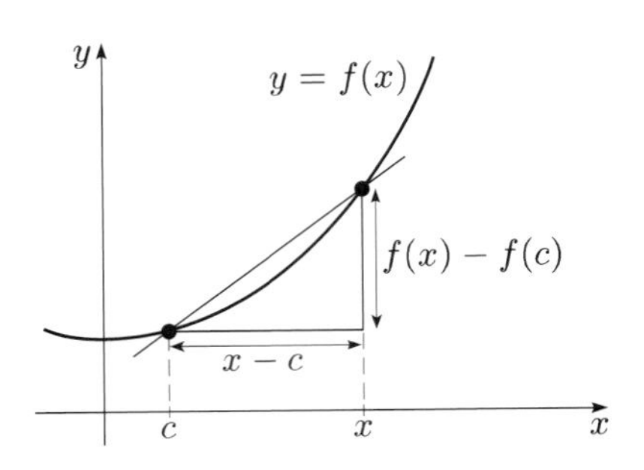


$$\frac{f(x) - f(c)}{x - c}, \quad \text{where } x \neq c.$$

This expression is called the **difference quotient** for $f$ at $c$. Thus the slope of the graph of $f$ at the point $(c, f(c))$ is

$$\lim_{x \to c} \frac{f(x) - f(c)}{x - c}, \tag{1.1}$$

provided that this limit exists.

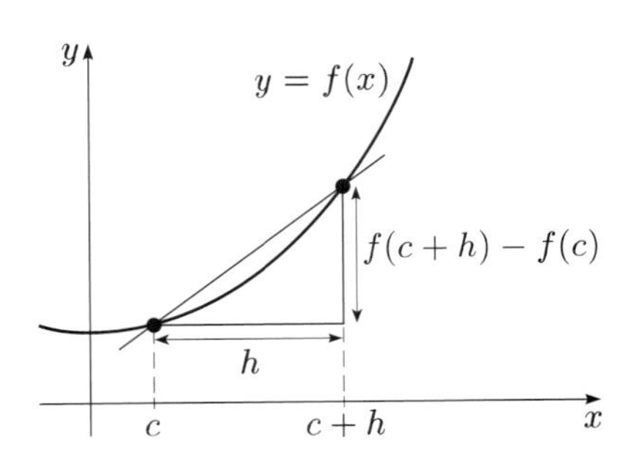


Sometimes it is more convenient to use an equivalent form of the difference quotient. If we replace $x$ by $c + h$, then '$x \to c$' in expression (1.1) is equivalent to '$h \to 0$'. The difference quotient for $f$ at $c$ is then

$$Q(h) = \frac{f(c+h) - f(c)}{h}, \quad \text{where } h \neq 0,$$

and the slope of the graph of $f$ at $(c, f(c))$ is

$$\lim_{h \to 0} Q(h), \tag{1.2}$$

Note that $Q(h)$ depends on $c$.

provided that this limit exists. We call this limit the *derivative* of $f$ at $c$.

To formalise this concept, we need to ensure that $f$ is defined near the point $c$, so we assume that $c$ lies in some open interval $I$ in the domain of $f$.

**Definition** Let $f$ be defined on an open interval $I$, and $c \in I$. Then the **derivative** of $f$ at $c$ is

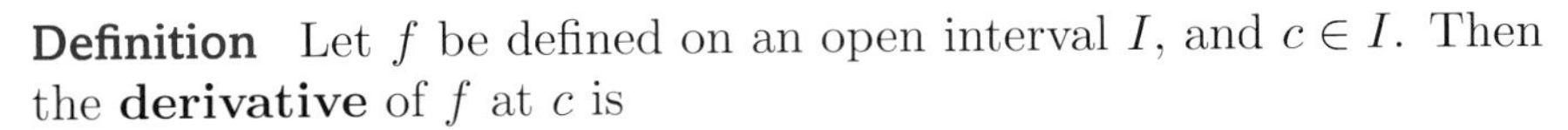

$$\lim_{x \to c} \frac{f(x) - f(c)}{x - c}, \quad \text{that is,} \quad \lim_{h \to 0} Q(h) = \lim_{h \to 0} \frac{f(c+h) - f(c)}{h},$$

provided that this limit exists. In this case, we say that $f$ is **differentiable** at $c$. If $f$ is differentiable at each point of its domain, then we say that $f$ is **differentiable** (on its domain).

The derivative of $f$ at $c$ is denoted by $f'(c)$ and the function $f' : x \longmapsto f'(x)$ is called the **derivative**, or sometimes the **derived function**, of $f$.

The operation of obtaining $f'(x)$ from $f(x)$ is called **differentiation**.

The word 'differentiable' arises because the definition involves the *differences* $f(x) - f(c)$ and $x - c$.

Sometimes $f'$ is denoted by $Df$ and $f'(x)$ is denoted by $Df(x)$.

In Leibniz notation, $f'(x)$ is written as $\dfrac{dy}{dx}$, where $y = f(x)$.

*Remarks*

1. The existence of the derivative $f'(c)$ is not quite equivalent to the existence of a tangent to the graph $y = f(x)$ at the point $(c, f(c))$. If

   $$\lim_{x \to c} \frac{f(x) - f(c)}{x - c} \quad \text{exists,}$$

   then the graph has a tangent at the point $(c, f(c))$, and the slope of the tangent is the value of the limit.

   However, the converse is not necessarily true. The graph may have a *vertical* tangent at the point $(c, f(c))$, in which case

   $$\frac{f(x) - f(c)}{x - c} \to \infty \text{ (or } -\infty) \quad \text{as } x \to c.$$

   In this case, limit (1.1) does not exist, so $f$ is not differentiable at $c$.

2. Historically, the idea of finding the slope of a graph which is not a straight line was one of the first steps in the development of calculus. The major figures in this development were Sir Isaac Newton (1642–1727) in England and Gottfried Wilhelm Leibniz (1646–1716) in Germany, to whom we owe the '$dy/dx$' notation and the names 'differential calculus' and 'integral calculus'. The names 'derived function' and 'derivative' and the notation $f'$ were introduced much later by Lagrange.

Another mathematician who played a role in the early development was Pierre de Fermat (1601–1665) in France.

**Example 1.1** Prove that the function $f(x) = x^3$ is differentiable at any point $c \in \mathbb{R}$, and determine $f'(c)$.

**Solution** The difference quotient for $f$ at $c$ is

$$\begin{aligned} Q(h) = \frac{f(c+h) - f(c)}{h} &= \frac{(c+h)^3 - c^3}{h} \\ &= \frac{(c^3 + 3c^2h + 3ch^2 + h^3) - c^3}{h} \\ &= 3c^2 + 3ch + h^2, \quad \text{where } h \neq 0. \end{aligned}$$

Thus $Q(h) \to 3c^2$ as $h \to 0$, so $f$ is differentiable at $c$, with $f'(c) = 3c^2$. ■

Here we use the Combination Rules for limits without mentioning them explicitly.

*Remark* We use $c$ to denote a particular point where we are testing for differentiability. However, when stating the rule of a derivative, we replace $c$ by the usual variable $x$. Thus the derivative of $f$ in Example 1.1 is $f'(x) = 3x^2$.

To prove from the definition that a function is *not* differentiable at a point, we can use the strategy for proving that a limit does not exist.

See Unit AB1, Section 1.

**Strategy 1.1** To prove that a function is not differentiable at a point.

Show that $\lim_{h \to 0} Q(h)$ does not exist, by:

EITHER

1. finding two null sequences $\{h_n\}$ and $\{h'_n\}$ with non-zero terms such that the sequences $\{Q(h_n)\}$ and $\{Q(h'_n)\}$ have different limits;

OR

2. finding a null sequence $\{h_n\}$ with non-zero terms such that $Q(h_n) \to \infty$ or $Q(h_n) \to -\infty$.

Here is an example.

**Example 1.2** Prove that the function

$$f(x) = \begin{cases} x \sin \dfrac{1}{x}, & x \neq 0, \\ 0, & x = 0, \end{cases}$$

is not differentiable at 0.

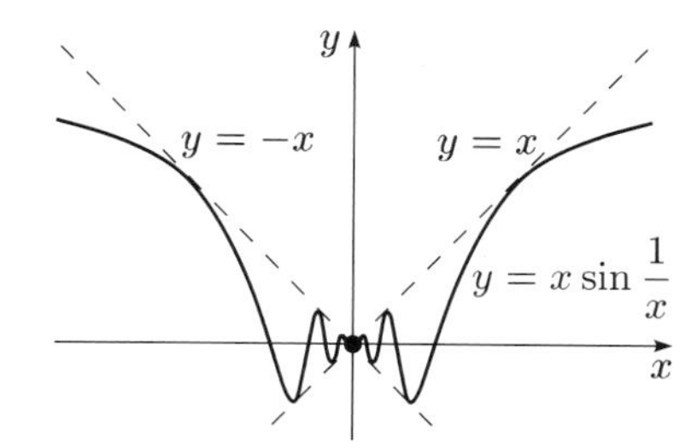

**Solution** The difference quotient for $f$ at $c=0$ is

$$\begin{aligned} Q(h) &= \frac{f(h)-f(0)}{h} \\ &= \frac{h\sin(1/h)-0}{h} = \sin(1/h), \quad \text{where } h \neq 0. \end{aligned}$$

Since $\sin(1/h)$ oscillates infinitely often for small values of $h$, we follow Strategy 1.1, part 1. Consider the two null sequences

$$h_n = \frac{1}{n\pi} \quad \text{and} \quad h_n' = \frac{1}{2n\pi + \frac{1}{2}\pi}, \quad n = 1, 2, \ldots,$$

Other choices of $\{h_n\}$ and $\{h_n'\}$ are possible; for example, $h_n = \dfrac{1}{2n\pi}$ and $h_n' = \dfrac{1}{2n\pi - \frac{1}{2}\pi}$.

with non-zero terms, which are chosen so that

$$Q(h_n) = \sin(1/h_n) = \sin(n\pi) = 0 \to 0 \ \text{ as } n \to \infty$$

and

$$Q(h_n') = \sin(1/h_n') = \sin(2n\pi + \tfrac{1}{2}\pi) = 1 \to 1 \ \text{ as } n \to \infty.$$

Since these limits are different, $f$ is not differentiable at 0. ■

Example 1.2 shows that the domain of a derivative $f'$ can be smaller than the domain of $f$.

**Exercise 1.1**

(a) Prove that the function $f(x) = 1/x$ is differentiable at any point $c \in \mathbb{R} - \{0\}$, and determine $f'(c)$.

(b) Prove that the function

$$f(x) = \begin{cases} x^2\cos(1/x), & x \neq 0, \\ 0, & x = 0, \end{cases}$$

is differentiable at 0, and determine $f'(0)$.

Hint: Use the Squeeze Rule for limits.

See Unit AB1, Subsection 1.3.

(c) Prove that the function $f(x) = |x|$ is not differentiable at 0.

(d) Prove that the function

$$f(x) = \begin{cases} |x|^{1/2}\sin(1/x), & x \neq 0, \\ 0, & x = 0, \end{cases}$$

is not differentiable at 0.

We now establish some basic derivatives.

**Theorem 1.1 Basic derivatives**

(a) If $f(x) = k$, where $k \in \mathbb{R}$, then $f'(x) = 0$.

(b) If $f(x) = x^n$, where $n \in \mathbb{N}$, then $f'(x) = nx^{n-1}$.

(c) If $f(x) = \sin x$, then $f'(x) = \cos x$.

(d) If $f(x) = \cos x$, then $f'(x) = -\sin x$.

(e) If $f(x) = e^x$, then $f'(x) = e^x$.

**Proof**

(a) If $f(x) = k$, then the difference quotient for $f$ at any point is 0, so $f'(x) = 0$.

(b) The proof of this part is similar to the reasoning in Example 1.1, using the Binomial Theorem applied to $(c+h)^n$. We omit the details.

(c) The difference quotient for $f$ at $c$ is

$$\begin{aligned} Q(h) &= \frac{\sin(c+h) - \sin c}{h} \\ &= \frac{\sin c \cos h + \cos c \sin h - \sin c}{h} \\ &= \cos c \left(\frac{\sin h}{h}\right) + \sin c \left(\frac{\cos h - 1}{h}\right), \quad \text{where } h \neq 0. \end{aligned}$$

Thus

$$Q(h) \to \cos c \times 1 + \sin c \times 0 = \cos c \quad \text{as } h \to 0,$$

so $f'(x) = \cos x$, as required.

(d) The proof of this part is similar to that of part (c). We omit the details.

(e) The difference quotient for $f$ at $c$ is

$$\begin{aligned} Q(h) &= \frac{e^{c+h} - e^c}{h} \\ &= e^c \left(\frac{e^h - 1}{h}\right), \quad \text{where } h \neq 0. \end{aligned}$$

Thus

$$Q(h) \to e^c \times 1 = e^c \quad \text{as } h \to 0,$$

so $f'(x) = e^x$, as required. ■

The limits

$$\lim_{h\to 0} \frac{\sin h}{h} = 1,$$

$$\lim_{h\to 0} \frac{\cos h - 1}{h} = 0,$$

$$\lim_{h\to 0} \frac{e^h - 1}{h} = 1$$

were found in Unit AB1, Section 1.

In general, when we differentiate a function $f$, we obtain a new function $f'$ whose domain may be smaller than that of $f$. The notion of differentiability can then be applied to the function $f'$, yielding another function, whose domain consists of those points where $f'$ is differentiable.

**Definition** Let $f$ be differentiable on an open interval $I$, and $c \in I$. If the derivative $f'$ is differentiable at $c$, then we say that $f$ is **twice differentiable** at $c$, and the number $f''(c) = (f')'(c)$ is called the **second derivative** of $f$ at $c$. The function $f''$, also denoted by $f^{(2)}$, is called the **second derivative** (or **second derived function**) of $f$.

Similarly, we can define the **higher-order derivatives** of $f$, denoted by $f^{(3)} = f'''$, $f^{(4)}$, and so on.

Sometimes $f''$ is denoted by $Df'$ or $D^2 f$ or $\dfrac{d^2y}{dx^2}$, where $y = f(x)$.

For example, if $f(x) = e^x$, then

$$f'(x) = e^x, \quad f''(x) = e^x, \quad f^{(3)}(x) = e^x, \quad \ldots.$$

However, not every derivative is differentiable at all points of its domain, as you will see.

See Exercise 1.2.

## 1.2 One-sided derivatives

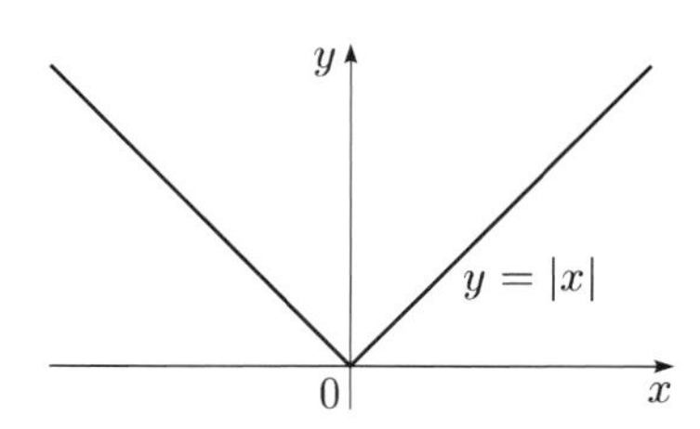


Although we know that the function $f(x) = |x|$ is not differentiable at 0, the graph of $f$ suggests that chords which join the origin $(0, 0)$ to points $(h, f(h))$ have slopes equal to 1 if $h > 0$, and equal to $-1$ if $h < 0$. This example suggests the concept of a *one-sided derivative*.

**Definition** Let $f$ be defined on an interval $I$, and $c \in I$. Then the **left derivative** of $f$ at $c$ is

$$f'_L(c) = \lim_{x \to c^-} \frac{f(x) - f(c)}{x - c} = \lim_{h \to 0^-} Q(h),$$

provided that this limit exists. In this case, we say that $f$ is **left differentiable** at $c$.

Similarly, the **right derivative** of $f$ at $c$ is

$$f'_R(c) = \lim_{x \to c^+} \frac{f(x) - f(c)}{x - c} = \lim_{h \to 0^+} Q(h),$$

provided that this limit exists. In this case, we say that $f$ is **right differentiable** at $c$.

Right and left limits were defined in Unit AB1, Section 1.

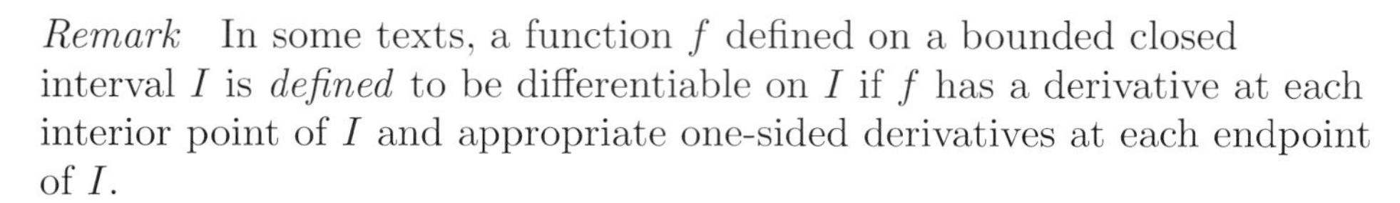

*Remark* In some texts, a function $f$ defined on a bounded closed interval $I$ is *defined* to be differentiable on $I$ if $f$ has a derivative at each interior point of $I$ and appropriate one-sided derivatives at each endpoint of $I$.

Interior points of intervals were defined in Unit AB1, Section 4.

Here is the relationship between derivatives and one-sided derivatives.

**Theorem 1.2** Let $f$ be defined on an open interval $I$, and $c \in I$.

(a) If $f$ is differentiable at $c$, then $f$ is both left differentiable and right differentiable at $c$, and

$$f'_L(c) = f'_R(c) = f'(c). \qquad (1.3)$$

(b) If $f$ is both left differentiable and right differentiable at $c$, and $f'_L(c) = f'_R(c)$, then $f$ is differentiable at $c$ and equation (1.3) holds.

We omit the proof of this result and the proof of the Glue Rule.

Theorem 1.2 is closely related to the Glue Rule for differentiability.

See Unit AA4, Section 2, for the Glue Rule for continuity.

**Glue Rule** Let $f$ be defined on an open interval $I$, and $c \in I$. If there are functions $g$ and $h$ defined on $I$ such that

1. $f(x) = g(x)$, for $x \in I$, $x < c$,
   $f(x) = h(x)$, for $x \in I$, $x > c$,
2. $f(c) = g(c) = h(c)$,
3. $g$ and $h$ are differentiable at $c$,

then $f$ is differentiable at $c$ if and only if $g'(c) = h'(c)$.

If $f$ is differentiable at $c$, then $f'(c) = g'(c) = h'(c)$.

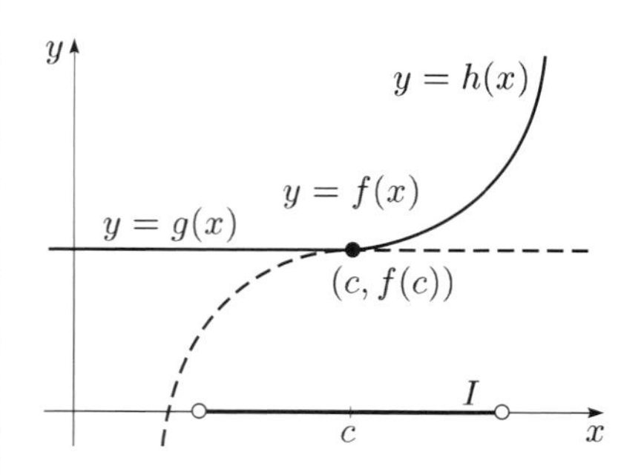


*Remark* In our discussion of continuity, we also introduced the Squeeze Rule. This rule has an analogue for differentiation, but we omit it.

See Unit AA4, Subsection 2.1, Frame 15.

The Glue Rule enables us to show that certain hybrid functions are differentiable (or not) at particular points without using the definition, as in the following example.

**Example 1.3** Use the Glue Rule to prove that the function

$$f(x) = \begin{cases} x, & x < 0, \\ \sin x, & x \geq 0, \end{cases}$$

is differentiable at 0, and determine $f'(0)$.

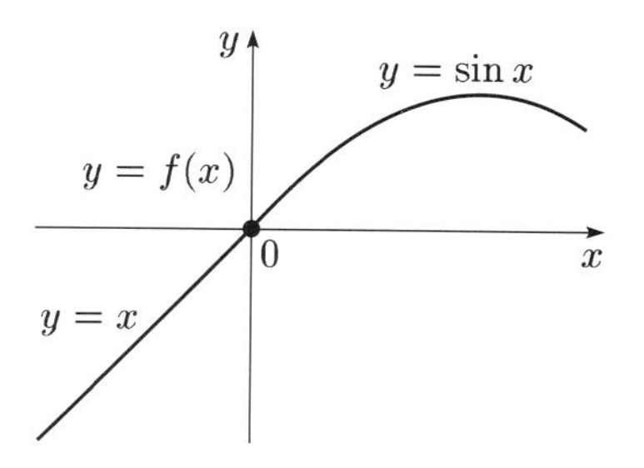


**Solution** Let $I$ be the open interval $\mathbb{R}$ and define

$$g(x) = x \quad (x \in \mathbb{R}) \quad \text{and} \quad h(x) = \sin x \quad (x \in \mathbb{R}).$$

Then $f$ is defined on $I$ and $0 \in I$. Also,

$$\begin{aligned} f(x) &= g(x), \quad \text{for } x < 0, \\ f(x) &= h(x), \quad \text{for } x > 0, \end{aligned}$$

so condition 1 holds with $a = 0$.

Now, $f(0) = g(0) = h(0) = 0$, so condition 2 holds. Also, $g$ and $h$ are differentiable with $g'(x) = 1$ and $h'(x) = \cos x$, so condition 3 holds.

Since $g'(0) = 1 = h'(0)$, we deduce that $f$ is differentiable at 0, with $f'(0) = 1$, by the Glue Rule. ■

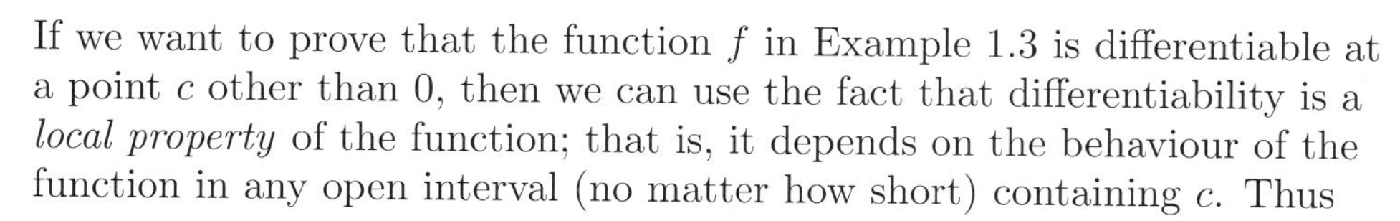

If we want to prove that the function $f$ in Example 1.3 is differentiable at a point $c$ other than 0, then we can use the fact that differentiability is a *local property* of the function; that is, it depends on the behaviour of the function in any open interval (no matter how short) containing $c$. Thus

Similarly, the *restriction* of a differentiable function to an open subinterval of its domain gives a new differentiable function.

$$f'(x) = \begin{cases} g'(x) = 1, & x < 0, \\ h'(x) = \cos x, & x > 0, \end{cases}$$

and hence, on combining this result with Example 1.2,

$$f'(x) = \begin{cases} 1, & x \leq 0, \\ \cos x, & x > 0. \end{cases}$$

You can use this approach in the following exercise.

**Exercise 1.2** Prove that the function

$$f(x) = \begin{cases} -x^2, & x < 0, \\ x^2, & x \geq 0, \end{cases}$$

is differentiable, and has derivative $f'(x) = 2|x|$.

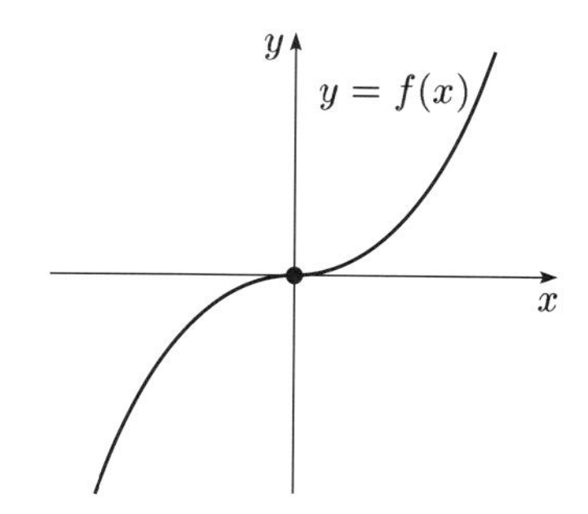


Since the function $f'(x) = 2|x|$ is not differentiable at 0, Exercise 1.2 shows that a derivative need not be differentiable at all points of its domain.

## 1.3 Continuity and differentiability

Next we discuss the relationship between continuity and differentiability. First we show that a differentiable function is continuous.

> **Theorem 1.3** Let $f$ be defined on an open interval $I$, and $c \in I$. If $f$ is differentiable at $c$, then $f$ is continuous at $c$.

**Proof** If $f$ is differentiable at $c$, then

$$\lim_{x\to c}\frac{f(x)-f(c)}{x-c}=f'(c).$$

For $x\in I$ and $x\neq c$, we have

$$f(x)-f(c)=\frac{f(x)-f(c)}{(x-c)}\times(x-c).$$

Hence, by the Combination Rules for limits,

See Unit AB1, Subsection 1.3.

$$f(x)-f(c)\to f'(c)\times 0=0 \quad\text{as } x\to c.$$

Thus $f(x)\to f(c)$ as $x\to c$, so $f$ is continuous at $c$. ■

Theorem 1.3 gives us a test for non-differentiability.

**Corollary** Let $f$ be defined on an open interval $I$, and $c\in I$. If $f$ is discontinuous at $c$, then $f$ is not differentiable at $c$.

This corollary is deduced from Theorem 1.3 by contraposition.

For example, the function

$$k(x)=\begin{cases}-1, & x<0,\\ 0, & x=0,\\ 1, & x>0,\end{cases}$$

is discontinuous at 0 because $\lim_{x\to 0^+} k(x)=1\neq k(0)$. Thus $k$ is not differentiable at 0, by the corollary to Theorem 1.3.

A continuous function need not be differentiable at every point of its domain; for example, the modulus function is continuous at all points of $\mathbb{R}$, but it is not differentiable at 0. This example can readily be modified to produce a continuous function which is not differentiable at any given finite set of points.

See Exercise 1.1(c).

## A continuous nowhere-differentiable function

The remainder of this section is optional, and is included only for your interest.

In the 19th century, when the concepts of continuity and differentiability were first made precise, it was widely believed that if a function is continuous at all points of an interval, then it must be differentiable at most points of that interval. However, it turns out that there exist functions which are continuous everywhere but differentiable *nowhere*. The first example was found as early as 1834 by Bolzano, but his pioneering work on analysis was not recognised by others. The first well-known example was constructed by Weierstrass in 1872. Such 'pathological' functions were regarded by some with suspicion. For example, the French mathematician Hermite wrote to a colleague in 1893: 'I recoil in fear and loathing from that deplorable evil: continuous functions with no derivatives.' However, in modern times it has been shown that such functions are in some sense normal and even useful.

Earlier, we showed that the blancmange function is continuous at all points. We now prove that this function is nowhere differentiable. Recall that the blancmange function $B$ is defined as follows:

See Unit AB1, Theorem 3.4.

$$B(x)=\sum_{n=0}^{\infty}\frac{1}{2^n}s(2^n x)=s(x)+\tfrac{1}{2}s(2x)+\tfrac{1}{4}s(4x)+\cdots \quad (x\in\mathbb{R}), \qquad (1.4)$$

where $s$ is the sawtooth function

$$s(x) = \begin{cases} x - [x], & 0 \leq x - [x] \leq \frac{1}{2}, \\ 1 - (x - [x]), & \frac{1}{2} < x - [x] < 1. \end{cases}$$

The graph of the function $s$ has a 'corner' at each point of the form $k/2$, where $k \in \mathbb{Z}$, so the graph of each function $x \longmapsto 2^{-n}s(2^n x)$ has a corner at each point of the form $k/2^{n+1}$, where $k \in \mathbb{Z}$. This suggests that the graph of the function $B$ is not smooth at any point of $\mathbb{R}$, and we now prove that this is the case.

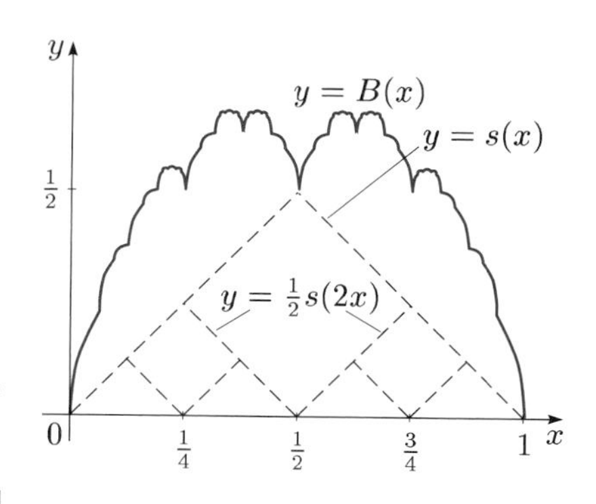


**Theorem 1.4** The blancmange function $B$ is not differentiable at any point $c \in \mathbb{R}$.

The name 'blancmange function' was used in the 1980s by the English mathematician David Tall, who remarked that $B$ is nowhere differentiable because it wobbles too much!

In the proof, we use the following notation for difference quotients, which shows the dependence on the point $c$ and the function $f$:

$$Q_{c,f}(h) = \frac{f(c+h) - f(c)}{h}, \quad \text{where } h \neq 0.$$

The proof is based on three facts.

**Fact 1** For $m = 1, 2, \ldots,$

$$B(x) = s(x) + \frac{1}{2}s(2x) + \cdots + \frac{1}{2^{m-1}}s(2^{m-1}x) + \frac{1}{2^m}B(2^m x),$$

and the function

$$x \longmapsto s(x) + \frac{1}{2}s(2x) + \cdots + \frac{1}{2^{m-1}}s(2^{m-1}x)$$

is linear on all intervals of the form $[p\,2^{-m}, (p+1)2^{-m}]$, where $p \in \mathbb{Z}$.

This fact follows immediately from equation (1.4) and the definition of $s$.

**Fact 2** For each $x \in [0,1]$, there exist $h, h' \neq 0$ such that

$$x + h,\ x + h' \in [0,1] \quad \text{and} \quad |Q_{x,B}(h) - Q_{x,B}(h')| \geq 1. \qquad (1.5)$$

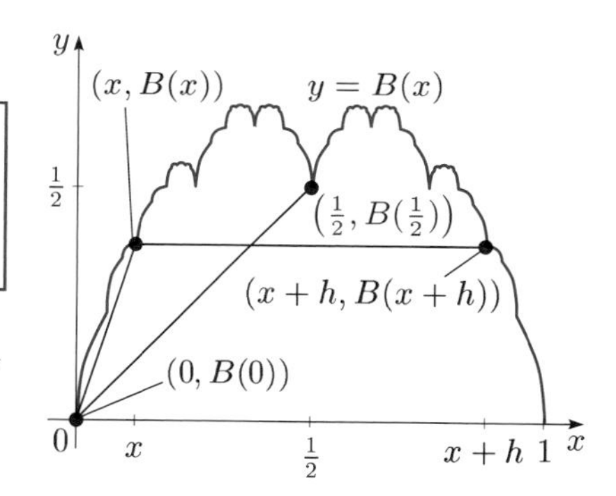


Here we can assume by symmetry (see the figure) that $0 \leq x \leq \frac{1}{2}$. We now choose $h$ so that $x + h = 1 - x$, and $h'$ so that $x + h' = 0$ (or $h' = \frac{1}{2}$ if $x = 0$). Then $Q_{x,B}(h) = 0$ and $Q_{x,B}(h') \geq 1$, so inequality (1.5) follows.

**Fact 3** Given any function $f$ and a linear function $g(x) = ax + b$, the corresponding difference quotients of the functions $f$ and $f + g$ always differ by $a$, the gradient of the linear function $g$.

Fact 3 holds because, for $c \in \mathbb{R}$ and $h \neq 0$, we have $(g(c+h) - g(c))/h = a$.

**Proof of Theorem 1.4**

Let $c \in \mathbb{R}$ and choose integers $p_m$, $m = 0, 1, 2, \ldots$, such that $c \in I_m$, where

$$I_m = \left[p_m 2^{-m},\ (p_m + 1)2^{-m}\right].$$

On the interval $I_m$ the function $B$ is, by Fact 1, the sum of a linear function and the function $B_m(x) = 2^{-m}B(2^m x)$, which is obtained from $B$ by scaling in both the $x$- and $y$-directions by the factor $2^{-m}$. Thus the graph of $B_m$ on the interval $I_m$ is a scaled-down copy of the graph of $B$ on $[0, 1]$. Difference quotients are unchanged by such a scaling, so Fact 2 implies that there exist $h_m, h'_m \neq 0$ such that

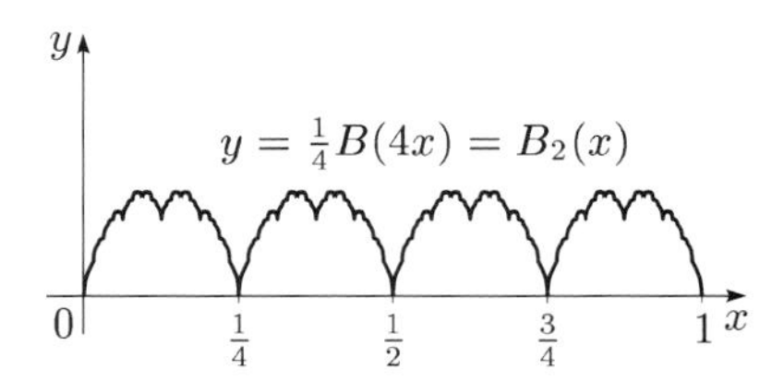


The graph $y = B_m(x)$ on $I_m$ is a mini-blancmange!

$$c + h_m,\ c + h'_m \in I_m \quad \text{and} \quad |Q_{c,B_m}(h_m) - Q_{c,B_m}(h'_m)| \geq 1.$$

Therefore, by Fact 3,

$$|Q_{c,B}(h_m) - Q_{c,B}(h'_m)| = |Q_{c,B_m}(h_m) - Q_{c,B_m}(h'_m)| \geq 1. \tag{1.6}$$

Since $c$, $c + h_m$, $c + h'_m \in I_m$, for $m = 1, 2, \ldots$, and $I_m$ has length $2^{-m}$, we have $h_m \to 0$ and $h'_m \to 0$. Thus if $B$ is differentiable at $c$, then

$$Q_{c,B}(h_m) \to B'(c) \quad \text{and} \quad Q_{c,B}(h'_m) \to B'(c) \quad \text{as } m \to \infty.$$

But this contradicts inequality (1.6), so $B$ is not differentiable at $c$. ■

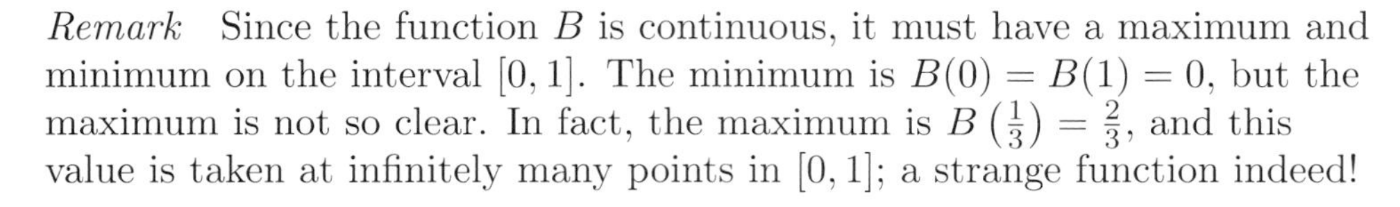

*Remark* Since the function $B$ is continuous, it must have a maximum and minimum on the interval $[0, 1]$. The minimum is $B(0) = B(1) = 0$, but the maximum is not so clear. In fact, the maximum is $B\left(\frac{1}{3}\right) = \frac{2}{3}$, and this value is taken at infinitely many points in $[0, 1]$; a strange function indeed!

This follows by the Extreme Value Theorem; see Unit AA4, Theorem 3.4.

# Further exercises

**Exercise 1.3** Determine, from the definition of differentiable, which of the following functions $f$ is differentiable at 0. If $f$ is differentiable at 0, then evaluate the derivative $f'(0)$.

(a) $f(x) = \begin{cases} x\sin(1/x^2), & x \neq 0, \\ 0, & x = 0. \end{cases}$ (b) $f(x) = \dfrac{x}{1 + x}$

**Exercise 1.4** Use the Glue Rule or the corollary to Theorem 1.3 to determine which of the following functions $f$ is differentiable at the given point $c$. If $f$ is differentiable at $c$, then evaluate the derivative $f'(c)$.

(a) $f(x) = \begin{cases} -x^2, & x \leq 0, \\ x^3, & x > 0, \end{cases}$ $c = 0$.

(b) $f(x) = \begin{cases} x, & x < 1, \\ x^2, & x \geq 1, \end{cases}$ $c = 1$.

(c) $f(x) = \begin{cases} x, & x < 1, \\ x - x^2, & x \geq 1, \end{cases}$ $c = 1$.

**Exercise 1.5** Prove that the function

$$f(x) = \begin{cases} 1, & x \leq 0, \\ \cos x, & x > 0, \end{cases}$$

is differentiable, and determine the rule of $f'$.

# 2 Rules for differentiation

After working through this section, you should be able to:

(a) use the table of standard derivatives;

(b) use the rules for differentiation to prove the differentiability of a particular function and to calculate its derivative.

In Section 1 we showed that various basic functions are differentiable on $\mathbb{R}$, by appealing directly to the definition of a differentiable function.

However, it would be tedious if we had to use the definition every time we wished to prove that a given function is differentiable and determine its derivative. Instead, we can often use the Combination Rules, the Composition Rule and the Inverse Function Rule for differentiable functions. Each of these rules enables us to find the derivatives of further functions, and we include the most important of these in a table of standard derivatives.

The proofs of these rules are in Subsection 2.4.

## 2.1 Combination Rules

The Combination Rules for differentiability are a consequence of the Combination Rules for limits.

See Unit AB1, Subsection 1.3.

**Combination Rules** Let $f$ and $g$ be defined on an open interval $I$, and $c \in I$. If $f$ and $g$ are differentiable at $c$, then so are the functions:

**Sum Rule** $f + g$, and

$$(f+g)'(c) = f'(c) + g'(c);$$

**Multiple Rule** $\lambda f$, for $\lambda \in \mathbb{R}$, and

$$(\lambda f)'(c) = \lambda f'(c);$$

**Product Rule** $fg$, and

$$(fg)'(c) = f'(c)g(c) + f(c)g'(c);$$

**Quotient Rule** $f/g$, provided that $g(c) \neq 0$, and

$$\left(\frac{f}{g}\right)'(c) = \frac{g(c)f'(c) - f(c)g'(c)}{(g(c))^2}.$$

In Leibniz notation:

if $y = uv$, then

$$\frac{dy}{dx} = \frac{du}{dx}v + u\frac{dv}{dx};$$

if $y = u/v$, then

$$\frac{dy}{dx} = \frac{v\dfrac{du}{dx} - u\dfrac{dv}{dx}}{v^2}.$$

We can use the fact that if $f(x) = x^n$, where $n \in \mathbb{N}$, then $f'(x) = nx^{n-1}$, together with the Combination Rules, to prove that any polynomial function is differentiable on $\mathbb{R}$, and that its derivative can be obtained by differentiating the polynomial term by term.

**Corollary** Let

$$p(x) = a_0 + a_1x + a_2x^2 + \cdots + a_nx^n \quad (x \in \mathbb{R}),$$

where $a_0, a_1, \ldots, a_n \in \mathbb{R}$. Then $p$ is differentiable on $\mathbb{R}$, with derivative

$$p'(x) = a_1 + 2a_2x + \cdots + na_nx^{n-1} \quad (x \in \mathbb{R}).$$

Since a rational function is a quotient of two polynomials, it follows from the corollary to the Combination Rules and from the Quotient Rule that a rational function is differentiable at all points where its denominator is non-zero, that is, at all points of the domain of the function. Here is an example.

**Example 2.1** Prove that the function

$$f(x) = \frac{x^3}{x^2 - 1} \quad (x \in \mathbb{R} - \{-1, 1\})$$

is differentiable on its domain, and find its derivative.

**Solution** The function $f$ is a rational function of the form $f = p/q$, where $p(x) = x^3$ and $q(x) = x^2 - 1$, whose denominator $q$ is non-zero on $\mathbb{R} - \{-1, 1\}$. Thus, by the Quotient Rule, the domain of $f'$ is $\mathbb{R} - \{-1, 1\}$.

Here we give full justification of the use of the Quotient Rule; usually less detail is required.

Now $p'(x) = 3x^2$ and $q'(x) = 2x$. Thus, by the Quotient Rule, the derivative of $f$ is

$$\begin{aligned} f'(x) &= \frac{(x^2 - 1)3x^2 - x^3(2x)}{(x^2 - 1)^2} \\ &= \frac{x^4 - 3x^2}{(x^2 - 1)^2} \quad (x \in \mathbb{R} - \{-1, 1\}). \quad \blacksquare \end{aligned}$$

*Remark* The Quotient Rule can also be used to show that the formula for differentiating $f(x) = x^n$, given in Theorem 1.1(b), remains valid if $n$ is a negative integer.

**Exercise 2.1** Find the derivative of each of the following functions.

(a) $f(x) = x^7 - 2x^4 + 3x^3 - 5x + 1 \quad (x \in \mathbb{R})$

(b) $f(x) = \dfrac{x^2 + 1}{x^3 - 1} \quad (x \in \mathbb{R} - \{1\})$

(c) $f(x) = \sin x \cos x \quad (x \in \mathbb{R})$

(d) $f(x) = \dfrac{e^x}{3 + \sin x - 2\cos x} \quad (x \in \mathbb{R})$

It is not necessary to work through all these exercises if you are confident that you can use the Combination Rules.

**Exercise 2.2** Find the third derivative of the function

$$f(x) = xe^{2x} \quad (x \in \mathbb{R}).$$

In Section 1 we differentiated the functions sin, cos and exp. We now ask you to find the derivatives of the other trigonometric functions and the three most common hyperbolic functions.

The derivatives of these functions are included in the table of standard derivatives on page 49.

**Exercise 2.3** Find the derivative of each of the following functions.

(a) $f(x) = \tan x \quad (x \neq \pm\frac{1}{2}\pi, \pm\frac{3}{2}\pi, \pm\frac{5}{2}\pi, \ldots)$

(b) $f(x) = \operatorname{cosec} x \quad (x \neq 0, \pm\pi, \pm 2\pi, \ldots)$

(c) $f(x) = \sec x \quad (x \neq \pm\frac{1}{2}\pi, \pm\frac{3}{2}\pi, \pm\frac{5}{2}\pi, \ldots)$

(d) $f(x) = \cot x \quad (x \neq 0, \pm\pi, \pm 2\pi, \ldots)$

**Exercise 2.4** Find the derivative of each of the following functions.

(a) $f(x) = \sinh x \quad (x \in \mathbb{R})$

(b) $f(x) = \cosh x \quad (x \in \mathbb{R})$

(c) $f(x) = \tanh x \quad (x \in \mathbb{R})$

## 2.2 Composition Rule

In Subsection 2.1 we extended our stock of differentiable functions to include all polynomial, rational, trigonometric and hyperbolic functions. We also need to be able to differentiate functions such as

$$f(x) = \sin(\cos x) \quad (x \in \mathbb{R}),$$

which is the composite of the two differentiable functions sin and cos. To do this, we use the Composition Rule.

> **Composition Rule** Let $f$ be defined on an open interval $I$, let $g$ be defined on an open interval $J$ such that $f(I) \subseteq J$ and let $c \in I$.
>
> If $f$ is differentiable at $c$ and $g$ is differentiable at $f(c)$, then $g \circ f$ is differentiable at $c$ and
>
> $$(g \circ f)'(c) = g'(f(c))f'(c).$$

*Remarks*

1. When written in Leibniz notation, the Composition Rule has a form that is easy to remember: if we put

   $$u = f(x) \quad \text{and} \quad y = g(u) = g(f(x)),$$

   then

   $$\frac{dy}{dx} = \frac{dy}{du} \times \frac{du}{dx}.$$

The Leibniz form of the Composition Rule is often called the *Chain Rule*.

2. The Composition Rule can be extended to a composite of three or more functions; for example,

   $$(h \circ g \circ f)'(x) = h'(g(f(x)))g'(f(x))f'(x).$$

   In Leibniz notation, if we put

   $$v = f(x), \quad u = g(v) \quad \text{and} \quad y = h(u) = h(g(f(x))),$$

   then

   $$\frac{dy}{dx} = \frac{dy}{du} \times \frac{du}{dv} \times \frac{dv}{dx}.$$

We usually use this extended form of the Composition Rule without mentioning it explicitly.

**Example 2.2** Prove that each of the following composite functions is differentiable on its domain, and find its derivative.

(a) $k(x) = \sin(\cos x) \quad (x \in \mathbb{R})$

(b) $k(x) = \cosh(e^{2x}) \quad (x \in \mathbb{R})$

(c) $k(x) = \tan(x^2) \quad (x \in (-1, 1))$

**Solution**

Here we give full justification of the use of the Composition Rule; usually less detail is required.

(a) Here $k(x) = \sin(\cos x)$, so let

$$f(x) = \cos x \quad \text{and} \quad g(x) = \sin x \quad (x \in \mathbb{R}).$$

Then $f$ and $g$ are differentiable on $\mathbb{R}$, and

$$f'(x) = -\sin x \quad \text{and} \quad g'(x) = \cos x \quad (x \in \mathbb{R}).$$

By the Composition Rule, $k = g \circ f$ is differentiable on $\mathbb{R}$, and

$$\begin{aligned} k'(x) &= g'(f(x))f'(x) \\ &= \cos(\cos x) \times (-\sin x) \\ &= -\cos(\cos x)\sin x. \end{aligned}$$

(b) Here $k(x) = \cosh(e^{2x})$, so let

$$f(x) = 2x, \quad g(x) = e^x \quad \text{and} \quad h(x) = \cosh x \quad (x \in \mathbb{R}).$$

Then $f$, $g$ and $h$ are differentiable on $\mathbb{R}$, and

$$f'(x) = 2, \quad g'(x) = e^x \quad \text{and} \quad h'(x) = \sinh x \quad (x \in \mathbb{R}).$$

By the Composition Rule, $k = h \circ g \circ f$ is differentiable on $\mathbb{R}$, and

Here we use the extended form of the Composition Rule.

$$\begin{aligned} k'(x) &= h'(g(f(x)))g'(f(x))f'(x) \\ &= \sinh(e^{2x}) \times e^{2x} \times 2 \\ &= 2e^{2x} \sinh(e^{2x}). \end{aligned}$$

(c) In the notation of the Composition Rule, we can write

$$f(x) = x^2 \quad (x \in I) \quad \text{and} \quad g(x) = \tan x,$$

where $I = (-1, 1)$. Then $f(I) = [0, 1)$, so if we choose $J = \left(-\frac{1}{2}\pi, \frac{1}{2}\pi\right)$, then $f(I) \subseteq J$, as required.

Now

$$f'(x) = 2x \quad (x \in (-1, 1))$$

and

$$g'(x) = \sec^2 x.$$

Thus, by the Composition Rule, $k = g \circ f$ is differentiable on $(-1, 1)$, and

$$\begin{aligned} k'(x) &= g'(f(x))f'(x) \\ &= 2x \sec^2(x^2) \quad (x \in (-1, 1)). \quad \blacksquare \end{aligned}$$

**Exercise 2.5** Find the derivative of each of the following functions.

(a) $f(x) = \sinh(x^2) \quad (x \in \mathbb{R})$

(b) $f(x) = \sin(\sinh 2x) \quad (x \in \mathbb{R})$

(c) $f(x) = \sin\left(\dfrac{\cos 2x}{x^2}\right) \quad (x \in (0, \infty))$

## 2.3 Inverse Function Rule

In Analysis Block A we discussed inverse functions and proved that if a function $f$ with domain an interval $I$ and image $J$ is strictly monotonic and continuous on $I$, then $f$ possesses a strictly monotonic and continuous inverse function $f^{-1}$ with domain $J$, and $J$ is an interval. In particular, the power functions, the trigonometric functions, the exponential function and the hyperbolic functions all have continuous inverse functions, provided that we restrict their domains where necessary.

See Unit AA4, Section 4.

Recall from Unit AA4, Section 1, that *strictly monotonic* means that $f$ is either strictly increasing or strictly decreasing.

These standard functions are all differentiable on their domains. Do their inverse functions also have this property, as their graphs suggest?

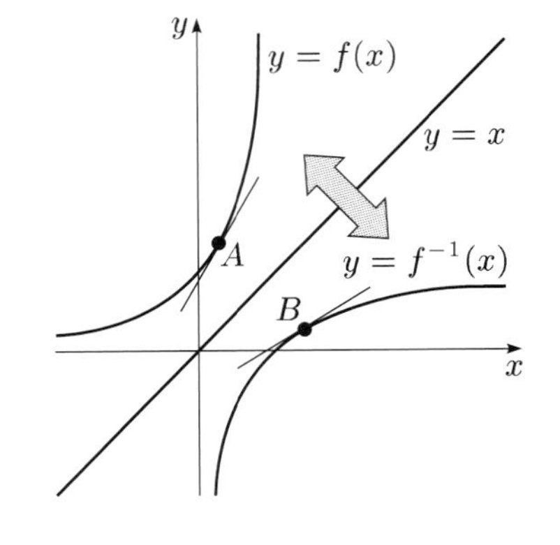


Also, recall that we obtain the graph $y = f^{-1}(x)$ by reflecting the graph $y = f(x)$ in the line $y = x$, which maps a typical point $A(c, d)$ on the graph $y = f(x)$ to the point $B(d, c)$ on the graph $y = f^{-1}(x)$. This suggests that if the slope of the tangent to the graph $y = f(x)$ at the point $A$ is $f'(c) = m$, then the slope of the tangent to the graph $y = f^{-1}(x)$ at $B$ is $(f^{-1})'(d) = 1/m$, provided that $m \neq 0$.

However, if the graph of $f$ has a horizontal tangent ($m = 0$) at a point $A$, then the graph of $f^{-1}$ has a vertical tangent at the corresponding point $B$; in this case, $f^{-1}$ is not differentiable at $B$, since $1/m$ is not defined for $m = 0$. We therefore require the condition '$f'(x)$ is non-zero' in our statement of the rule for differentiating inverse functions.

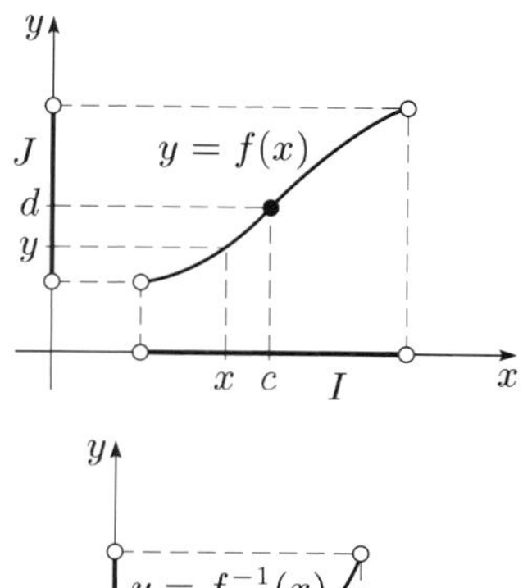


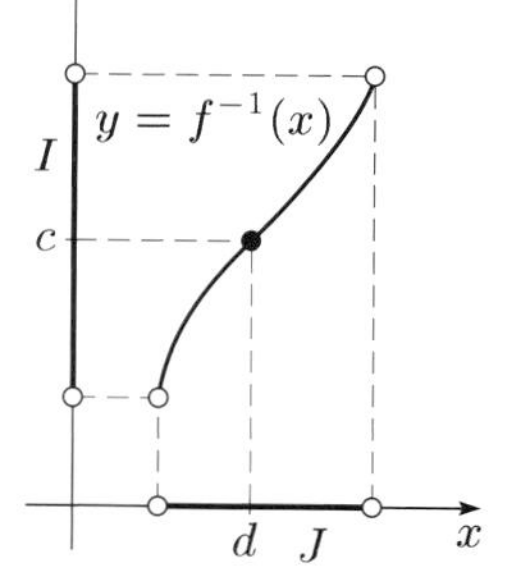


> **Inverse Function Rule** Let $f$ be a function whose domain is an open interval $I$ on which $f$ is continuous and strictly monotonic, with image $J = f(I)$.
>
> If $f$ is differentiable on $I$ and $f'(x) \neq 0$ for $x \in I$, then $f^{-1}$ is differentiable on its domain $J$. Also, if $c \in I$ and $d = f(c)$, then
>
> $$(f^{-1})'(d) = \frac{1}{f'(c)}.$$

*Remark* The Leibniz notation for derivatives can be used to express the Inverse Function Rule in a form that is easy to remember: if we put

$$y = f(x) \quad \text{and} \quad x = f^{-1}(y),$$

and write

$$\frac{dy}{dx} \text{ for } f'(x) \quad \text{and} \quad \frac{dx}{dy} \text{ for } (f^{-1})'(y),$$

then

$$\frac{dx}{dy} = 1 \Big/ \frac{dy}{dx}.$$

**Example 2.3** For each of the following functions $f$, state the domain and rule of $f^{-1}$, and show that $f^{-1}$ is differentiable and determine its derivative.

(a) $f(x) = x^n \quad (x \in \mathbb{R}^+)$, where $n \geq 2$.

(b) $f(x) = \tan x \quad (x \in (-\frac{1}{2}\pi, \frac{1}{2}\pi))$

(c) $f(x) = e^x \quad (x \in \mathbb{R})$

The derivatives of these inverse functions are included in the table of standard derivatives.

**Solution**

(a) The function

$$f(x) = x^n \quad (x \in \mathbb{R}^+)$$

is continuous and strictly increasing, and $f((0, \infty)) = (0, \infty)$. Also, $f$ is differentiable on $(0, \infty)$, and its derivative $f'(x) = nx^{n-1}$ is non-zero there. So $f$ satisfies the conditions of the Inverse Function Rule.

See Unit AA4, Subsection 4.2.

Hence $f^{-1}(y) = y^{1/n}$ is differentiable on its domain $(0, \infty)$, and if $y = f(x) = x^n$ (so $x = y^{1/n}$), then

$$(f^{-1})'(y) = \frac{1}{f'(x)} = \frac{1}{nx^{n-1}} = \frac{1}{n(y^{1/n})^{n-1}} = \frac{1}{n} y^{(1/n)-1}.$$

Replacing the domain variable $y$ by $x$, we obtain

$$(f^{-1})'(x) = \frac{1}{n} x^{(1/n)-1} \quad (x \in (0, \infty)).$$

(b) The function

$$f(x) = \tan x \quad (x \in (-\tfrac{1}{2}\pi, \tfrac{1}{2}\pi))$$

is continuous and strictly increasing, and $f\left((-\frac{1}{2}\pi, \frac{1}{2}\pi)\right) = \mathbb{R}$.

Also, $f$ is differentiable on $\left(-\frac{1}{2}\pi, \frac{1}{2}\pi\right)$, and its derivative $f'(x) = \sec^2 x$ is non-zero there. So $f$ satisfies the conditions of the Inverse Function Rule.

Hence $f^{-1}(y) = \tan^{-1} y$ is differentiable on its domain $\mathbb{R}$, and if $y = f(x) = \tan x$, then

$$(f^{-1})'(y) = \frac{1}{f'(x)} = \frac{1}{\sec^2 x} = \frac{1}{1 + \tan^2 x} = \frac{1}{1 + y^2}.$$

Replacing the domain variable $y$ by $x$, we obtain

$$(\tan^{-1})'(x) = \frac{1}{1 + x^2} \quad (x \in \mathbb{R}).$$

(c) The function

$$f(x) = e^x \quad (x \in \mathbb{R})$$

is continuous and strictly increasing, and $f(\mathbb{R}) = (0, \infty)$. Also, $f$ is differentiable on $\mathbb{R}$, and its derivative $f'(x) = e^x$ is non-zero there. So $f$ satisfies the conditions of the Inverse Function Rule.

Hence $f^{-1}(y) = \log_e y$ is differentiable on its domain $(0, \infty)$, and if $y = f(x) = e^x$, then

$$(f^{-1})'(y) = \frac{1}{f'(x)} = \frac{1}{e^x} = \frac{1}{y}.$$

Replacing the domain variable $y$ by $x$, we obtain

$$(\log_e)'(x) = \frac{1}{x} \quad (x \in (0, \infty)). \quad ■$$

**Exercise 2.6** For each of the following functions $f$, show that $f^{-1}$ is differentiable, and determine its derivative.

(a) $f(x) = \cos x \ (x \in (0, \pi))$ (b) $f(x) = \sinh x \ (x \in \mathbb{R})$

The Inverse Function Rule can sometimes be used to find values of the derivative of an inverse function $f^{-1}$ even when the equation $y = f(x)$ cannot be solved to give a formula for the rule of $f^{-1}$.

**Exercise 2.7** Let $f(x) = x^5 + x - 1 \ (x \in \mathbb{R})$.

(a) Prove that $f$ has an inverse function $f^{-1}$ which is differentiable on $\mathbb{R}$. (You may assume that $f(\mathbb{R}) = \mathbb{R}$.)

(b) Find the values of $(f^{-1})'(d)$ at those points $d = f(c)$ where $c = 0, 1, -1$.

## Exponential functions

In Analysis Block A we defined the number $a^x$, for $a > 0$, by the formula

See Unit AA4, Subsection 4.3.

$$a^x = \exp(x \log_e a).$$

Since the functions exp and $\log_e$ are differentiable on $\mathbb{R}$ and $\mathbb{R}^+$, respectively, it follows that we can use this formula to determine the derivatives of several related functions.

See Theorem 1.1(e) and Example 2.3(c).

**Example 2.4** Prove that, for $\alpha \in \mathbb{R}$, the function

$$f(x) = x^\alpha \quad (x \in \mathbb{R}^+)$$

is differentiable on its domain, and that

$$f'(x) = \alpha x^{\alpha - 1} \quad (x \in \mathbb{R}^+).$$

This derivative is included in the table of standard derivatives. Note that it agrees with the formula for the derivative of $f(x) = x^n$, where $n \in \mathbb{N}$.

**Solution** By definition,

$$f(x) = \exp(\alpha \log_e x) \quad (x \in \mathbb{R}^+).$$

The function $x \longmapsto \alpha \log_e x$ is differentiable on $\mathbb{R}^+$, with derivative $\alpha/x$. Thus, by the Composition Rule, $f$ is differentiable on $\mathbb{R}^+$, with derivative

$$\begin{aligned} f'(x) &= \exp(\alpha \log_e x) \times (\alpha/x) \\ &= x^\alpha(\alpha/x) = \alpha x^{\alpha-1} \quad (x \in \mathbb{R}^+). \quad \blacksquare \end{aligned}$$

**Example 2.5** Prove that, for $a > 0$, the function

$$f(x) = a^x \quad (x \in \mathbb{R})$$

is differentiable, and that

$$f'(x) = a^x \log_e a \quad (x \in \mathbb{R}).$$

**Solution** By definition,

$$f(x) = \exp(x \log_e a).$$

The function $x \longmapsto x \log_e a$ is differentiable on $\mathbb{R}$, with derivative $\log_e a$. By the Composition Rule, $f$ is differentiable on $\mathbb{R}$, with derivative

$$\begin{aligned} f'(x) &= \exp(x \log_e a) \times \log_e a \\ &= a^x \log_e a. \quad \blacksquare \end{aligned}$$

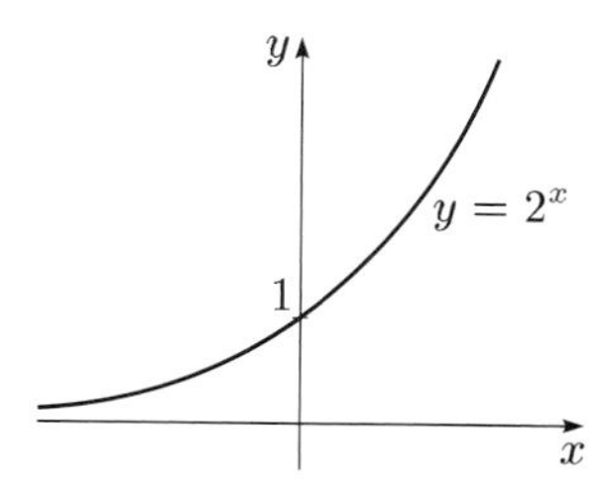


*Remark* At the beginning of the course, we posed the following question: does the graph of the function $f(x) = 2^x$ have a jump at the point $\sqrt{2}$? Since $f$ is continuous, its graph has no jumps. Example 2.5 shows that $f$ is also differentiable, so $f$ is smooth and its graph has no corners.

**Exercise 2.8** Prove that the function

$$f(x) = x^x \quad (x \in \mathbb{R}^+)$$

is differentiable, and find its derivative.

## 2.4 Proofs

We now supply the proofs of the Combination Rules, the Composition Rule and the Inverse Function Rule.

If you are short of time, omit these proofs.

**Combination Rules** Let $f$ and $g$ be defined on an open interval $I$, and $c \in I$. If $f$ and $g$ are differentiable at $c$, then so are the functions:

**Sum Rule** $f + g$ and

$$(f+g)'(c) = f'(c) + g'(c);$$

**Multiple Rule** $\lambda f$, for $\lambda \in \mathbb{R}$, and

$$(\lambda f)'(c) = \lambda f'(c);$$

**Product Rule** $fg$ and

$$(fg)'(c) = f'(c)g(c) + f(c)g'(c);$$

**Quotient Rule** $f/g$, provided that $g(c) \neq 0$, and

$$\left(\frac{f}{g}\right)'(c) = \frac{g(c)f'(c) - f(c)g'(c)}{(g(c))^2}.$$

**Proof** Suppose that $f$ and $g$ are both differentiable at $c$.

In this proof, we use the Combination Rules for limits, given in Unit AB1, Subsection 1.3.

**Sum Rule** Let $F = f + g$. Then

$$\begin{aligned}\frac{F(x)-F(c)}{x-c} &= \frac{(f(x)+g(x))-(f(c)+g(c))}{x-c}\\ &= \frac{f(x)-f(c)}{x-c} + \frac{g(x)-g(c)}{x-c}\\ &\to f'(c)+g'(c) \quad \text{as } x \to c.\end{aligned}$$

In the proof of each rule we need to express the difference quotient

$$\frac{F(x)-F(c)}{x-c}$$

in terms of the corresponding difference quotients for $f$ and $g$.

Thus $F$ is differentiable at $c$, with derivative

$$F'(c) = f'(c) + g'(c).$$

**Multiple Rule** This is a special case of the Product Rule, with $g(x) = \lambda$.

**Product Rule** Let $F = fg$. Then

$$\begin{aligned}\frac{F(x)-F(c)}{x-c} &= \frac{f(x)g(x)-f(c)g(c)}{x-c}\\ &= \frac{f(x)-f(c)}{x-c}\,g(x) + f(c)\,\frac{g(x)-g(c)}{x-c}\\ &\to f'(c)g(c)+f(c)g'(c) \quad \text{as } x \to c,\end{aligned}$$

since $f$ and $g$ are differentiable at $c$, and $g$ is continuous at $c$ by Theorem 1.3.

Thus $F$ is differentiable at $c$, with derivative

$$F'(c) = f'(c)g(c) + f(c)g'(c).$$

**Quotient Rule** Let $F = f/g$. Since $g$ is continuous at $c$ and $g(c) \neq 0$, there exists $\delta > 0$ such that $J = (c-\delta, c+\delta) \subseteq I$ and

$$|g(x)-g(c)| < \tfrac{1}{2}|g(c)|, \quad \text{for all } x \text{ with } |x-c| < \delta.$$

Take $\varepsilon = \frac{1}{2}|g(c)|$ in the $\varepsilon$–$\delta$ definition of continuity; see Unit AB1, Section 3.

In particular, $g(x) \neq 0$ for $x \in J$, so the domain of $F$ contains $J$. Then

$$\begin{aligned}\frac{F(x)-F(c)}{x-c} &= \frac{\dfrac{f(x)}{g(x)} - \dfrac{f(c)}{g(c)}}{x-c}\\ &= \frac{f(x)g(c)-f(c)g(x)}{(x-c)g(x)g(c)}\\ &= \frac{g(c)(f(x)-f(c)) - f(c)(g(x)-g(c))}{(x-c)g(x)g(c)}\\ &= \frac{g(c)\dfrac{f(x)-f(c)}{x-c} - f(c)\dfrac{g(x)-g(c)}{x-c}}{g(x)g(c)}\\ &\to \frac{g(c)f'(c)-f(c)g'(c)}{(g(c))^2} \quad \text{as } x \to c,\end{aligned}$$

since $f$ and $g$ are differentiable at $c$, and $g$ is continuous at $c$.

Thus $F$ is differentiable at $c$, with derivative

$$F'(c) = \frac{g(c)f'(c)-f(c)g'(c)}{(g(c))^2}. \quad \blacksquare$$

> **Composition Rule** Let $f$ be defined on an open interval $I$, let $g$ be defined on an open interval $J$ such that $f(I) \subseteq J$ and let $c \in I$.
>
> If $f$ is differentiable at $c$ and $g$ is differentiable at $f(c)$, then $g \circ f$ is differentiable at $c$ and
>
> $$(g \circ f)'(c) = g'(f(c))f'(c).$$

**Proof** Let $F = g \circ f$. The difference quotient for $F$ at $c$ is

$$\frac{F(x) - F(c)}{x - c} = \frac{g(f(x)) - g(f(c))}{x - c}. \tag{2.1}$$

Let $y = f(x)$, where $x \in I$, and let $d = f(c)$. Then the right-hand side of equation (2.1) is

$$\left(\frac{g(y) - g(d)}{y - d}\right)\left(\frac{f(x) - f(c)}{x - c}\right), \quad \text{provided that } y \neq d. \tag{2.2}$$

To avoid the difficulty that expression (2.2) expression (2.2) is undefined if $y = d$, which can occur in some situations, we introduce the function

$$h(y) = \begin{cases} \dfrac{g(y) - g(d)}{y - d}, & y \neq d, \\ g'(d), & y = d. \end{cases}$$

Since $g$ is differentiable at $d$,

$$h(y) \to g'(d) \quad \text{as } y \to d;$$

and since $h(d) = g'(d)$, it follows that $h$ is continuous at $d$.

By the Composition Rule for continuous functions, we deduce that

$$(h \circ f)(x) = \begin{cases} \dfrac{g(f(x)) - g(f(c))}{f(x) - f(c)}, & f(x) \neq f(c), \\ g'(f(c)), & f(x) = f(c), \end{cases}$$

is continuous at $c$.

Recall that $y = f(x)$ and $d = f(c)$.

Next, note that if $f(x) \neq f(c)$, then equation (2.1) and expression (2.2) give

$$\frac{F(x) - F(c)}{x - c} = (h \circ f)(x)\left(\frac{f(x) - f(c)}{x - c}\right). \tag{2.3}$$

Equation (2.3) is also true when $f(x) = f(c)$, since both sides are then 0.

If we now let $x$ tend to $c$ in equation (2.3) and use the continuity at $c$ of the function $h \circ f$, then we obtain

$$\frac{F(x) - F(c)}{x - c} \to g'(f(c))f'(c) \quad \text{as } x \to c.$$

Thus $F$ is differentiable at $c$, with derivative

$$F'(c) = g'(f(c))f'(c). \quad \blacksquare$$

**Inverse Function Rule** Let $f$ be a function whose domain is an open interval $I$ on which $f$ is continuous and strictly monotonic, with image $J = f(I)$.

If $f$ is differentiable on $I$ and $f'(x) \neq 0$ for $x \in I$, then $f^{-1}$ is differentiable on its domain $J$. Also, if $c \in I$ and $d = f(c)$, then

$$(f^{-1})'(d) = \frac{1}{f'(c)}.$$

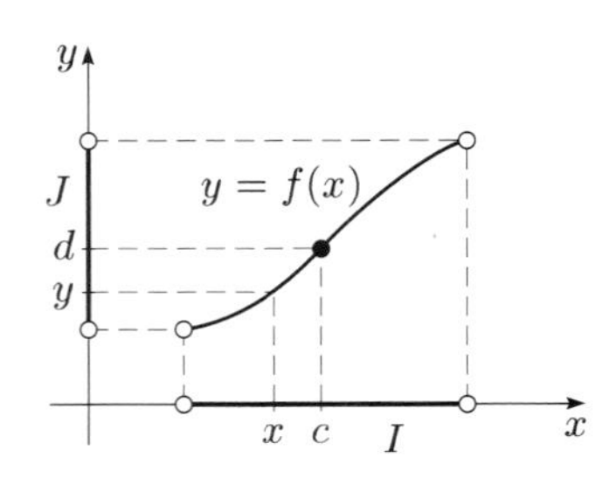


**Proof** First note that $f^{-1}$ has domain $J$ and is continuous there.

See Unit AA4, Subsection 4.1.

Let $y \in J$ and $y \neq d$, so $f^{-1}(y) = x$, where $x \in I$ and $x \neq c$.

Then the difference quotient for $f^{-1}$ at $d$ is

$$\begin{aligned}\frac{f^{-1}(y) - f^{-1}(d)}{y - d} &= \frac{x - c}{f(x) - f(c)} \\ &= 1\Big/\frac{f(x) - f(c)}{x - c}.\end{aligned}$$

As $y \to d$, we have $x = f^{-1}(y) \to c$, since $f^{-1}$ is continuous. So

$$\begin{aligned}\frac{f^{-1}(y) - f^{-1}(d)}{y - d} &= 1\Big/\frac{f(x) - f(c)}{x - c} \\ &\to 1/f'(c) \quad \text{as } y \to d \quad (\text{since } f'(c) \neq 0).\end{aligned}$$

Thus $f^{-1}$ is differentiable at $d$, with derivative $(f^{-1})'(d) = 1/f'(c)$. ■

# Further exercises

**Exercise 2.9** Verify that the following function is differentiable on $(-1, \infty)$ and determine its derivative, stating which rules you use:

$$f(x) = \log_e(1 + x) + e^{x^2}.$$

**Exercise 2.10** Find (without justification) the derivatives of the following functions.

(a) $f(x) = \dfrac{x^2 + 1}{x - 1} \quad (x \in (1, \infty))$

(b) $f(x) = \log_e(\sin x) \quad (x \in (0, \pi))$

(c) $f(x) = \log_e(\sec x + \tan x) \quad (x \in (-\frac{1}{2}\pi, \frac{1}{2}\pi))$

(d) $f(x) = \coth x \quad (x \in \mathbb{R} - \{0\})$

**Exercise 2.11** Prove that the function

$$f(x) = \tanh x \quad (x \in \mathbb{R})$$

has an inverse function $f^{-1}$ that is differentiable on $(-1, 1)$, and find a formula for $(f^{-1})'(x)$.

**Exercise 2.12** Prove that the function

$$f(x) = \tan x + 3x \quad \left(x \in \left(-\tfrac{1}{2}\pi, \tfrac{1}{2}\pi\right)\right)$$

has an inverse function $f^{-1}$ that is differentiable on $\mathbb{R}$, and find the value of $(f^{-1})'(0)$.

# 3 Rolle's Theorem

After working through this section, you should be able to:

(a) state and use the Local Extremum Theorem;

(b) state and use Rolle's Theorem.

In this section and in Section 4 we describe some of the fundamental properties of functions that are differentiable not just at a particular point, but *on an interval*. Our results are motivated by the geometric significance of differentiability in terms of tangents, and they explain why the graphs of differentiable functions possess certain geometric properties.

## 3.1 Local Extremum Theorem

In Analysis Block A we described some of the fundamental properties of functions which are continuous on a bounded closed interval. In particular, we proved the Extreme Value Theorem, which states that if a function $f$ is continuous on a closed interval $[a, b]$, then there are points $c$ and $d$ in $[a, b]$ such that

See Unit AA4, Section 3.

$$f(x) \le f(d), \quad \text{for } x \in [a, b],$$

and

$$f(x) \ge f(c), \quad \text{for } x \in [a, b].$$

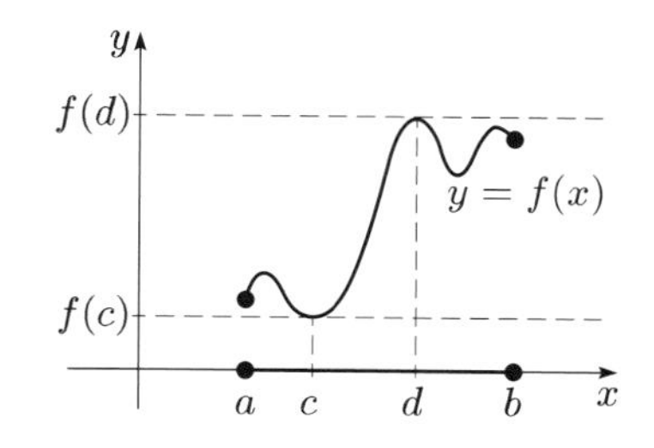


The value $f(d)$ is the **maximum** of $f$ on $[a, b]$, and the value $f(c)$ is the **minimum** of $f$ on $[a, b]$. A maximum or a minimum of $f$ is called an **extremum** of $f$.

But how do we determine the points $c$ and $d$ where these extrema occur? In general, this is not easy. However, if the function $f$ is differentiable, then we can, in principle, determine $c$ and $d$ by first finding any *local extrema* of the function $f$ on the interval $[a, b]$.

Roughly speaking, for a point $c$ in $(a, b)$, the value $f(c)$ is a *local maximum* of $f$ on $[a, b]$ if $f(c)$ is the greatest value of $f$ in the immediate vicinity of $c$, and a *local minimum* of $f$ on $[a, b]$ if $f(c)$ is the least value of $f$ in the immediate vicinity of $c$.

**Definition** The function $f$ has

(a) a **local maximum** $f(c)$ at $c$ if there is an open interval $I = (c - r, c + r)$, where $r > 0$, in the domain of $f$ such that

$$f(x) \le f(c), \quad \text{for } x \in I;$$

(b) a **local minimum** $f(c)$ at $c$ if there is an open interval $I = (c - r, c + r)$, where $r > 0$, in the domain of $f$ such that

$$f(x) \ge f(c), \quad \text{for } x \in I;$$

(c) a **local extremum** $f(c)$ at $c$ if $f(c)$ is either a local maximum or a local minimum.

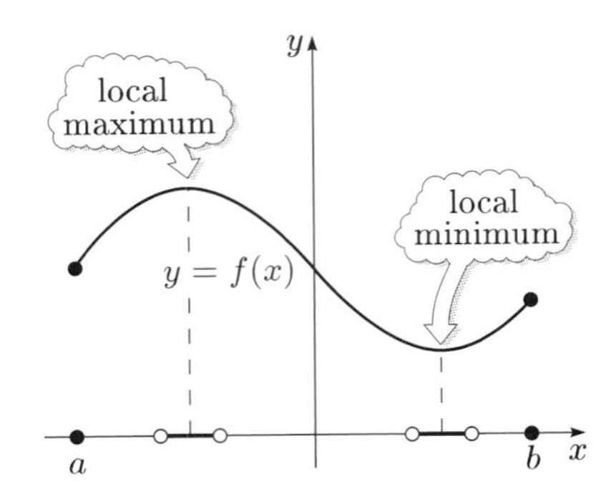


By definition, a local extremum of a function $f$ defined on a bounded closed interval $[a, b]$ is an interior point of $[a, b]$; that is, a local extremum cannot occur at either of the endpoints $a$ and $b$.

If we want to find the local extrema of a differentiable function $f$, then we can use the following result, which gives a connection between the local extrema of a function $f$ and the points $c$ where $f'(c) = 0$. A point $c$ such that $f'(c) = 0$ is called a **stationary point** of $f$; we sometimes say that $f'$ **vanishes** at $c$.

> **Theorem 3.1 Local Extremum Theorem**
>
> If $f$ has a local extremum at $c$ and $f$ is differentiable at $c$, then
>
> $$f'(c) = 0.$$

**Proof** Suppose that $f$ has a local maximum at $c$. Then there exists a positive number $r$ such that

We prove only the local maximum version; the proof of the local minimum version is similar.

$$f(x) \le f(c), \quad \text{for } c - r < x < c + r. \tag{3.1}$$

Now let

$$x_n = c + \frac{r}{n} \quad \text{and} \quad x'_n = c - \frac{r}{n}, \quad n = 2, 3, \ldots.$$

Then $c < x_n < c + r$, for $n = 2, 3, \ldots$, so

$$f(x_n) - f(c) \le 0 \quad \text{and} \quad x_n - c > 0, \quad \text{for } n = 2, 3, \ldots,$$

by inequality (3.1). Hence

$$\frac{f(x_n) - f(c)}{x_n - c} \le 0, \quad \text{for } n = 2, 3, \ldots.$$

Since $x_n \to c$, we deduce, by the Limit Inequality Rule, that

See Unit AA2, Subsection 3.3.

$$f'(c) = \lim_{n\to\infty} \frac{f(x_n) - f(c)}{x_n - c} \le 0. \tag{3.2}$$

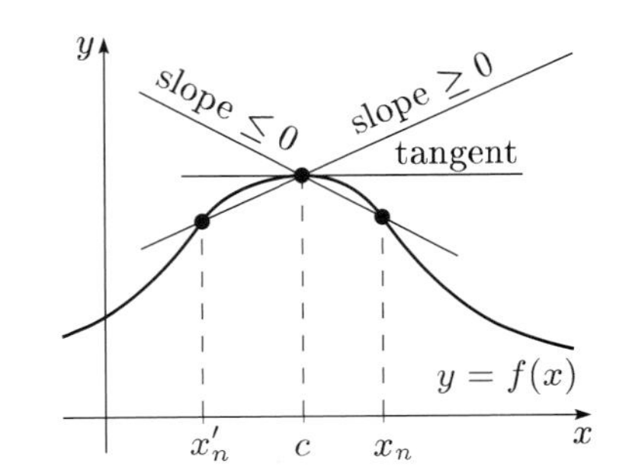


On the other hand, $c - r < x'_n < c$, for $n = 2, 3, \ldots$, so

$$f(x'_n) - f(c) \le 0 \quad \text{and} \quad x'_n - c < 0, \quad \text{for } n = 2, 3, \ldots,$$

by inequality (3.1). Hence

$$\frac{f(x'_n) - f(c)}{x'_n - c} \ge 0, \quad \text{for } n = 2, 3, \ldots.$$

Since $x'_n \to c$, we deduce that

$$f'(c) = \lim_{n\to\infty} \frac{f(x'_n) - f(c)}{x'_n - c} \ge 0. \tag{3.3}$$

Hence, by inequalities (3.2) and (3.3), we have $f'(c) = 0$, as required. ■

*Remark* The converse of the Local Extremum Theorem is not true; a point where the derivative vanishes (that is, equals zero) is not necessarily a local extremum. For example, the function $f(x) = x^3$ does not have a local extremum at 0, although $f'(0) = 0$.

Any extremum of a function $f$ on a bounded closed interval $[a, b]$ which is not $f(a)$ or $f(b)$ must also be a local extremum. Thus, by Theorem 3.1, such a point $x$ must satisfy $f'(x) = 0$. This gives the following property of the extrema of a differentiable function on a bounded closed interval.

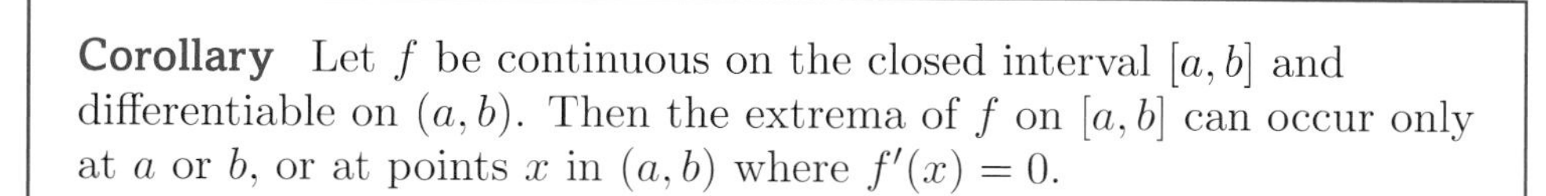

**Corollary** Let $f$ be continuous on the closed interval $[a, b]$ and differentiable on $(a, b)$. Then the extrema of $f$ on $[a, b]$ can occur only at $a$ or $b$, or at points $x$ in $(a, b)$ where $f'(x) = 0$.

We now reformulate this corollary to Theorem 3.1 as a strategy for locating maxima and minima.

**Strategy 3.1** To find the maximum and minimum of a function.

Let the function $f$ be continuous on $[a, b]$ and differentiable on $(a, b)$. To determine the maximum and the minimum of $f$ on $[a, b]$:

1. determine the points $c_1, c_2, \ldots$ in $(a, b)$ where $f'$ is zero;
2. amongst the values of

$$f(a),\ f(b),\ f(c_1),\ f(c_2),\ \ldots,$$

the greatest is the maximum and the least is the minimum.

In some cases, there may be infinitely many points in $(a, b)$ where $f'$ is zero.

**Exercise 3.1** Use Strategy 3.1 to determine the maximum and minimum of the function

$$f(x) = \sin^2 x + \cos x$$

on the interval $[0, \frac{1}{2}\pi]$.

## 3.2 Rolle's Theorem

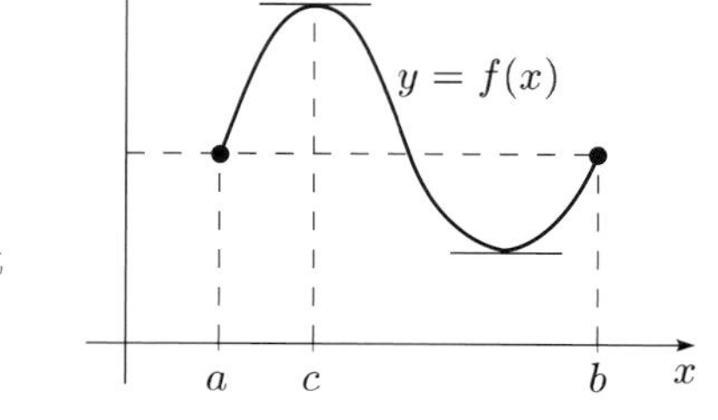


In Subsection 3.1 we saw that if a function $f$ is continuous on the closed interval $[a, b]$ and differentiable on the open interval $(a, b)$, then the extrema of $f$ can occur only at $a$ or $b$, or at some point $c$ in $(a, b)$ such that $f'(c) = 0$. If we also know that the values of $f(a)$ and $f(b)$ are equal, then it follows that there must be some point $c$ in $(a, b)$ where $f'(c) = 0$.

**Theorem 3.2 Rolle's Theorem**

Let $f$ be continuous on the closed interval $[a, b]$ and differentiable on $(a, b)$. If $f(a) = f(b)$, then there exists a point $c$, with $a < c < b$, such that

$$f'(c) = 0.$$

Michel Rolle (1652–1719) was a French mathematician who gave this result for polynomials.

This is an *existence theorem.* Often it is difficult to evaluate $c$ explicitly.

**Proof** Suppose that $f(a) = f(b)$.

If $f$ is constant on $[a, b]$, then $f'(x) = 0$ everywhere on $(a, b)$; in this case, we can take $c$ to be any point of $(a, b)$.

If $f$ is non-constant on $[a, b]$, then either the maximum or the minimum (or both) of $f$ on $[a, b]$ is different from the common value $f(a) = f(b)$. Since one of the extrema occurs at some point $c$ with $a < c < b$, the Local Extremum Theorem shows that $f'(c)$ must be zero. ■

Since $f$ is continuous on $[a, b]$, it must have both a maximum and a minimum on $[a, b]$, by the Extreme Value Theorem; see Unit AA4, Theorem 3.4.

*Remarks*

1. Rolle's Theorem is one of the most important theorems in analysis; for example, most of the results in Sections 4 and 5 depend on Rolle's Theorem.
2. In geometric terms, Rolle's Theorem states that if the line joining the points $(a, f(a))$, $(b, f(b))$ on the graph of $f$ is horizontal, then so is the tangent to the graph for some $c \in (a, b)$.
3. There may be more than one point $c$ in $(a, b)$ at which $f'$ vanishes.

We can use Rolle's Theorem to verify the existence of zeros of certain functions which are derivatives.

**Example 3.1** Use Rolle's Theorem to show that if

$$f(x) = 3x^4 - 2x^3 - 2x^2 + 2x,$$

then there is a value of $c$ in $(-1, 1)$ such that $f'(c) = 0$.

**Solution** Since $f$ is a polynomial function, $f$ is continuous on $[-1, 1]$ and differentiable on $(-1, 1)$. Also, $f(1) = f(-1) = 1$. Thus $f$ satisfies the conditions of Rolle's Theorem on $[-1, 1]$. It follows that there exists a point $c \in (-1, 1)$ such that $f'(c) = 0$. ■

*Remark* For the function in Example 3.1 we can find a value for $c$ directly by using the fact that

$$\begin{aligned} f'(x) &= 12x^3 - 6x^2 - 4x + 2 \\ &= 2(3x^2 - 1)(2x - 1). \end{aligned}$$

Thus $f'$ has a zero at each of the points $-1/\sqrt{3}$, $1/\sqrt{3}$ and $\frac{1}{2}$, which are all in $(-1, 1)$.

**Exercise 3.2** Use Rolle's Theorem to show that if

$$f(x) = x^4 - 4x^3 + 3x^2 + 2,$$

then there is a value of $c$ in $(1, 3)$ such that $f'(c) = 0$.

**Exercise 3.3** For each of the following functions, state whether Rolle's Theorem applies for the given interval.

(a) $f(x) = \tan x$, $[0, \pi]$.

(b) $f(x) = 3|x - 1| - x$, $[0, 3]$.

(c) $f(x) = x - 9x^{17} + 8x^{18}$, $[0, 1]$.

(d) $f(x) = \sin x + \tan^{-1} x$, $[0, \frac{1}{2}\pi]$.

## Further exercises

**Exercise 3.4** The function $f$ has domain $[-2, 2]$, and its graph consists of four line segments, as shown below.

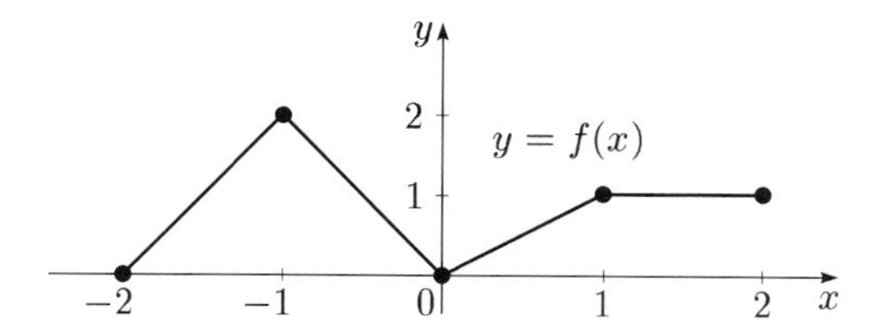


Identify any

(a) local minima (b) minima (c) local maxima (d) maxima

of $f$, and state where these occur.

**Exercise 3.5** Use Rolle's Theorem to show that if

$$f(x) = x^5 - 3x^4 + 2x^3 + 2x^2 - 6x + 1,$$

then there is a value of $c$ in $(1, 2)$ such that $f'(c) = 0$.

**Exercise 3.6** Use Rolle's Theorem to prove that if $p$ is a polynomial and $x_1, x_2, \ldots, x_n$ are distinct zeros of $p$, then $p'$ has at least $n - 1$ zeros.

**Exercise 3.7** Use Rolle's Theorem to prove that for any real number $\lambda$, the function

$$f(x) = x^3 - \tfrac{3}{2}x^2 + \lambda \quad (x \in \mathbb{R}),$$

does not have two distinct zeros in $[0, 1]$.

Hint: Assume that $f$ has two distinct zeros in $[0, 1]$, and deduce a contradiction.

# 4 Mean Value Theorem

After working through this section, you should be able to:

(a) state and use the Mean Value Theorem;

(b) state and use the Increasing–Decreasing Theorem and the Zero Derivative Theorem.

In this section we continue to study the geometric properties of functions that are differentiable on intervals, and describe some of their applications.

## 4.1 Mean Value Theorem

First we recall the geometric interpretation of Rolle's Theorem from the previous section. Rolle's Theorem tells us that, under suitable conditions, if the chord joining the points $(a, f(a))$ and $(b, f(b))$ on the graph of $f$ is horizontal, then so is the tangent to the graph for some $c$ in $(a, b)$.

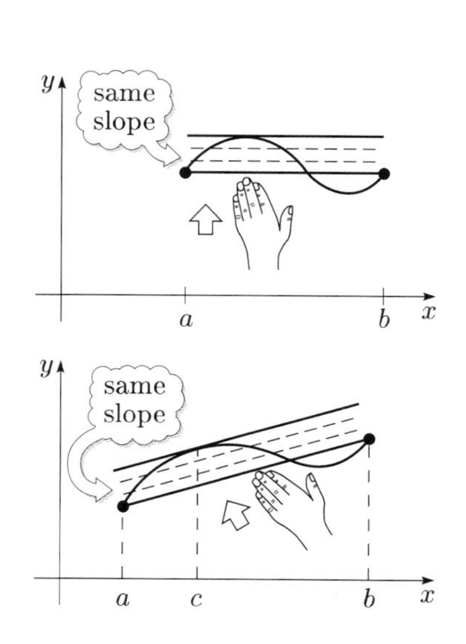


If you imagine pushing this horizontal chord, always parallel to its original position, until it is just about to lose contact with the graph of $f$, then it appears that at this point the chord is a tangent to the graph. This 'chord-pushing' approach suggests that even if the original chord is not horizontal (that is, if $f(a) \neq f(b)$), then there must still be a point $c$ in $(a, b)$ at which the tangent is parallel to the chord.

**Example 4.1** Consider the function

$$f(x) = x^3 - 3x + 3 \quad (x \in [1, 2]).$$

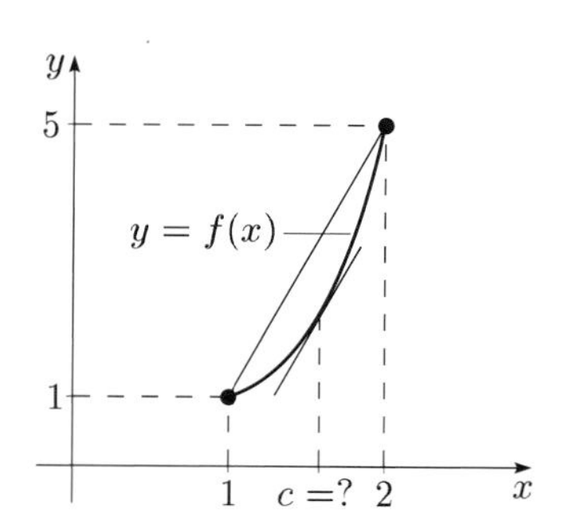


Find a point $c \in (1, 2)$ such that the tangent to the graph of $f$ is parallel to the chord joining $(1, f(1))$ to $(2, f(2))$.

**Solution** Since $f(1) = 1 - 3 + 3 = 1$ and $f(2) = 8 - 6 + 3 = 5$, the slope of the chord is

$$\frac{f(2) - f(1)}{2 - 1} = \frac{5 - 1}{2 - 1} = 4.$$

Since $f$ is a polynomial, it is differentiable on $(1, 2)$, and its derivative is $f'(x) = 3x^2 - 3$. Hence $f'(c) = 4$ when $3c^2 = 7$; that is, when $c = \sqrt{7/3} \simeq 1.53$.

Thus at the point $(c, f(c))$ the tangent to the graph is parallel to the chord joining the endpoints of the graph. ■

We now generalise Rolle's Theorem and show that there is always a point where the tangent to the graph is parallel to the chord joining the endpoints. This result is known as the *Mean Value Theorem*, so-called since

$$\frac{f(b) - f(a)}{b - a}$$

can be thought of as the *mean value* of the derivative between $a$ and $b$.

**Theorem 4.1 Mean Value Theorem**

Let $f$ be continuous on the closed interval $[a, b]$ and differentiable on $(a, b)$. Then there exists a point $c$ in $(a, b)$ such that

$$f'(c) = \frac{f(b) - f(a)}{b - a}.$$

Again, this is an *existence theorem.*

Note that when $f(a) = f(b)$, the Mean Value Theorem reduces to Rolle's Theorem.

**Proof** The slope of the chord joining the points $(a, f(a))$ and $(b, f(b))$ is

$$m = \frac{f(b) - f(a)}{b - a},$$

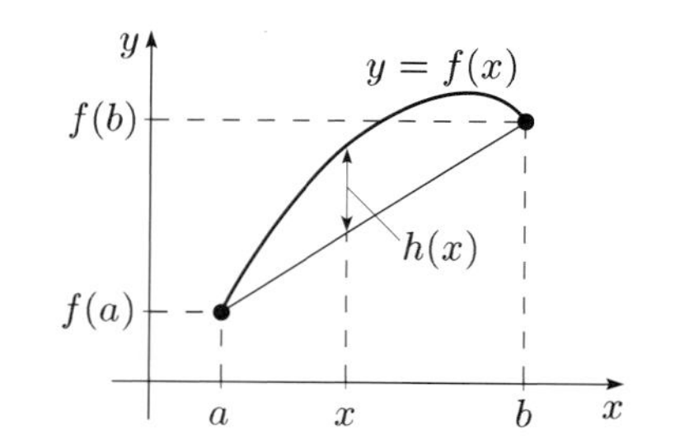


so the equation of the chord is

$$y = m(x - a) + f(a).$$

It follows that the vertical distance, $h(x)$, from the point $(x, f(x))$ to the chord is given by the function

$$h(x) = f(x) - (m(x - a) + f(a)).$$

Now $h(a) = h(b) = 0$, and $h$ is continuous on $[a, b]$ and differentiable on $(a, b)$. Thus $h$ satisfies all the conditions of Rolle's Theorem.

It follows that there exists a point $c$ in $(a, b)$ such that $h'(c) = 0$. Since $h'(c) = f'(c) - m$, we have

$$f'(c) = m = \frac{f(b) - f(a)}{b - a},$$

as required. ■

**Example 4.2** Use the Mean Value Theorem to show that if

$$f(x) = \frac{x-1}{x+1},$$

then there is a point $c$ in $\left(1, \frac{7}{2}\right)$ such that $f'(c) = \frac{2}{9}$.

**Solution** The function $f$ is a rational function whose denominator is non-zero on $\left[1, \frac{7}{2}\right]$, so $f$ is continuous on $\left[1, \frac{7}{2}\right]$ and differentiable on $\left(1, \frac{7}{2}\right)$. Thus $f$ satisfies the conditions of the Mean Value Theorem.

Now

$$\frac{f\left(\frac{7}{2}\right) - f(1)}{\frac{7}{2} - 1} = \frac{\frac{5}{9} - 0}{\frac{5}{2}} = \frac{2}{9}.$$

Thus, by the Mean Value Theorem, there exists a point $c$ in $\left(1, \frac{7}{2}\right)$ such that $f'(c) = \frac{2}{9}$. ■

*Remark* For the function in Example 4.2 we can find a value for $c$ directly. Since $f'(x) = 2/(x+1)^2$, the point $c$ satisfies

$$f'(c) = \frac{2}{(c+1)^2} = \frac{2}{9}; \quad \text{that is,} \quad (c+1)^2 = 9.$$

This equation has solutions 2 and $-4$, so $c = 2$ $\left(\text{since } 2 \in \left(1, \frac{7}{2}\right)\right)$.

In the following exercise, a value for $c$ cannot be found in this direct way.

**Exercise 4.1** Use the Mean Value Theorem to show that if

$$f(x) = xe^x,$$

then there is a point $c$ in $(0, 2)$ such that $f'(c) = e^2$.

## 4.2 Positive, negative and zero derivatives

We now study some consequences of the Mean Value Theorem for functions whose derivatives are always positive, always negative, or always zero. First we prove a fundamental result about monotonic functions, used in the Introduction Block to help in graph sketching.

See Unit I1, Section 2.

For any interval $I$, the **interior** of $I$, denoted by $\mathrm{Int}(I)$, is the largest open subinterval of $I$.

Thus $\mathrm{Int}(I)$ is obtained from $I$ by removing any endpoints of $I$, so it consists of all the interior points of $I$.

**Theorem 4.2 Increasing–Decreasing Theorem**

Let $f$ be continuous on an interval $I$ and differentiable on $\mathrm{Int}(I)$.

(a) If $f'(x) \geq 0$ for $x \in \mathrm{Int}(I)$, then $f$ is increasing on $I$.

(b) If $f'(x) \leq 0$ for $x \in \mathrm{Int}(I)$, then $f$ is decreasing on $I$.

**Proof** Choose any two points $x_1$ and $x_2$ in $I$, with $x_1 < x_2$. The function $f$ satisfies the conditions of the Mean Value Theorem on the interval $[x_1, x_2]$, so there exists a point $c$ in $(x_1, x_2)$ such that

$$\frac{f(x_2) - f(x_1)}{x_2 - x_1} = f'(c).$$

Hence $f(x_2) - f(x_1)$ has the same sign as $f'(c)$, so

(a) if $f'(x) \geq 0$ for $x \in \text{Int}(I)$, then $f(x_2) - f(x_1) \geq 0$, so $f(x_2) \geq f(x_1)$ and hence $f$ is increasing on $I$;

(b) if $f'(x) \leq 0$ for $x \in \text{Int}(I)$, then $f(x_2) - f(x_1) \leq 0$, so $f(x_2) \leq f(x_1)$ and hence $f$ is decreasing on $I$. ■

*Remark* If the weak inequalities are replaced by strict inequalities in Theorem 4.2, then the conclusions are as follows.

(a) If $f'(x) > 0$ for $x \in \text{Int}(I)$, then $f$ is strictly increasing on $I$.

(b) If $f'(x) < 0$ for $x \in \text{Int}(I)$, then $f$ is strictly decreasing on $I$.

The converse of these two statements is false. For example, $f(x) = x^3$ is strictly increasing on $[-1, 1]$, but $f'(0) = 0$.

**Exercise 4.2** For each of the following functions $f$, determine whether $f$ is increasing, strictly increasing, decreasing or strictly decreasing on the given interval $I$.

(a) $f(x) = 3x^{4/3} - 4x, \quad I = [1, \infty)$.

(b) $f(x) = x - \log_e x, \quad I = (0, 1]$.

The following corollary to Theorem 4.2 is useful in later units.

**Corollary Zero Derivative Theorem**

Let $f$ be continuous on an interval $I$ and differentiable on $\text{Int}(I)$. If

$$f'(x) = 0, \quad \text{for } x \in \text{Int}(I),$$

then

$f$ is constant on $I$.

**Proof** Theorem 4.2(a) and (b) both apply, so $f$ is both increasing and decreasing on $I$. Hence $f$ is constant on $I$. ■

We can often determine whether a point $c$ such that $f'(c) = 0$ is a local maximum or local minimum of a function $f$ by using the following test.

**Second Derivative Test** Let $f$ be a twice-differentiable function defined on an open interval containing a point $c$ for which $f'(c) = 0$ and $f''$ is continuous at $c$.

(a) If $f''(c) > 0$, then $f(c)$ is a local minimum of $f$.

(b) If $f''(c) < 0$, then $f(c)$ is a local maximum of $f$.

The following diagrams may be helpful in remembering this result.

**Proof** We prove part (a), so we assume that $f''(c) > 0$.

The proof of part (b) is similar.

Then there exists $\delta > 0$ such that $f''(x) > 0$ for $x \in (c - \delta, c + \delta)$, and hence $f'$ is strictly increasing on the open interval $(c - \delta, c + \delta)$, by the strict version of the Increasing–Decreasing Theorem.

This follows by the $\varepsilon$–$\delta$ definition of continuity, by taking $\varepsilon = \frac{1}{2}f''(c)$ and choosing a corresponding $\delta > 0$.

Since $f'(c) = 0$, we deduce that

$$f'(x) < 0, \quad \text{for } x \in (c-\delta, c),$$
$$f'(x) > 0, \quad \text{for } x \in (c, c+\delta).$$

Thus $f$ has a local minimum at $c$, by the Increasing–Decreasing Theorem. ■

*Remark* If $f''(c) = 0$, then the Second Derivative Test gives no information about local extrema.

For example, the function $f(x) = x^3$ satisfies $f'(0) = 0$ and $f''(0) = 0$, but it has neither a local maximum nor a local minimum at 0.

**Exercise 4.3** Consider the function

$$f(x) = x^3 - 3x^2 + 1.$$

(a) Determine those points $c$ such that $f'(c) = 0$.

(b) Using the Second Derivative Test, determine whether the points $c$ found in part (a) correspond to local maxima or local minima.

## Proving inequalities

We now demonstrate how the Increasing–Decreasing Theorem can be used to prove certain inequalities involving differentiable functions.

**Example 4.3** Let $\alpha > 1$. Prove that

$$(1+x)^\alpha \geq 1 + \alpha x, \quad \text{for } x \geq -1.$$

This is a version of Bernoulli's Inequality:

$$(1+x)^n \geq 1 + nx, \quad \text{for } x \geq -1,$$

where $n \in \mathbb{N}$; see Unit AA1, Section 3, Frame 7.

**Solution** Suppose that $\alpha > 1$, and define the function

$$f(x) = (1+x)^\alpha - (1+\alpha x) \quad (x \in [-1, \infty)).$$

We want to show that $f(x) \geq 0$ for $x \in [-1, \infty)$. Since $f(0) = 1 - 1 = 0$, it is equivalent to show that

$$f(x) \geq f(0), \quad \text{for } x \in [-1, \infty).$$

Thus it is sufficient to show that

$$f \text{ is increasing on } (0, \infty) \text{ and decreasing on } [-1, 0). \tag{4.1}$$

The function $f$ is continuous on $[-1, \infty)$ and differentiable on $(-1, \infty)$, and

$$\begin{aligned} f'(x) &= \alpha(1+x)^{\alpha-1} - \alpha \\ &= \alpha((1+x)^{\alpha-1} - 1), \quad \text{for } x \in (-1, \infty). \end{aligned} \tag{4.2}$$

If $x > 0$, then $1 + x > 1$, so

$$(1+x)^{\alpha-1} > 1, \quad \text{for } x > 0.$$

Since $\alpha - 1 > 0$, we can use Rule 5 for inequalities, introduced in Unit AA1, Section 2.

Hence, by equation (4.2),

$$f'(x) > 0, \quad \text{for } x > 0, \tag{4.3}$$

so $f$ is increasing on $(0, \infty)$, by the Increasing–Decreasing Theorem.

If $-1 < x < 0$, then $0 < 1 + x < 1$, so

$$(1+x)^{\alpha-1} < 1, \quad \text{for } -1 < x < 0.$$

Hence, by equation (4.2),

$$f'(x) < 0, \quad \text{for } -1 < x < 0, \tag{4.4}$$

so $f$ is decreasing on $(-1, 0)$. This proves statement (4.1). ■

Example 4.3 illustrates the following general strategy for using the Increasing–Decreasing Theorem to prove inequalities.

**Strategy 4.1** To prove an inequality.

To prove that $g(x) \geq h(x)$, for $x \in [a, b]$, carry out the following.

1. Let

   $$f(x) = g(x) - h(x),$$

   and show that $f$ is continuous on $[a, b]$ and differentiable on $(a, b)$.

2. Prove

   EITHER $f(a) \geq 0$ and $f'(x) \geq 0$ for $x \in (a, b)$,

   OR $f(b) \geq 0$ and $f'(x) \leq 0$ for $x \in (a, b)$.

There is a corresponding version of Strategy 4.1 in which the weak inequalities are replaced by strict inequalities.

This result also holds if $b$ is $\infty$.

This result also holds if $a$ is $-\infty$.

The diagrams below illustrate why this strategy works.

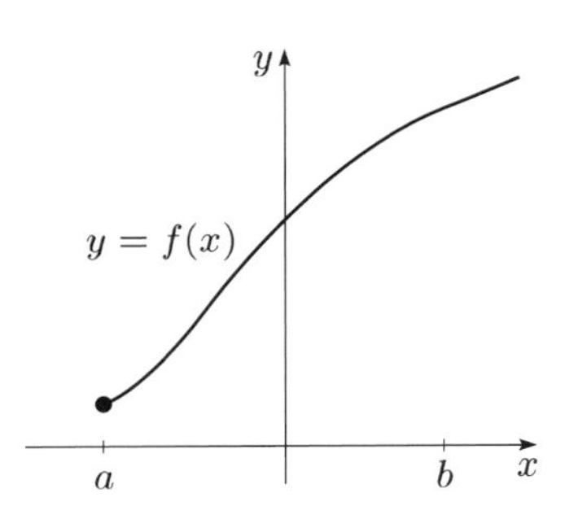


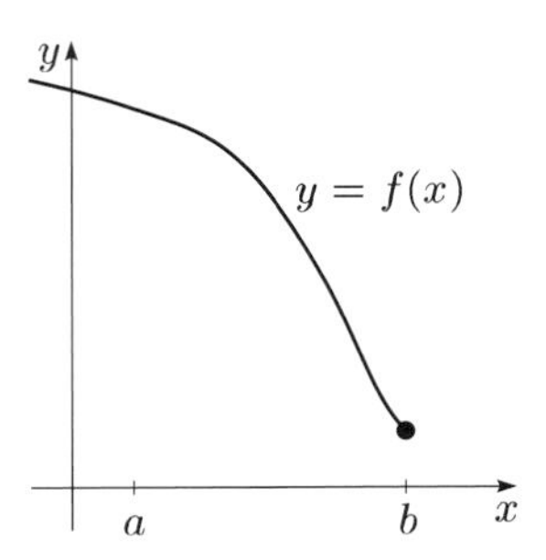


**Exercise 4.4** Prove the following inequalities.

(a) $\sin x \leq x$, for $x \in [0, \infty)$. (b) $\frac{2}{3}x + \frac{1}{3} \geq x^{2/3}$, for $x \in [0, 1]$.

# Further exercises

**Exercise 4.5** Use the Mean Value Theorem to show that if

$$f(x) = x^3 + 2x^2 + x,$$

then there is a point $c \in (0, 1)$ such that $f'(c) = 4$.

**Exercise 4.6** Let $f$ be continuous on $[0, 2]$ and differentiable on $(0, 2)$, with

$$f(0) = 10 \quad \text{and} \quad |f'(x)| \leq 3, \quad \text{for } x \in (0, 2).$$

Use the Mean Value Theorem to deduce that

$$4 \leq f(2) \leq 16.$$

**Exercise 4.7** For the function

$$f(x) = x^3 - 2x^2 + x \quad (x \in \mathbb{R}),$$

determine the points $c$ such that $f'(c) = 0$. Using the Second Derivative Test, decide whether these points correspond to local maxima or local minima.

**Exercise 4.8** Prove the following inequalities.

(a) $\log_e x \geq 1 - \dfrac{1}{x}$, for $x \in [1, \infty)$.

(b) $4x^{1/4} \leq x + 3$, for $x \in [0, 1]$.

(c) $\log_e(1 + x) > x - \frac{1}{2}x^2$, for $x \in (0, \infty)$.

# 5 L'Hôpital's Rule

After working through this section, you should be able to:

(a) understand the statements of Cauchy's Mean Value Theorem and l'Hôpital's Rule;

(b) use l'Hôpital's Rule to evaluate certain limits of the form $\lim_{x \to c} f(x)/g(x)$, where $f(c) = g(c) = 0$.

## 5.1 Limits of quotients

In Section 1 we found the derivatives of sin and exp by using the results

$$\lim_{x \to 0} \frac{\sin x}{x} = 1 \quad \text{and} \quad \lim_{x \to 0} \frac{e^x - 1}{x} = 1.$$

These limits were evaluated from basic principles in Unit AB1, Section 1.

Each of the above limits is of the form

$$\lim_{x \to c} \frac{f(x)}{g(x)},$$

where $f$ and $g$ are continuous functions with $f(c) = g(c) = 0$. Such limits cannot be evaluated by the Quotient Rule for limits, because this rule requires $\lim_{x \to c} g(x) \neq 0$.

We meet similar problems with the following more complicated limits:

$$\lim_{x \to \pi/2} \frac{\cos 3x}{\sin x - e^{\cos x}} \quad \text{and} \quad \lim_{x \to 0} \frac{x^2}{\cosh x - 1}.$$

Do they exist? And if they do, what are their values?

The video programme introduces l'Hôpital's Rule, which enables us to tackle such questions.

**Watch the video programme 'L'Hôpital's Rule'.**

Video

## 5.2 Review of the video programme

The programme begins by outlining the proofs of Rolle's Theorem and the Mean Value Theorem.

It then reminds you how to describe a curve in $\mathbb{R}^2$ by specifying the $x$- and $y$-coordinates of its points using two functions, $f$ and $g$, to define parametric equations

$$x = g(t), \quad y = f(t),$$

You met the idea of parametric equations in Unit I1, Section 5; here we have interchanged the roles of $f$ and $g$ for convenience in the proof of Theorem 5.2.

where the parameter $t$ belongs to some suitable interval $[a, b]$. The curve can then be thought of as the path in $\mathbb{R}^2$ of a particle moving from an initial point $(g(a), f(a))$ to a final point $(g(b), f(b))$ as the time $t$ increases from $t = a$ to $t = b$.

Here are two examples of curves described in this way.

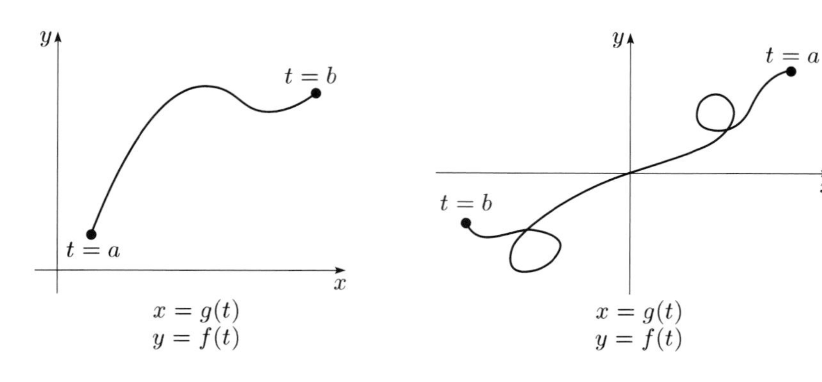


The formula for the slope of the tangent to a curve given in parametric form is given in the following theorem.

**Theorem 5.1** The tangent to the curve with parametric equations

$$x = g(t), \quad y = f(t),$$

at the point with parameter $t$ has slope $f'(t)/g'(t)$, provided that $g'(t) \neq 0$.

This result follows from the Chain Rule, which gives

$$\frac{dy}{dx} = \frac{dy}{dt} \Big/ \frac{dx}{dt}.$$

The Mean Value Theorem asserts that, under certain conditions, a function defined on a closed interval has the property that at some intermediate point, the tangent to the graph is parallel to the chord joining the endpoints. The next result states that this geometric property also holds for suitable curves.

The proofs of Theorem 5.2 and l'Hôpital's Rule are in Subsection 5.4.

**Theorem 5.2 Cauchy's Mean Value Theorem**

Let $f$ and $g$ be continuous on $[a, b]$ and differentiable on $(a, b)$. Then there exists a point $c \in (a, b)$ such that

$$f'(c)(g(b) - g(a)) = g'(c)(f(b) - f(a));$$

in particular, if $g(b) \neq g(a)$ and $g'(c) \neq 0$, then

$$\frac{f'(c)}{g'(c)} = \frac{f(b) - f(a)}{g(b) - g(a)}.$$

Baron Augustin Louis Cauchy (1789–1857) was a French mathematician who made many important contributions to analysis, especially to the theory of complex functions.

When $g(x) = x$, Theorem 5.2 reduces to the usual Mean Value Theorem.

To appreciate this result geometrically, note that

$\dfrac{f'(c)}{g'(c)}$ is the slope of the tangent to the curve at the point $(g(c), f(c))$;

$\dfrac{f(b) - f(a)}{g(b) - g(a)}$ is the slope of the chord joining $(g(a), f(a))$ and $(g(b), f(b))$.

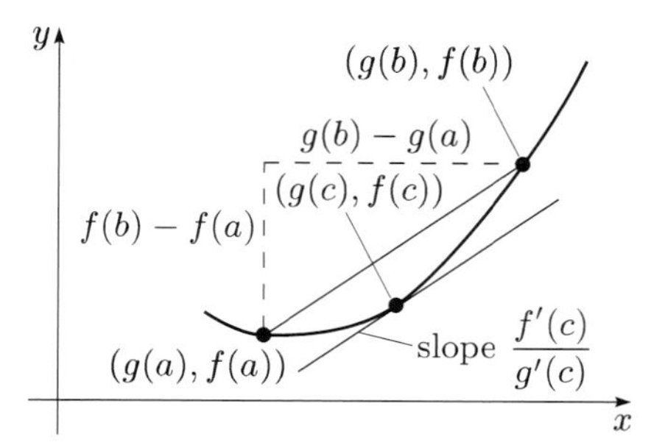


Cauchy's Mean Value Theorem is used to prove l'Hôpital's Rule, which is the main result in the video programme.

**L'Hôpital's Rule** Let $f$ and $g$ be differentiable on an open interval $I$ containing the point $c$, and suppose that $f(c) = g(c) = 0$. Then

$$\lim_{x \to c} \frac{f(x)}{g(x)} \text{ exists and equals } \lim_{x \to c} \frac{f'(x)}{g'(x)},$$

provided that the latter limit exists.

G. F. A. de l'Hôpital (1661–1704) was a French marquis who included this result (due to Jean Bernoulli) in his textbook on calculus.

It is important not to ignore this proviso.

# Solutions to the exercises

**1.1 (a)** The difference quotient for $f$ at $c$, where $c \neq 0$, is

$$Q(h) = \frac{f(c+h) - f(c)}{h} = \frac{\dfrac{1}{c+h} - \dfrac{1}{c}}{h} = \frac{-1}{(c+h)c}, \quad \text{where } h \neq 0.$$

Thus $Q(h) \to -1/c^2$ as $h \to 0$. Hence $f$ is differentiable at $c$, with $f'(c) = -1/c^2$.

**(b)** The difference quotient for $f$ at 0 is

$$Q(h) = \frac{f(h) - f(0)}{h} = \frac{h^2 \cos(1/h) - 0}{h} = h\cos(1/h), \quad \text{where } h \neq 0.$$

Now, $|\cos(1/h)| \leq 1$ for $h \neq 0$, so

$$|Q(h)| \leq |h|, \quad \text{for } h \neq 0.$$

Thus $Q(h) \to 0$ as $h \to 0$, by the Squeeze Rule for limits. Hence $f$ is differentiable at 0, with $f'(0) = 0$.

**(c)** The difference quotient for $f$ at 0 is

$$Q(h) = \frac{f(h) - f(0)}{h} = \frac{|h| - 0}{h} = \begin{cases} 1, & h > 0, \\ -1, & h < 0. \end{cases}$$

Now consider the two sequences

$$h_n = \frac{1}{n} \quad \text{and} \quad h_n' = -\frac{1}{n}, \quad n = 1, 2, \ldots.$$

These give

$$Q(h_n) = 1 \to 1 \text{ as } n \to \infty,$$

and

$$Q(h_n') = -1 \to -1 \text{ as } n \to \infty.$$

Since these limits are different, $f$ is not differentiable at 0.

**(d)** The difference quotient for $f$ at 0 is

$$Q(h) = \frac{f(h) - f(0)}{h} = \frac{|h|^{1/2}\sin(1/h) - 0}{h} = \begin{cases} \dfrac{\sin(1/h)}{h^{1/2}}, & h > 0, \\ -\dfrac{\sin(1/h)}{|h|^{1/2}}, & h < 0. \end{cases}$$

Now consider the null sequence

$$h_n = \frac{1}{2n\pi + \frac{1}{2}\pi}, \quad n = 1, 2, \ldots,$$

with positive terms. This gives

$$\begin{aligned} Q(h_n) &= \frac{\sin(1/h_n)}{h_n^{1/2}} \\ &= (2n\pi + \tfrac{1}{2}\pi)^{1/2}\sin(2n\pi + \tfrac{1}{2}\pi) \\ &= (2n\pi + \tfrac{1}{2}\pi)^{1/2} \to \infty \text{ as } n \to \infty. \end{aligned}$$

Hence $f$ is not differentiable at 0.

**1.2** Let $I = \mathbb{R}$ and define

$$g(x) = -x^2 \quad (x \in \mathbb{R}) \quad \text{and} \quad h(x) = x^2 \quad (x \in \mathbb{R}),$$

so

$$g'(x) = -2x \quad (x \in \mathbb{R}) \quad \text{and} \quad h'(x) = 2x \quad (x \in \mathbb{R}).$$

Then

$$\begin{aligned} f(x) &= g(x), \quad \text{for } x < 0, \\ f(x) &= h(x), \quad \text{for } x > 0. \end{aligned} \qquad \text{(S.1)}$$

Now, $f(0) = g(0) = h(0) = 0$ and $g'(0) = h'(0) = 0$. Thus $f$ is differentiable at 0 and $f'(0) = 0$, by the Glue Rule.

Also, by statements (S.1),

$$\begin{aligned} f'(x) &= g'(x) = -2x, \quad \text{for } x < 0, \\ f'(x) &= h'(x) = 2x, \quad \text{for } x > 0, \end{aligned}$$

since differentiability is a local property.

Hence $f$ is differentiable (on $\mathbb{R}$), and

$$f'(x) = \begin{cases} -2x, & x < 0, \\ 0, & x = 0, \\ 2x, & x > 0. \end{cases}$$

Thus

$$f'(x) = 2|x| \quad (x \in \mathbb{R}).$$

**1.3 (a)**

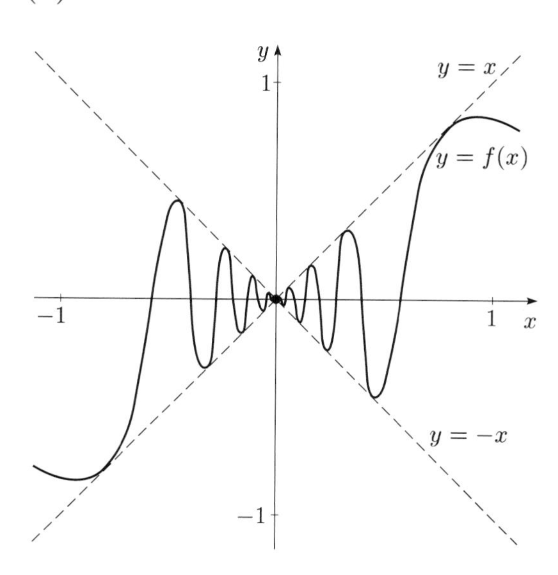

We guess that $f$ is not differentiable at 0.

The difference quotient for $f$ at 0 is

$$Q(h) = \frac{f(h)-f(0)}{h} = \frac{h\sin(1/h^2)-0}{h} = \sin(1/h^2), \quad \text{where } h \neq 0.$$

First, let $\{h_n\}$ be the null sequence

$$h_n = 1/\sqrt{2n\pi + \tfrac{1}{2}\pi}, \quad n = 0, 1, 2, \ldots,$$

with non-zero terms. Then

$$Q(h_n) = \sin(1/h_n^2) = \sin(2n\pi + \tfrac{1}{2}\pi) = 1, \quad \text{for } n = 0, 1, 2, \ldots,$$

so

$$Q(h_n) \to 1 \text{ as } n \to \infty.$$

Next, let $\{h'_n\}$ be the null sequence

$$h'_n = 1/\sqrt{2n\pi + \tfrac{3}{2}\pi}, \quad n = 0, 1, 2, \ldots,$$

with non-zero terms. Then

$$Q(h'_n) = \sin(1/h'^2_n) = \sin(2n\pi + \tfrac{3}{2}\pi) = -1, \quad \text{for } n = 0, 1, 2, \ldots,$$

so

$$Q(h'_n) \to -1 \text{ as } n \to \infty.$$

Thus

$$\lim_{n\to\infty} Q(h_n) = 1 \neq -1 = \lim_{n\to\infty} Q(h'_n).$$

Hence $f$ is not differentiable at 0.

**(b)** The difference quotient for $f$ at 0 is

$$Q(h) = \frac{f(h)-f(0)}{h} = \frac{\frac{h}{1+h} - 0}{h} = \frac{1}{1+h}, \quad \text{where } h \neq 0.$$

Thus $Q(h) \to 1$ as $h \to 0$. Hence $f$ is differentiable at 0, with $f'(0) = 1$.

**1.4 (a)** Let $I = \mathbb{R}$ and define

$$g(x) = -x^2 \quad (x \in \mathbb{R}) \quad \text{and} \quad h(x) = x^3 \quad (x \in \mathbb{R}),$$

so

$$g'(x) = -2x \quad (x \in \mathbb{R}) \quad \text{and} \quad h'(x) = 3x^2 \quad (x \in \mathbb{R}).$$

Then $f(x) = g(x)$ for $x < 0$ and $f(x) = h(x)$ for $x > 0$.

Now, $f(0) = g(0) = h(0) = 0$ and $g'(0) = h'(0) = 0$. Thus $f$ is differentiable at 0 and $f'(0) = 0$, by the Glue Rule.

**(b)** Let $I = \mathbb{R}$ and define

$$g(x) = x \quad (x \in \mathbb{R}) \quad \text{and} \quad h(x) = x^2 \quad (x \in \mathbb{R}),$$

so

$$g'(x) = 1 \quad (x \in \mathbb{R}) \quad \text{and} \quad h'(x) = 2x \quad (x \in \mathbb{R}),$$

Then $f(x) = g(x)$ for $x < 1$ and $f(x) = h(x)$ for $x > 1$.

Now, $f(1) = g(1) = h(1) = 1$, but $g'(1) = 1$ and $h'(1) = 2$, so $g'(1) \neq h'(1)$. Thus, by the Glue Rule, $f$ is not differentiable at 1.

**(c)** The function $f$ is not continuous at the point 1, since

$$f(1) = 0, \quad \text{because } f(x) = x - x^2 \text{ for } x \geq 1,$$

but

$$\lim_{x\to 1^-} f(x) = 1, \quad \text{because } f(x) = x \text{ for } x < 1.$$

Thus $f$ is not differentiable at 1, by the corollary to Theorem 1.3.

**1.5** First, let

$$g(x) = 1 \quad (x \in \mathbb{R}) \quad \text{and} \quad h(x) = \cos x \quad (x \in \mathbb{R}),$$

so

$$g'(x) = 0 \quad (x \in \mathbb{R}) \quad \text{and} \quad h'(x) = -\sin x \quad (x \in \mathbb{R}).$$

Then

$$\begin{aligned} f(x) &= g(x), \quad \text{for } x < 0, \\ f(x) &= h(x), \quad \text{for } x > 0. \end{aligned} \tag{S.2}$$

Now, $f(0) = g(0) = h(0) = 1$ and $g'(0) = h'(0) = 0$. Thus $f$ is differentiable at 0 and $f'(0) = 0$, by the Glue Rule.

Also, by statements (S.2),

$$\begin{aligned} f'(x) &= g'(x) = 0, \quad \text{for } x < 0, \\ f'(x) &= h'(x) = -\sin x, \quad \text{for } x > 0, \end{aligned}$$

since differentiability is a local property.

Hence $f$ is differentiable, and

$$f'(x) = \begin{cases} 0, & x \leq 0, \\ -\sin x, & x > 0. \end{cases}$$

**2.1** In each case we use the Combination Rules.

**(a)** $f'(x) = 7x^6 - 8x^3 + 9x^2 - 5 \quad (x \in \mathbb{R})$

**(b)** $$f'(x) = \frac{(x^3-1)2x - (x^2+1)3x^2}{(x^3-1)^2} = \frac{-x^4 - 3x^2 - 2x}{(x^3-1)^2} \quad (x \in \mathbb{R} - \{1\})$$

**(c)** $$f'(x) = \cos^2 x - \sin^2 x = \cos 2x \quad (x \in \mathbb{R})$$

**(d)** $$f'(x) = \frac{(3+\sin x - 2\cos x)e^x - e^x(\cos x + 2\sin x)}{(3 + \sin x - 2\cos x)^2} = \frac{e^x(3 - \sin x - 3\cos x)}{(3+\sin x - 2\cos x)^2} \quad (x \in \mathbb{R})$$

**2.2** We have

$$\begin{aligned} f'(x) &= e^{2x} + 2xe^{2x} = e^{2x}(1+2x), \\ f''(x) &= 2e^{2x}(1+2x) + 2e^{2x} = e^{2x}(4+4x), \\ f^{(3)}(x) &= 2e^{2x}(4+4x) + 4e^{2x} = e^{2x}(12+8x). \end{aligned}$$

**2.3** In each case, we use the Quotient Rule and the derivatives of sin and cos.

(a) $f(x) = \tan x = \sin x / \cos x$, so

$$f'(x) = \frac{\cos x \cos x - \sin x(-\sin x)}{\cos^2 x} = \frac{1}{\cos^2 x} = \sec^2 x$$

on the domain of $f$.

(b) $f(x) = \operatorname{cosec} x = 1/\sin x$, so

$$f'(x) = -\frac{\cos x}{\sin^2 x} = -\operatorname{cosec} x \cot x$$

on the domain of $f$.

(c) $f(x) = \sec x = 1/\cos x$, so

$$f'(x) = \frac{\sin x}{\cos^2 x} = \sec x \tan x$$

on the domain of $f$.

(d) $f(x) = \cot x = \cos x / \sin x$, so

$$f'(x) = \frac{\sin x(-\sin x) - \cos x \cos x}{\sin^2 x} = -\frac{1}{\sin^2 x} = -\operatorname{cosec}^2 x$$

on the domain of $f$.

**2.4** In each case we use the Combination Rules.

(a) $f(x) = \sinh x = \frac{1}{2}(e^x - e^{-x})$, so

$$f'(x) = \tfrac{1}{2}(e^x + e^{-x}) = \cosh x.$$

(b) $f(x) = \cosh x = \frac{1}{2}(e^x + e^{-x})$, so

$$f'(x) = \tfrac{1}{2}(e^x - e^{-x}) = \sinh x.$$

(c) $f(x) = \tanh x = \sinh x / \cosh x$, so

$$f'(x) = \frac{\cosh x \cosh x - \sinh x \sinh x}{\cosh^2 x} = \frac{1}{\cosh^2 x} = \operatorname{sech}^2 x.$$

**2.5** (a) $f(x) = \sinh(x^2)$, so

$$f'(x) = 2x\cosh(x^2).$$

(b) $f(x) = \sin(\sinh 2x)$, so

$$f'(x) = 2\cos(\sinh 2x)\cosh 2x.$$

(c) $f(x) = \sin\left(\frac{\cos 2x}{x^2}\right) \quad (x \in (0, \infty))$,

so on this interval

$$f'(x) = \cos\left(\frac{\cos 2x}{x^2}\right)\left(\frac{x^2(-2\sin 2x) - 2x\cos 2x}{x^4}\right) = -\frac{2}{x^3}(x\sin 2x + \cos 2x)\cos\left(\frac{\cos 2x}{x^2}\right).$$

**2.6** (a) The function

$$f(x) = \cos x \quad (x \in (0, \pi))$$

is continuous and strictly decreasing, and

$$f((0, \pi)) = (-1, 1).$$

Also, $f$ is differentiable on $(0, \pi)$, and its derivative $f'(x) = -\sin x$ is non-zero there.

Thus $f$ satisfies the conditions of the Inverse Function Rule.

Hence $f^{-1} = \cos^{-1}$ is differentiable on $(-1, 1)$, and if $y = f(x) = \cos x$, then

$$(f^{-1})'(y) = \frac{1}{f'(x)} = -\frac{1}{\sin x}.$$

Since $\sin x > 0$ on $(0, \pi)$ and $\sin^2 x + \cos^2 x = 1$, it follows that

$$\sin x = \sqrt{1 - \cos^2 x} = \sqrt{1 - y^2},$$

so

$$(f^{-1})'(y) = \frac{-1}{\sqrt{1 - y^2}}.$$

Replacing the domain variable $y$ by $x$, we obtain

$$(\cos^{-1})'(x) = \frac{-1}{\sqrt{1 - x^2}} \quad (x \in (-1, 1)).$$

(b) The function

$$f(x) = \sinh x \quad (x \in \mathbb{R})$$

is continuous and strictly increasing, and $f(\mathbb{R}) = \mathbb{R}$.

Also, $f$ is differentiable on $\mathbb{R}$, and its derivative $f'(x) = \cosh x$ is non-zero there.

Thus $f$ satisfies the conditions of the Inverse Function Rule.

Hence $f^{-1} = \sinh^{-1}$ is differentiable on $\mathbb{R}$, and if $y = f(x) = \sinh x$, then

$$(f^{-1})'(y) = \frac{1}{f'(x)} = \frac{1}{\cosh x}.$$

Since $\cosh x > 0$ on $\mathbb{R}$ and $\cosh^2 x = 1 + \sinh^2 x$, it follows that

$$\cosh x = \sqrt{1 + \sinh^2 x} = \sqrt{1 + y^2},$$

so

$$(f^{-1})'(y) = \frac{1}{\sqrt{1 + y^2}}.$$

Replacing the domain variable $y$ by $x$, we obtain

$$(\sinh^{-1})'(x) = \frac{1}{\sqrt{1 + x^2}} \quad (x \in \mathbb{R}).$$

**2.7** (a) If $x_1 < x_2$, then $x_1^5 < x_2^5$, so $f(x_1) < f(x_2)$. Thus $f$ is strictly increasing and continuous on $\mathbb{R}$, and $f(\mathbb{R}) = \mathbb{R}$. Hence $f$ has a continuous inverse function $f^{-1}$ with domain $\mathbb{R}$, by the Inverse Function Rule for continuity.

(b) We have

$$f'(x) = 5x^4 + 1 \neq 0, \quad \text{for } x \in \mathbb{R}.$$

Thus $f$ satisfies the conditions of the Inverse Function Rule (for differentiability).

Now, $f(0) = -1$, $f(1) = 1$ and $f(-1) = -3$. Hence, by the Inverse Function Rule,

$$(f^{-1})'(-1) = \frac{1}{f'(0)} = 1,$$

$$(f^{-1})'(1) = \frac{1}{f'(1)} = \tfrac{1}{6},$$

$$(f^{-1})'(-3) = \frac{1}{f'(-1)} = \tfrac{1}{6}.$$

**2.8** By definition,

$$f(x) = x^x = \exp(x \log_e x) \quad (x \in \mathbb{R}^+).$$

The functions $x \longmapsto x$ and $x \longmapsto \log_e x$ are differentiable on $\mathbb{R}^+$, and exp is differentiable on $\mathbb{R}$. It follows by the Product Rule and the Composition Rule that $f$ is differentiable on $\mathbb{R}^+$, and that

$$\begin{aligned} f'(x) &= \exp(x \log_e x)(\log_e x + x \times (1/x)) \\ &= x^x(\log_e x + 1) \quad (x \in \mathbb{R}^+). \end{aligned}$$

**2.9** The functions $x \longmapsto 1 + x$ and $x \longmapsto x^2$ are differentiable on $\mathbb{R}$, with derivatives $x \longmapsto 1$ and $x \longmapsto 2x$, respectively.

Since $\log_e$ is differentiable on $\mathbb{R}^+$ and $1 + x$ lies in $\mathbb{R}^+$ whenever $x \in (-1, \infty)$, the function $x \longmapsto \log_e(1 + x)$ is differentiable on $(-1, \infty)$, with derivative $x \longmapsto 1/(1 + x)$, by the Composition Rule.

Since exp is differentiable on $\mathbb{R}$, the function $x \longmapsto e^{x^2}$ is differentiable on $\mathbb{R}$, with derivative $x \longmapsto 2xe^{x^2}$, by the Composition Rule.

It follows by the Sum Rule that $f$ is differentiable on $(-1, \infty)$, with derivative

$$f'(x) = \frac{1}{x+1} + 2xe^{x^2}.$$

**2.10** (a) $$f'(x) = \frac{(x-1)2x - (x^2+1)1}{(x-1)^2} = \frac{x^2 - 2x - 1}{(x-1)^2} \quad (x \in (1, \infty))$$

(b) $$f'(x) = \frac{1}{\sin x}\cos x = \cot x \quad (x \in (0, \pi))$$

(c) $$f'(x) = \frac{1}{\sec x + \tan x}(\sec x \tan x + \sec^2 x) = \sec x \quad (x \in (-\tfrac{1}{2}\pi, \tfrac{1}{2}\pi))$$

(d) $f(x) = \coth x = \cosh x / \sinh x$, so

$$f'(x) = \frac{\sinh^2 x - \cosh^2 x}{\sinh^2 x} = \frac{-1}{\sinh^2 x} = -\operatorname{cosech}^2 x \quad (x \in \mathbb{R} - \{0\}).$$

**2.11** The function

$$f(x) = \tanh x \quad (x \in \mathbb{R})$$

is continuous and strictly increasing on $\mathbb{R}$, and $f(\mathbb{R}) = (-1, 1)$.

Also, $f$ is differentiable on $\mathbb{R}$, and

$$f'(x) = \operatorname{sech}^2 x \neq 0, \quad \text{for } x \in \mathbb{R}.$$

Thus $f$ satisfies the conditions of the Inverse Function Rule, so $f^{-1}$ exists and is differentiable on $(-1, 1)$.

If $y = f(x) = \tanh x$, then

$$(f^{-1})'(y) = \frac{1}{f'(x)} = \frac{1}{\operatorname{sech}^2 x}.$$

Now, $\cosh^2 x = 1 + \sinh^2 x$, so $1 = \operatorname{sech}^2 x + \tanh^2 x$, and hence

$$(f^{-1})'(y) = \frac{1}{1 - \tanh^2 x} = \frac{1}{1 - y^2}.$$

Replacing the domain variable $y$ by $x$, we obtain

$$(\tanh^{-1})'(x) = \frac{1}{1 - x^2} \quad (x \in (-1, 1)).$$

**2.12** Since both of the functions

$$x \longmapsto \tan x \quad \text{and} \quad x \longmapsto 3x$$

are continuous and strictly increasing on $(-\tfrac{1}{2}\pi, \tfrac{1}{2}\pi)$, so is their sum $f$, and $f((-\tfrac{1}{2}\pi, \tfrac{1}{2}\pi)) = \mathbb{R}$.

Also, $f$ is differentiable on $(-\tfrac{1}{2}\pi, \tfrac{1}{2}\pi)$, and

$$f'(x) = \sec^2 x + 3 \neq 0, \quad \text{for } x \in (-\tfrac{1}{2}\pi, \tfrac{1}{2}\pi).$$

Thus $f$ satisfies the conditions of the Inverse Function Rule, so $f^{-1}$ exists and is differentiable on $\mathbb{R}$.

Now, $f(0) = 0$. Hence, by the Inverse Function Rule,

$$(f^{-1})'(0) = \frac{1}{f'(0)} = \frac{1}{\sec^2 0 + 3} = \tfrac{1}{4}.$$

**3.1** Since the functions sin and cos are continuous and differentiable on $\mathbb{R}$, so also is $f$, by the Combination Rules.

Now,

$$f'(x) = 2\sin x \cos x - \sin x = \sin x(2\cos x - 1);$$

thus $f'$ vanishes on $(0, \tfrac{1}{2}\pi)$ when $\cos x = \tfrac{1}{2}$, that is, for $x = \tfrac{1}{3}\pi$.

Since $f(0) = 1$, $f(\tfrac{1}{2}\pi) = 1$ and

$$f(\tfrac{1}{3}\pi) = (\sqrt{3}/2)^2 + \tfrac{1}{2} = \tfrac{3}{4} + \tfrac{1}{2} = \tfrac{5}{4},$$

it follows that on $[0, \tfrac{1}{2}\pi]$:

the minimum of $f$ is 1 (occurring at $x = 0$ and $\tfrac{1}{2}\pi$);

the maximum of $f$ is $\tfrac{5}{4}$ (occurring at $x = \tfrac{1}{3}\pi$).

**3.2** Since $f$ is a polynomial function, $f$ is continuous on $[1, 3]$ and differentiable on $(1, 3)$. Also, $f(1) = 2$ and $f(3) = 2$, so $f(1) = f(3)$.

Thus $f$ satisfies the conditions of Rolle's Theorem on $[1, 3]$, so there exists $c$ in $(1, 3)$ such that $f'(c) = 0$.

(Since

$$f'(x) = 4x^3 - 12x^2 + 6x = 2x(2x^2 - 6x + 3),$$

and $2x^2 - 6x + 3 = 0$ for $x = \tfrac{1}{2}(3 \pm \sqrt{3})$, we have $c = \tfrac{1}{2}(3 + \sqrt{3}) \simeq 2.37$.)

**3.3** **(a)** No: $f$ is not defined at $\frac{1}{2}\pi$.

**(b)** No: $f$ is not differentiable at 1.

**(c)** Yes: all the conditions are satisfied.

**(d)** No: $f(0) \neq f(\frac{1}{2}\pi)$.

**3.4** **(a)** 0, occurring at 0;
1, occurring at all points in $(1, 2)$.

(Note that local minima do not occur at $-2$ and 2 because no open interval containing either $-2$ or 2 lies in the domain of $f$.)

**(b)** 0, occurring at $-2$ and 0.

(Note that a function cannot have more than one minimum, but the minimum may occur at more than one point.)

**(c)** 2, occurring at $-1$;
1, occurring at all points in $[1, 2)$.

**(d)** 2, occurring at $-1$.

**3.5** Since $f$ is a polynomial function, $f$ is continuous on $[1, 2]$ and differentiable on $(1, 2)$. Also, $f(1) = -3$ and $f(2) = -3$, so $f(1) = f(2)$.

Thus $f$ satisfies the conditions of Rolle's Theorem on $[1, 2]$, so there exists a point $c \in (1, 2)$ such that $f'(c) = 0$.

**3.6** We can assume that

$$x_1 < x_2 < \cdots < x_{n-1} < x_n.$$

Since $p$ is a polynomial function, $p$ is continuous on each closed interval $[x_i, x_{i+1}]$ and differentiable on each $(x_i, x_{i+1})$, for $i = 1, 2, \ldots, n-1$. Also, $p(x_i) = 0 = p(x_{i+1})$.

Thus $p$ satisfies the conditions of Rolle's Theorem on each interval $[x_i, x_{i+1}]$.

It follows by Rolle's Theorem that $p'$ vanishes at some point in each interval $(x_i, x_{i+1})$. Since there are $n-1$ such intervals, $p'$ must have at least $n-1$ zeros.

**3.7** We suppose that $f$ has two zeros, $a$ and $b$ in $[0, 1]$, with $a < b$, and deduce a contradiction.

Since $f$ is a polynomial function, $f$ is continuous on $[a, b]$ and differentiable on $(a, b)$. Also, we are assuming that $f(a) = f(b) = 0$.

Thus $f$ satisfies the conditions of Rolle's Theorem on $[a, b]$, so there exists a point $c \in (a, b)$ such that $f'(c) = 0$.

Now,

$$f'(c) = 3c^2 - 3c = 3c(c-1).$$

Since $c \in (0, 1)$, it follows that $3c(c-1)$ cannot be zero. This is the required contradiction.

**4.1** The function $f(x) = xe^x$ is continuous on $[0, 2]$ and differentiable on $(0, 2)$. Thus $f$ satisfies the conditions of the Mean Value Theorem on $[0, 2]$.

Now,

$$\frac{f(2) - f(0)}{2 - 0} = \frac{2e^2 - 0}{2} = e^2.$$

Thus, by the Mean Value Theorem, there exists a point $c$ in $(0, 2)$ such that $f'(c) = e^2$.

**4.2** **(a)** We have $f'(x) = 4x^{1/3} - 4 = 4(x^{1/3} - 1)$. Thus $f'(x) > 0$ for $x \in (1, \infty)$, so $f$ is strictly increasing on $[1, \infty)$, by the Increasing–Decreasing Theorem.

**(b)** We have $f'(x) = 1 - 1/x = (x-1)/x$. Thus $f'(x) < 0$ for $x \in (0, 1)$, so $f$ is strictly decreasing on $(0, 1]$, by the Increasing–Decreasing Theorem.

**4.3** **(a)** We have

$$f'(x) = 3x^2 - 6x = 3x(x-2).$$

Thus $f'(x) = 0$ for $x = 0$ and 2, so $c = 0, 2$.

**(b)** We have

$$f''(x) = 6x - 6,$$

so

$$f''(0) = -6 < 0 \quad \text{and} \quad f''(2) = 6 > 0.$$

Also, $f(0) = 1$ and $f(2) = -3$.

Thus, by the Second Derivative Test, $f$ has a local maximum 1 that occurs at 0, and a local minimum $-3$ that occurs at 2.

**4.4** In each case we use Strategy 4.1.

**(a)** 1. Let

$$f(x) = x - \sin x \quad (x \in [0, \infty)).$$

Then $f$ is continuous on $[0, \infty)$ and differentiable on $(0, \infty)$.

2. We have

$$f'(x) = 1 - \cos x \geq 0, \quad \text{for } x \in (0, \infty),$$

and $f(0) = 0$.

Thus $f$ is increasing on $(0, \infty)$, by the Increasing–Decreasing Theorem, so

$$f(x) \geq f(0) = 0, \quad \text{for } x \in [0, \infty).$$

Hence

$$\sin x \leq x, \quad \text{for } x \in [0, \infty).$$

**(b)** 1. Let

$$f(x) = \tfrac{2}{3}x + \tfrac{1}{3} - x^{2/3} \quad (x \in [0, 1]).$$

Then $f$ is continuous on $[0, 1]$ and differentiable on $(0, 1)$.

2. We have

$$f'(x) = \tfrac{2}{3} - \tfrac{2}{3}x^{-1/3}$$
$$= \tfrac{2}{3}(1 - x^{-1/3}) < 0, \quad \text{for } x \in (0,1),$$

and $f(1) = \frac{2}{3} + \frac{1}{3} - 1 = 0$.

Thus $f$ is decreasing on $(0,1)$, by the Increasing–Decreasing Theorem, so

$$f(x) \geq f(1) = 0, \quad \text{for } x \in [0,1].$$

Hence

$$\tfrac{2}{3}x + \tfrac{1}{3} \geq x^{2/3}, \quad \text{for } x \in [0,1].$$

**4.5** Since $f(x) = x^3 + 2x^2 + x$ is a polynomial function, $f$ is continuous on $[0,1]$ and differentiable on $(0,1)$. Thus $f$ satisfies the conditions of the Mean Value Theorem on $[0,1]$. Hence there is a point $c$ in $(0,1)$ such that

$$f'(c) = \frac{f(1) - f(0)}{1 - 0} = \frac{4 - 0}{1} = 4, \qquad \text{(S.3)}$$

as required.

(Since

$$f'(x) = 3x^2 + 4x + 1,$$

equation (S.3) can be written as

$$f'(c) = 3c^2 + 4c + 1 = 4.$$

Thus $c = \frac{1}{3}(-2 \pm \sqrt{13})$, so $c = \frac{1}{3}(\sqrt{13} - 2) \simeq 0.54$.)

**4.6** The function $f$ satisfies the conditions of the Mean Value Theorem on $[0,2]$. Hence there exists a point $c \in (0,2)$ such that

$$\frac{f(2) - f(0)}{2 - 0} = f'(c).$$

Since $|f'(c)| \leq 3$ and $f(0) = 10$, we have

$$|f(2) - 10| = 2|f'(c)| \leq 6.$$

Hence

$$-6 \leq f(2) - 10 \leq 6, \quad \text{so} \quad 4 \leq f(2) \leq 16,$$

as required.

**4.7** We have

$$f'(x) = 3x^2 - 4x + 1$$
$$= (3x - 1)(x - 1).$$

Thus $f'(x) = 0$ for $x = \frac{1}{3}$ and 1, so $c = \frac{1}{3}, 1$.

Now,

$$f''(x) = 6x - 4,$$

so

$$f''(\tfrac{1}{3}) = -2 < 0 \quad \text{and} \quad f''(1) = 2 > 0.$$

Also, $f(\frac{1}{3}) = \frac{4}{27}$ and $f(1) = 0$.

Thus, by the Second Derivative Test, $f$ has a local maximum $\frac{4}{27}$ at $\frac{1}{3}$ and a local minimum 0 at 1.

**4.8** In each case we use Strategy 4.1.

**(a)** 1. Let

$$f(x) = \log_e x - \left(1 - \frac{1}{x}\right) \quad (x \in [1,\infty)).$$

Then $f$ is continuous on $[1,\infty)$ and differentiable on $(1,\infty)$.

2. We have

$$f'(x) = \frac{1}{x} - \frac{1}{x^2} = \frac{x-1}{x^2} \geq 0, \quad \text{for } x \in (1,\infty),$$

and $f(1) = \log_e 1 - 0 = 0$.

Thus $f$ is increasing on $(1,\infty)$, by the Increasing–Decreasing Theorem, so

$$f(x) \geq f(1) = 0, \quad \text{for } x \in [1,\infty).$$

Hence

$$\log_e x \geq 1 - \frac{1}{x}, \quad \text{for } x \in [1,\infty).$$

**(b)** 1. Let

$$f(x) = x + 3 - 4x^{1/4} \quad (x \in [0,1]).$$

Then $f$ is continuous on $[0,1]$ and differentiable on $(0,1)$.

2. We have

$$f'(x) = 1 - x^{-3/4} \leq 0, \quad \text{for } x \in (0,1),$$

and $f(1) = 1 + 3 - 4 = 0$.

Thus $f$ is decreasing on $(0,1)$, by the Increasing–Decreasing Theorem, so

$$f(x) \geq f(1) = 0, \quad \text{for } x \in [0,1].$$

Hence

$$x + 3 \geq 4x^{1/4}, \quad \text{for } x \in [0,1].$$

**(c)** 1. Let

$$f(x) = \log_e(1+x) - (x - \tfrac{1}{2}x^2) \quad (x \in [0,\infty)).$$

Then $f$ is continuous on $[0,\infty)$ and differentiable on $(0,\infty)$.

2. We have

$$f'(x) = \frac{1}{1+x} - (1-x)$$
$$= \frac{1 - (1 - x^2)}{1+x}$$
$$= \frac{x^2}{1+x} > 0, \quad \text{for } x \in (0,\infty),$$

and $f(0) = \log_e 1 - 0 = 0$.

It follows that $f$ is *strictly* increasing on $[0,\infty)$, so

$$f(x) > f(0) = 0, \quad \text{for } x \in (0,\infty).$$

Hence

$$\log_e(1+x) > x - \tfrac{1}{2}x^2, \quad \text{for } x \in (0,\infty).$$

**5.1** Let

$$g(t) = t - \sin t \quad \text{and} \quad f(t) = 1 - \cos t \quad (t \in \mathbb{R}).$$

Then $f$ and $g$ are differentiable on $\mathbb{R}$, and

$$g'(t) = 1 - \cos t \quad \text{and} \quad f'(t) = \sin t \quad (t \in \mathbb{R}).$$

In particular,

$$g'(\tfrac{1}{3}\pi) = 1 - \tfrac{1}{2} = \tfrac{1}{2} \quad \text{and} \quad f'(\tfrac{1}{3}\pi) = \tfrac{1}{2}\sqrt{3}.$$

Hence, by Theorem 5.1, the slope of the tangent at the point with parameter $t = \frac{1}{3}\pi$ is

$$\frac{f'(\frac{1}{3}\pi)}{g'(\frac{1}{3}\pi)} = \frac{\sqrt{3}/2}{1/2} = \sqrt{3}.$$

**5.2** (a) Let

$$f(x) = \sinh 2x \quad \text{and} \quad g(x) = \sin 3x \quad (x \in \mathbb{R}).$$

Then $f$ and $g$ are differentiable on $\mathbb{R}$, and

$$f(0) = g(0) = 0.$$

Thus $f$ and $g$ satisfy the conditions of l'Hôpital's Rule at 0.

Now,

$$f'(x) = 2\cosh 2x \quad \text{and} \quad g'(x) = 3\cos 3x.$$

Since $g'(0) = 3 \neq 0$, we deduce, by the Combination Rules for continuous functions, that

$$\lim_{x\to 0} \frac{f'(x)}{g'(x)} = \frac{f'(0)}{g'(0)} = \tfrac{2}{3}.$$

Thus, by l'Hôpital's Rule, the required limit exists and equals $\frac{2}{3}$.

(b) Let

$$f(x) = (1+x)^{1/5} - (1-x)^{1/5}$$

and

$$g(x) = (1+2x)^{2/5} - (1-2x)^{2/5},$$

where $x \in (-\frac{1}{2}, \frac{1}{2})$, say. (This interval contains 0 and lies in the domains of both $f$ and $g$.)

Then $f$ and $g$ are differentiable on $(-\frac{1}{2}, \frac{1}{2})$, and

$$f(0) = g(0) = 0.$$

Thus $f$ and $g$ satisfy the conditions of l'Hôpital's Rule at 0.

Now,

$$f'(x) = \tfrac{1}{5}(1+x)^{-4/5} + \tfrac{1}{5}(1-x)^{-4/5}$$

and

$$g'(x) = \tfrac{4}{5}(1+2x)^{-3/5} + \tfrac{4}{5}(1-2x)^{-3/5}.$$

Since $g'(0) = \frac{4}{5} + \frac{4}{5} \neq 0$, we deduce, by the Combination Rules for continuous functions, that

$$\lim_{x\to 0} \frac{f'(x)}{g(x)} = \frac{f'(0)}{g'(0)} = \frac{\frac{1}{5}+\frac{1}{5}}{\frac{4}{5}+\frac{4}{5}} = \tfrac{1}{4}.$$

Thus, by l'Hôpital's Rule, the required limit exists and equals $\frac{1}{4}$.

(c) Let

$$f(x) = \sin(x^2) \quad \text{and} \quad g(x) = 1 - \cos 4x \quad (x \in \mathbb{R}).$$

Then $f$ and $g$ are differentiable on $\mathbb{R}$, and

$$f(0) = g(0) = 0.$$

Thus $f$ and $g$ satisfy the conditions of l'Hôpital's Rule at 0.

Now,

$$f'(x) = 2x\cos(x^2) \quad \text{and} \quad g'(x) = 4\sin 4x.$$

Thus, by l'Hôpital's Rule, the required limit exists and equals

$$\lim_{x\to 0} \frac{f'(x)}{g'(x)}, \qquad \text{(S.4)}$$

provided that limit (S.4) exists.

Here $f'(0) = g'(0) = 0$, so we cannot apply l'Hôpital's Rule at this stage. However, $f'$ and $g'$ are differentiable on $\mathbb{R}$, so $f'$ and $g'$ satisfy the conditions of l'Hôpital's Rule at 0.

Now,

$$f''(x) = -(2x)^2\sin(x^2) + 2\cos(x^2)$$

and

$$g''(x) = 16\cos 4x.$$

Thus, by l'Hôpital's Rule, the required limit exists and equals

$$\lim_{x\to 0} \frac{f''(x)}{g''(x)}, \qquad \text{(S.5)}$$

provided that limit (S.5) exists.

Since $g''(0) = 16 \neq 0$, we deduce, by the Combination Rules for continuous functions, that

$$\lim_{x\to 0} \frac{f''(x)}{g''(x)} = \frac{f''(0)}{g''(0)} = \frac{2}{16} = \tfrac{1}{8}.$$

Hence limit (S.5) exists and equals $\frac{1}{8}$.

Thus limit (S.4) exists and equals $\frac{1}{8}$, so the required limit also exists and equals $\frac{1}{8}$.

(d) Let

$$f(x) = \sin x - x\cos x \quad \text{and} \quad g(x) = x^3 \quad (x \in \mathbb{R}).$$

Then $f$ and $g$ are differentiable on $\mathbb{R}$, and $f(0) = g(0) = 0$. Thus $f$ and $g$ satisfy the conditions of l'Hôpital's Rule at 0.

Now,

$$f'(x) = x\sin x \quad \text{and} \quad g'(x) = 3x^2.$$

Thus, by l'Hôpital's Rule, the required limit exists and equals

$$\lim_{x\to 0} \frac{f'(x)}{g'(x)},$$

provided that this limit exists. But

$$\lim_{x\to 0} \frac{f'(x)}{g'(x)} = \lim_{x\to 0} \frac{x\sin x}{3x^2} = \frac{1}{3}\lim_{x\to 0} \frac{\sin x}{x} = \frac{1}{3}.$$

Hence, the required limit exists and equals $\frac{1}{3}$.

**5.3** (a) Let

$$g(t) = t^2 - 1 \quad \text{and} \quad f(t) = t^3 - t \quad (t \in \mathbb{R}).$$

Then $g$ and $f$ are differentiable, and

$$g'(t) = 2t \quad \text{and} \quad f'(t) = 3t^2 - 1 \quad (t \in \mathbb{R}).$$

In particular,

$$g'(-1) = -2 \quad \text{and} \quad f'(-1) = 3 - 1 = 2.$$

Hence, by Theorem 5.1, the slope of the tangent to the curve at the point with parameter $t = -1$ is

$$\frac{f'(-1)}{g'(-1)} = \frac{2}{-2} = -1.$$

(b) Let

$$g(t) = \sin t \quad \text{and} \quad f(t) = e^t \quad (t \in \mathbb{R}).$$

Then $g$ and $f$ are differentiable, and

$$g'(t) = \cos t \quad \text{and} \quad f'(t) = e^t \quad (t \in \mathbb{R}).$$

In particular,

$$g'(0) = \cos 0 = 1 \quad \text{and} \quad f'(0) = e^0 = 1.$$

Hence, by Theorem 5.1, the slope of the tangent to the curve at the point with parameter $t = 0$ is

$$\frac{f'(0)}{g'(0)} = \frac{1}{1} = 1.$$

**5.4** **(a)** Let

$$f(x) = 1 - \cos x \quad \text{and} \quad g(x) = x^2 \quad (x \in \mathbb{R}).$$

Then $f$ and $g$ are differentiable, and

$$f(0) = g(0) = 0.$$

Thus $f$ and $g$ satisfy the conditions of l'Hôpital's Rule at 0.

Now,

$$f'(x) = \sin x \quad \text{and} \quad g'(x) = 2x.$$

Thus, by l'Hôpital's Rule, the required limit exists and equals

$$\lim_{x\to 0} \frac{f'(x)}{g'(x)} = \lim_{x\to 0} \frac{\sin x}{2x} = \frac{1}{2} \lim_{x\to 0} \frac{\sin x}{x} = \tfrac{1}{2}.$$

**(b)** Let

$$f(x) = (5x+3)^{1/3} - (x+3)^{1/2} \quad \text{and} \quad g(x) = x - 1,$$

where $x \in (0, 2)$, say.

Then $f$ and $g$ are differentiable on $(0, 2)$, and

$$f(1) = g(1) = 0.$$

Thus $f$ and $g$ satisfy the conditions of l'Hôpital's Rule at 1.

Now,

$$f'(x) = \tfrac{5}{3}(5x+3)^{-2/3} - \tfrac{1}{2}(x+3)^{-1/2}$$

and

$$g'(x) = 1.$$

Since $g'(1) = 1 \neq 0$, we deduce, by the Combination Rules for continuous functions, that

$$\lim_{x\to 1} \frac{f'(x)}{g'(x)} = \frac{f'(1)}{g'(1)} = \frac{\frac{5}{3} \times \frac{1}{4} - \frac{1}{2} \times \frac{1}{2}}{1} = \tfrac{1}{6}.$$

Thus, by l'Hôpital's Rule, the required limit exists and equals $\frac{1}{6}$.

**(c)** Let

$$f(x) = \sinh x - x \quad \text{and} \quad g(x) = \sin(x^2) \quad (x \in \mathbb{R}).$$

Then $f$ and $g$ are differentiable on $\mathbb{R}$, and

$$f(0) = g(0) = 0.$$

Thus $f$ and $g$ satisfy the conditions of l'Hôpital's Rule at 0.

Now,

$$f'(x) = \cosh x - 1 \quad \text{and} \quad g'(x) = 2x\cos(x^2).$$

Thus, by l'Hôpital's Rule, the required limit exists and equals

$$\lim_{x\to 0} \frac{f'(x)}{g'(x)} = \lim_{x\to 0} \frac{\cosh x - 1}{2x\cos(x^2)}, \qquad \text{(S.6)}$$

provided that limit (S.6) exists.

Here, both $f'$ and $g'$ are differentiable on $\mathbb{R}$, and

$$f'(0) = g'(0) = 0.$$

Thus $f'$ and $g'$ satisfy the conditions of l'Hôpital's Rule at 0.

Now,

$$f''(x) = \sinh x$$

and

$$g''(x) = 2\cos(x^2) - 4x^2 \sin(x^2) \quad (x \in \mathbb{R}).$$

Thus, by l'Hôpital's Rule, the required limit exists and equals

$$\lim_{x\to 0} \frac{f''(x)}{g''(x)} = \lim_{x\to 0} \frac{\sinh x}{2\cos(x^2) - 4x^2\sin(x^2)}, \qquad \text{(S.7)}$$

provided that limit (S.7) exists.

Since $g''(0) = 2 \neq 0$, we deduce, by the Combination Rules for continuous functions, that

$$\lim_{x\to 0} \frac{f''(x)}{g''(x)} = \frac{f''(0)}{g''(0)} = \frac{0}{2} = 0.$$

Hence limit (S.7) exists and equals 0.

It follows that limit (S.6) exists and equals 0, so the required limit also exists and equals 0.

**(d)** Let

$$f(x) = \sinh(x + \sin x) \quad \text{and} \quad g(x) = \sin x \quad (x \in \mathbb{R}).$$

Then $f$ and $g$ are differentiable on $\mathbb{R}$, and

$$f(0) = g(0) = 0.$$

Thus $f$ and $g$ satisfy the conditions of l'Hôpital's Rule at 0.

Now

$$f'(x) = (1 + \cos x)\cosh(x + \sin x)$$

and

$$g'(x) = \cos x.$$

Since $g'(0) = 1 \neq 0$, we deduce, by the Combination Rules for continuous functions, that

$$\lim_{x\to 0} \frac{f'(x)}{g'(x)} = \frac{f'(0)}{g'(0)} = \frac{2\cosh 0}{1} = 2.$$

Thus, by l'Hôpital's Rule, the required limit exists and equals 2.

# Standard derivatives

| $f(x)$ | $f'(x)$ | Domain |
|---|---|---|
| $k$ | $0$ | $\mathbb{R}$ |
| $x$ | $1$ | $\mathbb{R}$ |
| $x^n,\ n \in \mathbb{Z} - \{0\}$ | $nx^{n-1}$ | $\mathbb{R}$ or $\mathbb{R} - \{0\}$ |
| $x^\alpha,\ \alpha \in \mathbb{R}$ | $\alpha x^{\alpha-1}$ | $\mathbb{R}^+$ |
| $a^x,\ a > 0$ | $a^x \log_e a$ | $\mathbb{R}$ |
| $\sin x$ | $\cos x$ | $\mathbb{R}$ |
| $\cos x$ | $-\sin x$ | $\mathbb{R}$ |
| $\tan x$ | $\sec^2 x$ | $\mathbb{R} - \{(n + \frac{1}{2})\pi : n \in \mathbb{Z}\}$ |
| $\operatorname{cosec} x$ | $-\operatorname{cosec} x \cot x$ | $\mathbb{R} - \{n\pi : n \in \mathbb{Z}\}$ |
| $\sec x$ | $\sec x \tan x$ | $\mathbb{R} - \{(n + \frac{1}{2})\pi : n \in \mathbb{Z}\}$ |
| $\cot x$ | $-\operatorname{cosec}^2 x$ | $\mathbb{R} - \{n\pi : n \in \mathbb{Z}\}$ |
| $\sin^{-1} x$ | $1/\sqrt{1 - x^2}$ | $(-1, 1)$ |
| $\cos^{-1} x$ | $-1/\sqrt{1 - x^2}$ | $(-1, 1)$ |
| $\tan^{-1} x$ | $1/(1 + x^2)$ | $\mathbb{R}$ |
| $e^x$ | $e^x$ | $\mathbb{R}$ |
| $\log_e x$ | $1/x$ | $\mathbb{R}^+$ |
| $\sinh x$ | $\cosh x$ | $\mathbb{R}$ |
| $\cosh x$ | $\sinh x$ | $\mathbb{R}$ |
| $\tanh x$ | $\operatorname{sech}^2 x$ | $\mathbb{R}$ |
| $\sinh^{-1} x$ | $1/\sqrt{1 + x^2}$ | $\mathbb{R}$ |
| $\cosh^{-1} x$ | $1/\sqrt{x^2 - 1}$ | $(1, \infty)$ |
| $\tanh^{-1} x$ | $1/(1 - x^2)$ | $(-1, 1)$ |

# Index

The Open University

M208 Pure

# GTB1

## Conjugacy

This publication forms part of an Open University course. Details of this and other Open University courses can be obtained from the Student Registration and Enquiry Service, The Open University, PO Box 197, Milton Keynes, MK7 6BJ, United Kingdom: tel. +44 (0)870 300 6090, e-mail general-enquiries@open.ac.uk

Alternatively, you may visit the Open University website at http://www.open.ac.uk where you can learn more about the wide range of courses and packs offered at all levels by The Open University.

To purchase a selection of Open University course materials, visit http://www.ouw.co.uk, or contact Open University Worldwide, Michael Young Building, Walton Hall, Milton Keynes, MK7 6AA, United Kingdom, for a brochure: tel. +44 (0)1908 858793, fax +44 (0)1908 858787, e-mail ouw-customer-services@open.ac.uk

The Open University, Walton Hall, Milton Keynes, MK7 6AA.

First published 2006. Reprinted with amendments 2007.



Edited, designed and typeset by The Open University, using the Open University TEX System.

Printed and bound in the United Kingdom by Hobbs the Printers Limited, Brunel Road, Totton, Hampshire SO40 3WX.

ISBN 0 7492 0219 X

1.2

# Contents

# Introduction to Group Theory Block B

In Group Theory Block A you met many of the basic ideas of group theory. In this block we build on the theory covered there, to give you a taste of more advanced group theory. You will see deeper examples of how group theory can make us aware of links and similarities in topics that seem unrelated, giving us a greater understanding of these topics. You will also see examples of how group theory can simplify, and hence make it possible to solve, problems that at first sight appear prohibitively complicated.

# Introduction

This unit is mainly concerned with *conjugacy*. In Unit GTA3 we investigated conjugacy in the symmetric group $S_n$ and discovered that *two permutations are conjugate in $S_n$* if and only if they have the *same cycle structure*. In this unit we generalise the definition of conjugacy so that it applies to any group. We explore general properties of conjugacy and *conjugate subgroups*. With these new ideas in mind, we revisit normal subgroups, introduced in Unit GTA4.

In Section 1 we revise some of the basic ideas from Group Theory Block A that you will need in Group Theory Block B.

In Section 2 we review conjugacy in $S_n$. We then generalise the definition of conjugate elements in $S_n$ and investigate conjugacy in some groups of small order. We discover that the relation *is conjugate to* is an equivalence relation on the set of elements of a group and so partitions a group into *conjugacy classes*.

In Section 3 we explore connections between normal subgroups and conjugacy. We begin by reviewing the definition of normality from Group Theory Block A. We then develop alternative ways of characterising normality and alternative strategies for testing whether subgroups are normal.

In Section 4 we concentrate on geometric aspects of conjugacy. We relate two partitions of the symmetry group of a figure: the partition into conjugacy classes and the natural partition of the group into elements of the same 'geometric type'.

In Section 5 we introduce a new family of groups: the *matrix groups*. We begin by investigating subgroups of the group of invertible $2 \times 2$ matrices with real entries. We then use the ideas about conjugacy that we have developed to look at normality of subgroups of matrix groups.

## Study guide

Section 1 is a revision section: it contains the basic ideas from the first three units of Group Theory Block A. It is important that you have a good working knowledge of this material before you embark on Group Theory Block B. You should be able to read through most of it fairly quickly; you need to study in depth only those parts which seem unfamiliar.

Subsections 2.1, 3.1 and 5.1 also contain only revision material, and the same comments apply to these subsections.

The ideas of Section 2 are central to this unit, so a good understanding of them is essential before you move on to later sections. This section contains a number of short proofs using standard techniques, which you should read.

Section 3 is the most important section of the unit. It contains many exercises illustrating the general theory, and we recommend that you work through them all. The proof that is given at the end of the section is quite technical; you may wish to omit it and come back to it when you have read the rest of the unit, or omit it altogether if you are short of time.

Section 4 is the video section. The video programme can be watched at any time after Section 2.

Section 5 is the audio section, which can be studied at any time after Section 3. Subsection 5.3 is probably the hardest in the unit.

# 1 Groups (revision)

In this section we revise some work from the first three units of Group Theory Block A that will be needed in Block B. The section contains no new material. Each topic is covered only briefly and justification of statements is often not included; if you find that you need more detail on a particular topic, then you should read it again in Group Theory Block A.

Some work from Unit GTA4 is revised later in this unit.

After working through this section, you should be able to:

(a) explain the terms *group*, *Abelian group*, *finite group*, *group of order n*, *subgroup*, *order of an element* and *cyclic group*;

(b) work with the groups $S_n$ and $A_n$, and know how to find composites, inverses and parities of permutations in cycle form;

(c) work with the groups $S(\triangle)$, $S(\square)$, $\mathbb{Z}_n$ and $\mathbb{Z}_p^*$.

## 1.1 Definition of a group

We begin by recalling the definition of a *group*.

**Definition** Let $G$ be a set and $\circ$ be a binary operation defined on $G$. Then $(G, \circ)$ is a **group** if the following four axioms hold.

G1 CLOSURE — For all $g_1, g_2 \in G$,

$$g_1 \circ g_2 \in G.$$

G2 IDENTITY — There exists an identity element $e \in G$ such that, for all $g \in G$,

$$g \circ e = g = e \circ g.$$

G3 INVERSES — For each $g \in G$, there exists an inverse element $g^{-1} \in G$ such that

$$g \circ g^{-1} = e = g^{-1} \circ g.$$

G4 ASSOCIATIVITY — For all $g_1, g_2, g_3 \in G$,

$$g_1 \circ (g_2 \circ g_3) = (g_1 \circ g_2) \circ g_3.$$

In order to specify a group, it is necessary to state both the *set* and the *binary operation*; for example, the group of integers under addition is denoted by $(\mathbb{Z}, +)$. However, when it is clear which binary operation is involved, we often suppress mention of it and refer to the group $G$, rather than the group $(G, \circ)$. In some settings we omit the binary operation in composites also, writing $xy$ instead of $x \circ y$. When we do this, we sometimes say that the elements $x$ and $y$ are 'multiplied' rather than 'composed'.

It follows from the axioms that, in any group, *the identity element is unique* and *each element has a unique inverse*.

In an additive group (one where the operation is some kind of addition), we usually denote the inverse of an element $x$ by $-x$ rather than by $x^{-1}$.

Since the binary operation of a group $(G, \circ)$ is associative, we can write composites of three or more elements without brackets: for example, we can write

$$g_1 \circ g_2 \circ g_3$$

and this can be evaluated as

$$\text{either} \quad g_1 \circ (g_2 \circ g_3) \quad \text{or} \quad (g_1 \circ g_2) \circ g_3;$$

both give the same answer. However, in general, we cannot change the order of the elements in such a composite: for example, $g_1 \circ g_2 \circ g_3$ is not necessarily equal to $g_2 \circ g_1 \circ g_3$.

If a group $(G, \circ)$ has the additional property that, for all $g_1, g_2 \in G$,

$$g_1 \circ g_2 = g_2 \circ g_1$$

(that is, the group operation $\circ$ is *commutative*), then we say that the group is **Abelian**.

A group $(G, \circ)$ is a *finite group* if $G$ is a set with a finite number of elements. If the set $G$ contains $n$ elements, then we say that $G$ is a group of **order** $n$ and we write $|G| = n$. For example, $S(\triangle)$, the group of symmetries of an equilateral triangle, is a group of order 6, so we write $|S(\triangle)| = 6$. A group such as $(\mathbb{Z}, +)$, where the underlying set is infinite, is said to be an *infinite group*.

An important example of a finite group is the group $\mathbb{Z}_n$, where the underlying set is $\{0, 1, 2, \ldots, n-1\}$ and the binary operation is addition modulo $n$, written $+_n$. The identity element is 0. For example, the group table for $\mathbb{Z}_6$ is as follows.

| $+_6$ | 0 | 1 | 2 | 3 | 4 | 5 |
|---|---|---|---|---|---|---|
| 0 | 0 | 1 | 2 | 3 | 4 | 5 |
| 1 | 1 | 2 | 3 | 4 | 5 | 0 |
| 2 | 2 | 3 | 4 | 5 | 0 | 1 |
| 3 | 3 | 4 | 5 | 0 | 1 | 2 |
| 4 | 4 | 5 | 0 | 1 | 2 | 3 |
| 5 | 5 | 0 | 1 | 2 | 3 | 4 |

In a group table, the composite $x \circ y$ is in the row labelled $x$ and the column labelled $y$. For example, in this table the entry in the row labelled 4 and the column labelled 3 is $4 +_6 3 = 1$.

We can find inverse elements from a group table by looking for the location of the identity element. For example, the identity element 0 appears in the row labelled 4 and column labelled 2 (and vice versa) of the group table for $\mathbb{Z}_6$, so 2 and 4 are inverses of each other in $\mathbb{Z}_6$.

In the group $\mathbb{Z}_n$ we usually attach the suffix $n$ to the notation for the inverse of an element, so the inverse of the element $x \in \mathbb{Z}_n$ is denoted by $-_n x$. For example, in $\mathbb{Z}_6$ we have $-_6 2 = 4$.

**Exercise 1.1** In each of the following cases, decide whether the given set and binary operation form a group. In each case, if they do not form a group, then indicate a group axiom that fails to hold; if they do form a group, then construct the group table.

(a) $(\{0, 2, 4, 6\}, \times_8)$ (b) $(\{1, 2, 3, 4\}, \times_5)$

The symbol $\times_n$ denotes multiplication modulo $n$.

For any prime $p$, we denote the set $\mathbb{Z}_p - \{0\} = \{1, 2, \ldots, p-1\}$ by $\mathbb{Z}_p^*$. Exercise 1.1(b) illustrates the fact that, for any prime $p$, $(\mathbb{Z}_p^*, \times_p)$ is a group of order $p - 1$.

The following **Cancellation Laws** are satisfied by any elements $a, b$ and $x$ of any group $(G, \circ)$:

$$\text{if } x \circ a = x \circ b, \quad \text{then} \quad a = b;$$
$$\text{if } a \circ x = b \circ x, \quad \text{then} \quad a = b.$$

## 1.2 Permutations

A **permutation** of the set $S = \{1, 2, \ldots, n\}$ is a one-one function from $S$ onto $S$. In this block we shall write permutations in **cycle form**; that is, as a product of disjoint cycles.

For example, consider the following permutation of $\{1, 2, 3, 4, 5, 6\}$:

$$f = (1\ 5)(2\ 6\ 4)(3).$$

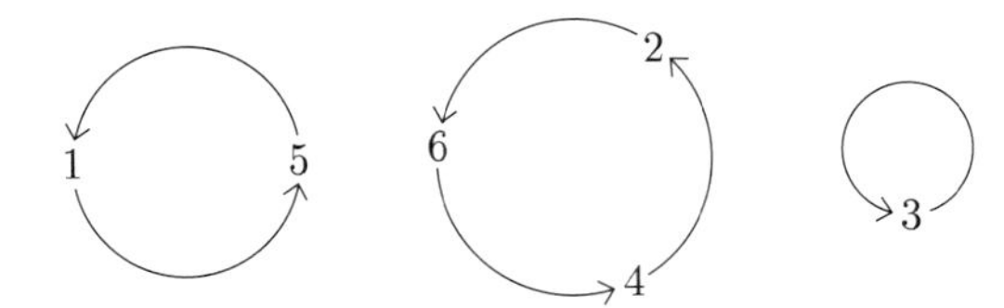


The cycle $(1\ 5)$ indicates that $f$ maps 1 to 5 and 5 to 1. Similarly, the cycle $(2\ 6\ 4)$ indicates that $f$ maps 2 to 6, 6 to 4 and 4 to 2, and the cycle $(3)$ indicates that $f$ fixes 3 (maps 3 to itself). We usually omit 1-cycles (cycles of length 1) from the cycle form of a permutation, so we would write the above permutation as

$$\begin{array}{ccccccc} & 1 & 2 & 3 & 4 & 5 & 6 \\ f & \downarrow & \downarrow & \downarrow & \downarrow & \downarrow & \downarrow \\ & 5 & 6 & 3 & 2 & 1 & 4 \end{array}$$

$$f = (1\ 5)(2\ 6\ 4).$$

The permutation $f$ can also be written as a *two-line symbol*:

$$f = \begin{pmatrix} 1 & 2 & 3 & 4 & 5 & 6 \\ 5 & 6 & 3 & 2 & 1 & 4 \end{pmatrix}.$$

However the cycle form is usually more convenient.

There are other ways to write $f$ in cycle form; for example,

$$f = (6\ 4\ 2)(5\ 1),$$

but we usually write the smallest symbol in each cycle first and arrange the cycles with their smallest symbols in increasing order. (Sometimes, however, it is more convenient to use other cycle forms.)

A method for composing permutations in cycle form is illustrated in the following example. Consider the permutation $g = (1\ 5\ 4\ 3\ 6)$ of $\{1, 2, 3, 4, 5, 6\}$. To find the composite permutation

$$g \circ f = (1\ 5\ 4\ 3\ 6) \circ (1\ 5)(2\ 6\ 4)$$

Note that $f$ fixes 3 and that $g$ fixes 2.

and to write it in cycle form, we begin by considering the symbol 1. The permutation $f$ maps 1 to 5 and then $g$ maps 5 to 4, so the composite $g \circ f$ maps 1 to 4. Thus one cycle of $g \circ f$ begins

Remember that $g \circ f$ means do $f$ then $g$.

$$(1\ 4\ \ldots).$$

The image under $g \circ f$ obtained above was 4, so we now consider this symbol. The permutation $f$ maps 4 to 2 and $g$ fixes 2, so $g \circ f$ maps 4 to 2. Thus the cycle continues

$$(1\ 4\ 2\ \ldots).$$

Continuing in this way, we find that $g \circ f$ maps 2 to 1, so one of the cycles of $g \circ f$ is

$$(1\ 4\ 2).$$

We now consider the smallest symbol whose image under $g \circ f$ we have not yet found, and continue in a similar way. In the end we find that the composite can be written as

$$g \circ f = (1\ 4\ 2)(3\ 6)(5) = (1\ 4\ 2)(3\ 6).$$

$$\begin{array}{ccccccc} & 1 & 2 & 3 & 4 & 5 & 6 \\ f & \downarrow & \downarrow & \downarrow & \downarrow & \downarrow & \downarrow \\ & 5 & 6 & 3 & 2 & 1 & 4 \\ g & \downarrow & \downarrow & \downarrow & \downarrow & \downarrow & \downarrow \\ & 4 & 1 & 6 & 2 & 5 & 3 \end{array}$$

The above method of composing permutations can be extended to composites of three or more permutations.

**Exercise 1.2** Determine the cycle form of each of the following composites of permutations in $S_8$.

(a) $(1\ 2\ 7\ 5)(3\ 8\ 4) \circ (1\ 3\ 6\ 7\ 5)$ (b) $(1\ 3\ 7)(2\ 5\ 4) \circ (2\ 4)(3\ 8)(5\ 6)$

The *inverse* of a permutation in cycle form is found by reversing all the cycles. For example, if $f = (1\ 5)(2\ 6\ 4)$, as above, then

$$f^{-1} = (5\ 1)(4\ 6\ 2).$$

$$\begin{array}{ccccccc} & 1 & 2 & 3 & 4 & 5 & 6 \\ f^{-1} & \uparrow & \uparrow & \uparrow & \uparrow & \uparrow & \uparrow \\ & 5 & 6 & 3 & 2 & 1 & 4 \end{array}$$

Since we usually prefer to write the smallest symbol in each cycle first, we would normally write this as

$$f^{-1} = (1\ 5)(2\ 4\ 6).$$

**Exercise 1.3** Find the inverse of each of the following permutations in $S_8$.

(a) $(1\ 7\ 5\ 2)(3\ 8\ 4)$ (b) $(1\ 4)(2\ 3)(6\ 8)$

The technique of reversing the cycles works only if the permutation is in cycle form. For example, the inverse of the composite permutation $(1\ 2\ 3) \circ (3\ 4)$ is not obtained by reversing the cycles $(1\ 2\ 3)$ and $(3\ 4)$, since these cycles are not disjoint (they have the symbol 3 in common).

The set of all permutations of the set $\{1, 2, \ldots, n\}$ forms a group called the **symmetric group of degree** $n$, denoted by $S_n$. The binary operation of this group is composition of functions. The order of $S_n$ is $n!$.

Each permutation in $S_n$ can be expressed as a composite of transpositions (cycles of length 2). For example, in $S_6$,

$$(1\ 2\ 3\ 4\ 5\ 6) = (1\ 6) \circ (1\ 5) \circ (1\ 4) \circ (1\ 3) \circ (1\ 2).$$

There are many ways to express a given permutation as a composite of transpositions, but

a permutation cannot be expressed *both* as a composite of an even number of transpositions *and* as a composite of an odd number of transpositions.

This result is the Parity Theorem.

We say that a permutation is **even** if it can be expressed as a composite of an even number of transpositions and **odd** if it can be expressed as a composite of an odd number of transpositions. The evenness or oddness of a permutation is called its **parity**.

Any $r$-cycle can be expressed as a composite of $r - 1$ transpositions in a similar way to the 6-cycle $(1\ 2\ 3\ 4\ 5\ 6)$ above. Hence a cycle of odd length is an even permutation and a cycle of even length is an odd permutation. The composite of two odd or two even permutations is even, and the composite of an even and an odd permutation is odd. We can use these facts to determine the parity of any permutation in cycle form. For example, the permutation

$$f = (1\ 3\ 4)(2\ 6)(5\ 9\ 7\ 8)$$

in $S_9$ is even + odd + odd = even.

Recall that a product of disjoint cycles is also a composite of these cycles.

**Exercise 1.4** Determine the parity of each of the following permutations in $S_8$.

(a) $(1\ 5\ 8)(2\ 7\ 3\ 4)$ (b) $(1\ 8)(2\ 7)(3\ 5\ 4\ 6)$

We can see from the above method of determining parity that any two permutations with the same *cycle structure* (the same number of cycles of each length) have the same parity. In particular, a permutation and its inverse have the same parity.

The set of all even permutations in $S_n$ itself forms a group, which we call the **alternating group of degree** $n$ and denote by $A_n$. The order of $A_n$ is $\frac{1}{2}n!$.

Thus $A_n$ is a subgroup of $S_n$.

## 1.3 Symmetry groups

A rich source of examples of groups is the symmetry of figures. The symmetry group of a figure $F$ is denoted by $S(F)$. The binary operation in symmetry groups is composition of functions (since symmetries are particular examples of functions).

For example, we have met $S(\triangle)$, $S(\square)$, $S(\sqsubset\!\sqsupset)$ and $S(\hexagon)$, the symmetry groups of an equilateral triangle, a square, a rectangle and a regular hexagon, with orders 6, 8, 4 and 12, respectively.

Let us consider the groups $S(\triangle)$ and $S(\square)$ in more detail, beginning with $S(\triangle)$. Each of the six elements of $S(\triangle)$ can be represented as a permutation of the three vertex labels of the triangle, as follows:

For convenience, we often write 'vertex 1' and refer to 'vertex labels' when, strictly speaking, we should write 'the vertex which is at location 1 before applying the symmetry' and 'location labels', respectively.

We express the angles of rotation in radians *anticlockwise*.

| | | |
|---|---|---|
| $e$ | (the identity) | $e$, |
| $a$ | (rotation though $2\pi/3$) | $(1\ 2\ 3)$, |
| $b$ | (rotation though $4\pi/3$) | $(1\ 3\ 2)$, |
| $r$ | (reflection in axis through vertex 1) | $(2\ 3)$, |
| $s$ | (reflection in axis through vertex 2) | $(1\ 3)$, |
| $t$ | (reflection in axis through vertex 3) | $(1\ 2)$. |

One way to compose these symmetries is to compose the permutations that represent them. For example,

$$b \circ s = (1\ 3\ 2) \circ (1\ 3) = (1\ 2)(3) = (1\ 2) = t.$$

By combining all pairs of symmetries in this way, we obtain the following group table for $S(\triangle)$.

| $\circ$ | $e$ | $a$ | $b$ | $r$ | $s$ | $t$ |
|---|---|---|---|---|---|---|
| $e$ | $e$ | $a$ | $b$ | $r$ | $s$ | $t$ |
| $a$ | $a$ | $b$ | $e$ | $t$ | $r$ | $s$ |
| $b$ | $b$ | $e$ | $a$ | $s$ | $t$ | $r$ |
| $r$ | $r$ | $s$ | $t$ | $e$ | $a$ | $b$ |
| $s$ | $s$ | $t$ | $r$ | $b$ | $e$ | $a$ |
| $t$ | $t$ | $r$ | $s$ | $a$ | $b$ | $e$ |

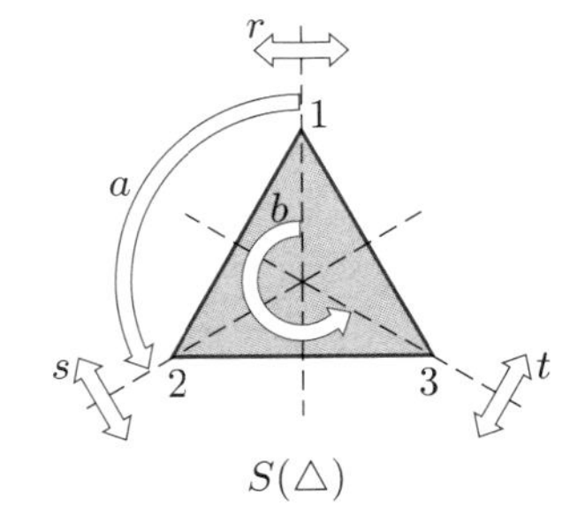

$S(\triangle)$

**Exercise 1.5** Use the group table for $S(\triangle)$ to determine the following.

(a) $a \circ s$ (b) $b^{-1}$ (c) $b \circ r \circ a$

As the binary operation in a group is associative, the composite in part (c) can be calculated by first composing either the two elements on the right or the two on the left. That is,

$$\begin{aligned} b \circ r \circ a &= (b \circ r) \circ a \\ &= b \circ (r \circ a). \end{aligned}$$

A symmetry of a plane figure is *direct* if its effect can be demonstrated using a model of the figure without removing the model from the plane. For a solid (that is, three-dimensional) figure, a symmetry is *direct* if its effect can be demonstrated directly in space using a model of the figure. If the figure (plane or solid) is bounded, then the direct symmetries are just the rotations. The symmetries that are not direct are called *indirect*.

In any finite symmetry group, either all the symmetries are direct or half are direct and half are indirect. In $S(\triangle)$, the symmetries $e$, $a$ and $b$ are direct, and the symmetries $r$, $s$ and $t$ are indirect. The group table of $S(\triangle)$ illustrates the general fact that the composite of two direct symmetries or two indirect symmetries is direct, whereas the composite of a direct symmetry and an indirect symmetry is indirect.

We now consider $S(\square)$, the symmetry group of the square. The elements of this group are

| | | |
|---|---|---|
| $e$ | (the identity) | $e$, |
| $a$ | (rotation through $\pi/2$) | $(1\ 2\ 3\ 4)$, |
| $b$ | (rotation through $\pi$) | $(1\ 3)(2\ 4)$, |
| $c$ | (rotation through $3\pi/2$) | $(1\ 4\ 3\ 2)$, |
| $r$ | (reflection in vertical axis) | $(1\ 4)(2\ 3)$, |
| $s$ | (reflection in diagonal through vertex 1) | $(2\ 4)$, |
| $t$ | (reflection in horizontal axis) | $(1\ 2)(3\ 4)$, |
| $u$ | (reflection in diagonal through vertex 2) | $(1\ 3)$. |

It has the following group table.

| $\circ$ | $e$ | $a$ | $b$ | $c$ | $r$ | $s$ | $t$ | $u$ |
|---|---|---|---|---|---|---|---|---|
| $e$ | $e$ | $a$ | $b$ | $c$ | $r$ | $s$ | $t$ | $u$ |
| $a$ | $a$ | $b$ | $c$ | $e$ | $s$ | $t$ | $u$ | $r$ |
| $b$ | $b$ | $c$ | $e$ | $a$ | $t$ | $u$ | $r$ | $s$ |
| $c$ | $c$ | $e$ | $a$ | $b$ | $u$ | $r$ | $s$ | $t$ |
| $r$ | $r$ | $u$ | $t$ | $s$ | $e$ | $c$ | $b$ | $a$ |
| $s$ | $s$ | $r$ | $u$ | $t$ | $a$ | $e$ | $c$ | $b$ |
| $t$ | $t$ | $s$ | $r$ | $u$ | $b$ | $a$ | $e$ | $c$ |
| $u$ | $u$ | $t$ | $s$ | $r$ | $c$ | $b$ | $a$ | $e$ |

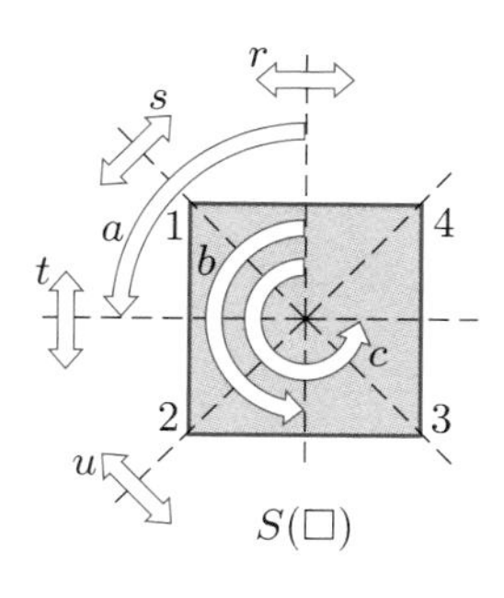


The symmetries $e$, $a$, $b$ and $c$ are direct, and the symmetries $r$, $s$, $t$ and $u$ are indirect.

## 1.4 Subgroups

Earlier we mentioned that, for any positive integer $n$, the set of all even permutations in the symmetric group $S_n$ forms a group under the same binary operation as in $S_n$, namely composition of functions. We say that this group (the alternating group of degree $n$) is a *subgroup* of $S_n$.

> **Definition** A **subgroup** of a group $(G, \circ)$ is a group $(H, \circ)$, where $H$ is a subset of $G$.

The binary operation must be the *same* for $G$ and $H$. It follows from the definition that if $H$ is a subgroup of $G$, then the identity element of $H$ is the same as that of $G$ and the inverse of an element in $H$ is the same as its inverse in $G$.

To show that a subset of a group is a subgroup, we do not need to verify all four group axioms. We use the following strategy.

> **Strategy 1.1 (Unit GTA2, Strategy 1.2)**
>
> To determine whether $(H, \circ)$ is a subgroup of $(G, \circ)$, where $H \subseteq G$,
>
> GUESS behaviour, ... CHECK definition.
>
> To show that $(H, \circ)$ is a subgroup, show that EACH of the following properties holds.
>
> SG1 CLOSURE For all $h_1, h_2 \in H$, the composite $h_1 \circ h_2 \in H$.
>
> SG2 IDENTITY The identity element $e \in H$.
>
> SG3 INVERSES For each $h \in H$, the inverse element $h^{-1} \in H$.
>
> To show that $(H, \circ)$ is not a subgroup, show that ANY ONE of the properties SG1, SG2 or SG3 fails; that is,
>
> show that $\circ$ is not closed on $H$,
>
> OR show that $e \notin H$,
>
> OR find one element $h \in H$ for which $h^{-1} \notin H$.

If $H \not\subseteq G$, then $(H, \circ)$ cannot be a subgroup of $(G, \circ)$.

Property SG1 fails.
Property SG2 fails.
Property SG3 fails.

The closure property SG1 is the same as the corresponding group axiom G1; to verify it we need to check that the binary operation is closed on the subset $H$.

However, the identity and inverse properties SG2 and SG3 differ somewhat from their counterpart group axioms in that they are concerned with *belonging to*, not *existence*. To verify property SG2, we must check that the identity element of $G$ belongs to $H$.

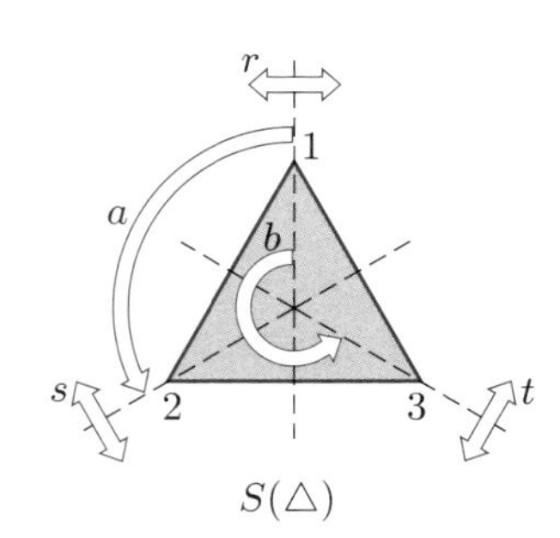

$S(\triangle)$

To verify property SG3, we must check that the inverse in $G$ of each element of $H$ belongs to $H$.

Let us consider some subgroups of $S(\triangle)$. The sets $\{e\}$ and $S(\triangle)$ are both subgroups of $S(\triangle)$. Each reflection in $S(\triangle)$, being self-inverse, forms a subgroup with $e$, so $S(\triangle)$ has the following three subgroups of order 2:

$$\{e, r\}, \quad \{e, s\}, \quad \{e, t\}.$$

There is one further subgroup of $S(\triangle)$. The direct symmetries of any figure $F$ form a subgroup of its symmetry group, denoted by $S^+(F)$. Thus $S^+(\triangle) = \{e, a, b\}$ is a subgroup of $S(\triangle)$.

**Exercise 1.6** The symmetry group $S(\square)$ has

(a) one subgroup of order 1;

(b) five subgroups of order 2;

(c) three subgroups of order 4;

(d) one subgroup of order 8.

Write down as many of these subgroups as you can.

## 1.5 Order of a group element

As you have seen, the *order of a group* is the number of elements in the group. The *order of an element* is a different concept, but it is closely related.

> **Definition** Let $x$ be an element of a group $G$. If $n$ is the least positive integer such that $x^n = e$, then $x$ has **order** $n$.

Convention: We define $x^0 = e$. Then we define the powers of $x$ inductively:

$$x^n = x^{n-1} \circ x, \quad \text{for all } n \in \mathbb{N}.$$

For example,

$$x^1 = x^0 \circ x = e \circ x = x,$$
$$x^2 = x \circ x,$$
$$x^3 = x^2 \circ x = x \circ x \circ x.$$

In an *additive* group, the $n$th power of $x$ is usually called the $n$th multiple of $x$ or $n$ times $x$; it is denoted by $nx$. For example,

$$2x = x + x,$$
$$3x = x + x + x.$$

For example, in $S(\square)$, the element $c$ has order 4 because

$$c^1 = c,$$
$$c^2 = c \circ c = b,$$
$$c^3 = c^2 \circ c = b \circ c = a,$$
$$c^4 = c^3 \circ c = a \circ c = e.$$

The order of any element $x$ of a finite group can be found by determining the successive powers

$$x,\ x^2,\ x^3,\ \ldots$$

until an integer $n$ such that $x^n = e$ is reached; then the order of $x$ is $n$. In particular, the order of the identity element in a group is 1.

However, if $x$ is an element of an *infinite* group, then there *may* not be any positive integer $n$ such that $x^n = e$; in this case, we say that $x$ has *infinite* order.

For example, in the multiplicative group $(\mathbb{R}^+, \times)$, the successive powers of 2 are

$$2, 4, 8, 16, 32, \ldots.$$

No matter how long we keep going, we shall not reach a positive integer $n$ such that $2^n = 1$ (the identity element).

**Exercise 1.7** Determine the order of each of the following elements:

(a) $a$, $b$ and $r$ in $S(\square)$;

(b) 0, 1, 2, 3, 4 and 5 in $\mathbb{Z}_6$. (Remember that the binary operation in $\mathbb{Z}_6$ is $+_6$.)

As you saw in Unit GTA3, there is an easy way to find the order of a permutation in cycle form: its order is the least common multiple of the lengths of its cycles. For example, the permutation (1 3 4)(2 6)(5 9 7 8) in $S_9$ has cycles of lengths 3, 2 and 4, so its order is 12.

## 1.6 Cyclic groups

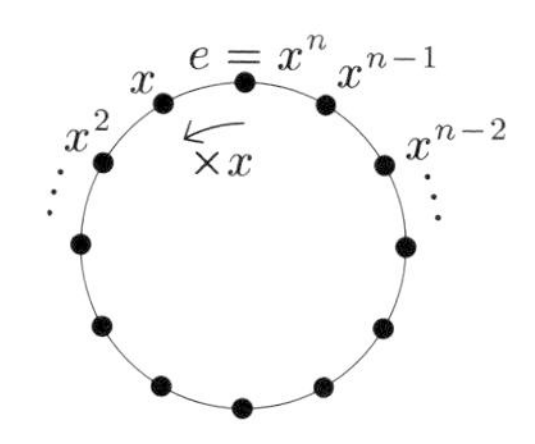


Let $x$ be an element of a group $G$. It is easy to check that the set $\{x^k : k \in \mathbb{Z}\}$, containing all the powers of $x$, is a subgroup of $G$. This subgroup is called the subgroup **generated by** $x$ and is denoted by $\langle x \rangle$. If $x$ has order $n$, then there are only $n$ distinct powers of $x$ and

$$\langle x \rangle = \{e, x, x^2, x^3, \dots, x^{n-1}\}.$$

If $x$ is an element of an *additive* group, then

$$\langle x \rangle = \{kx : k \in \mathbb{Z}\}$$

and this is the set consisting of all the multiples of $x$. If $x$ has order $n$, then this is the set

$$\{0, x, 2x, \dots, (n-1)x\}.$$

Thus there is a close connection between the two meanings of the word *order* in group theory: the order of an element $x$ is equal to the order of the subgroup generated by $x$. For example, in $S(\square)$, the element $c$ has order 4 and the subgroup

$$\langle c \rangle = \{e, c, c^2, c^3\} = \{e, a, b, c\}$$

has order 4.

**Exercise 1.8** Determine the subgroup generated by each element in $\mathbb{Z}_6$.

The group $\mathbb{Z}_6$ has the property that one of its elements generates the whole group: the subgroup generated by 1 is the whole set $\{0, 1, 2, 3, 4, 5\}$. A group that is generated by one of its elements is called a *cyclic* group.

The element 5 also generates $\mathbb{Z}_6$.

> **Definition** A group $G$ is **cyclic** if it contains an element $x$ such that $G = \langle x \rangle$. Such an element $x$ is called a **generator** of the group.

**Exercise 1.9** Determine which of the following groups are cyclic. State all the generators of each cyclic group.

(a) $S(\square)$ (b) $S^+(\square)$ (c) $\mathbb{Z}_5$

If $x$ is an element of a group $G$, then the subgroup $\langle x \rangle$ is by definition a cyclic group; we often refer to it as the *cyclic subgroup generated by* $x$. In Exercise 1.8 we found all the cyclic subgroups of $\mathbb{Z}_6$. The same technique can be applied to find all the cyclic subgroups of any given finite group. But notice that different elements can generate the same cyclic subgroup. For example, in $\mathbb{Z}_6$,

the elements 2 and 4 each generate the subgroup $\{0, 2, 4\}$,

the elements 1 and 5 each generate the whole group $\mathbb{Z}_6$.

In particular, in any group, an element $x$ and its inverse $x^{-1}$ generate the same cyclic subgroup; that is, $\langle x \rangle = \langle x^{-1} \rangle$.

Or, in an additive group, $\langle x \rangle = \langle -x \rangle$.

**Exercise 1.10** Determine all the distinct cyclic subgroups of the following.

(a) $S(\square)$ (b) $\mathbb{Z}_9$ (c) $\mathbb{Z}_7^*$ (d) $S_3$

The binary operation in $\mathbb{Z}_7^*$ is $\times_7$.

# 2 Conjugate elements

After working through this section, you should be able to:

(a) explain the terms *conjugate element* and *conjugacy class*;

(b) state some properties of conjugate elements;

(c) determine the conjugacy classes of certain groups of small order.

## 2.1 Conjugacy in symmetric groups (revision)

In Group Theory Block A we studied conjugacy in the symmetric group $S_n$, the group of all permutations of the set $\{1, 2, \ldots, n\}$. We defined an element $y \in S_n$ to be a *conjugate* of an element $x \in S_n$ if there is an element $g \in S_n$ such that

You may find it helpful to look back at the audio frames in Unit GTA3, Section 3.

$$y = g \circ x \circ g^{-1}.$$

For example, the element $(2\ 3\ 5)(4\ 6)$ is a conjugate of $(1\ 4\ 3)(2\ 6)$ in $S_6$ because $(1\ 3\ 2\ 4\ 5) \in S_6$ and

$$(\mathbf{2\ 3\ 5})(\mathbf{4\ 6}) = (1\ 3\ 2\ 4\ 5) \circ (\mathbf{1\ 4\ 3})(\mathbf{2\ 6}) \circ (1\ 3\ 2\ 4\ 5)^{-1},$$

as you can check. We say that the element $(1\ 3\ 2\ 4\ 5)$ *conjugates* $(1\ 4\ 3)(2\ 6)$ to $(2\ 3\ 5)(4\ 6)$ in the group $S_6$.

To check the equation above, we have to simplify the expression on the right-hand side; that is, we have to find the conjugate of $(1\ 4\ 3)(2\ 6)$ by $(1\ 3\ 2\ 4\ 5)$. One way to do this is to find the inverse of the permutation $(1\ 3\ 2\ 4\ 5)$, then compose the permutations in the usual way. However, we saw earlier that there is a quicker way to find conjugates in $S_n$. If $x$ and $g$ are permutations in $S_n$, then $g \circ x \circ g^{-1}$ is the permutation obtained by 'renaming' each symbol in $x$ using $g$. That is, we replace each symbol in the cycle form of $x$ by its image under $g$. For example, for $x = (1\ 4\ 3)(2\ 6)$ and $g = (1\ 3\ 2\ 4\ 5)$, the renaming is carried out as illustrated below.

$$\begin{array}{cccccc} & (1 & 4 & 3) & (2 & 6) \\ g & \downarrow & \downarrow & \downarrow & \downarrow & \downarrow \\ & (g(1) & g(4) & g(3)) & (g(2) & g(6)) \\ = & (3 & 5 & 2) & (4 & 6) \end{array}$$

In this way we obtain

$$g \circ x \circ g^{-1} = (3\ 5\ 2)(4\ 6) = (2\ 3\ 5)(4\ 6),$$

as expected.

**Exercise 2.1**

(a) To which element of $S_5$ does $(1\ 3\ 5)$ conjugate $(1\ 2\ 4\ 3\ 5)$?

(b) To which element of $S_5$ does $(1\ 3)(2\ 4\ 5)$ conjugate $(1\ 5\ 2)$?

From the renaming method we can see that any conjugate of a permutation has the same cycle structure as the original permutation.

Conversely, if two permutations in $S_n$ have the same cycle structure, then they are conjugate in $S_n$. This is because if two permutations $x$ and $y$ have the same cycle structure, then there is always at least one permutation $g$ that renames $x$ to $y$. There is usually more than one such permutation $g$.

For example, we saw above that the permutation (1 3 2 4 5) conjugates (1 4 3)(2 6) to (2 3 5)(4 6). Another permutation that does the same job is (1 5)(2 4), since

$$(\mathbf{2\ 3\ 5})(\mathbf{4\ 6}) = (1\ 5)(2\ 4) \circ (\mathbf{1\ 4\ 3})(\mathbf{2\ 6}) \circ ((1\ 5)(2\ 4))^{-1}.$$

$$\begin{array}{rl} & (1\ 4\ 3)\ (2\ 6) \\ (1\ 5)(2\ 4) & \downarrow\downarrow\downarrow\ \ \downarrow\downarrow \\ & (5\ 2\ 3)\ (4\ 6) \\ & = (2\ 3\ 5)\ (4\ 6) \end{array}$$

**Exercise 2.2** There are six elements of $S_6$ that conjugate (1 4 3)(2 6) to (2 3 5)(4 6). Two of these are given in this subsection, namely (1 3 2 4 5) and (1 5)(2 4). Determine the other four elements.

Hint: You will need to find all possible ways of writing the permutation (2 3 5)(4 6) in the form (− − −)(− −).

From the discussion in this subsection we have the following theorem, which we met earlier.

**Theorem 2.1 (Unit GTA3, Theorem 3.1)**

Two elements of $S_n$ are conjugate in $S_n$ if and only if they have the same cycle structure.

## 2.2 Conjugacy and conjugacy classes

We now extend the idea of conjugacy to a general group. For convenience, from now on, when considering a general group $G$, we often omit the symbol $\circ$ and write $gxg^{-1}$ rather than $g \circ x \circ g^{-1}$. We sometimes retain the symbol $\circ$ when dealing with a particular group for which the group operation is composition.

**Definition** Let $x$ and $y$ be elements of a group $G$; then $y$ is a **conjugate** of $x$ in $G$ if there exists an element $g \in G$ such that

$$y = gxg^{-1}.$$

We then also say that $g$ **conjugates** $x$ to $y$, that $g$ is a **conjugating element** and that $y$ is the conjugate of $x$ by $g$.

**Example 2.1** In the group $S(\triangle)$, find the elements that are conjugate to the rotation $a$.

**Solution** The element $a$ is conjugate to all elements of the form

$$g \circ a \circ g^{-1}, \quad \text{where } g \in S(\triangle).$$

As there are six choices for the element $g$, there are six conjugates to calculate:

$$\begin{aligned} e \circ a \circ e^{-1} &= e \circ (a \circ e) = e \circ a = a, \\ a \circ a \circ a^{-1} &= a \circ (a \circ b) = a \circ e = a, \\ b \circ a \circ b^{-1} &= b \circ (a \circ a) = b \circ b = a, \\ r \circ a \circ r^{-1} &= r \circ (a \circ r) = r \circ t = b, \\ s \circ a \circ s^{-1} &= s \circ (a \circ s) = s \circ r = b, \\ t \circ a \circ t^{-1} &= t \circ (a \circ t) = t \circ s = b. \end{aligned}$$

This gives all the elements that are conjugate to $a$. There are two: $a$ and $b$. ■

| $\circ$ | $e$ | $a$ | $b$ | $r$ | $s$ | $t$ |
|---|---|---|---|---|---|---|
| $e$ | $e$ | $a$ | $b$ | $r$ | $s$ | $t$ |
| $a$ | $a$ | $b$ | $e$ | $t$ | $r$ | $s$ |
| $b$ | $b$ | $e$ | $a$ | $s$ | $t$ | $r$ |
| $r$ | $r$ | $s$ | $t$ | $e$ | $a$ | $b$ |
| $s$ | $s$ | $t$ | $r$ | $b$ | $e$ | $a$ |
| $t$ | $t$ | $r$ | $s$ | $a$ | $b$ | $e$ |

$S(\triangle)$

We have established that, in $S(\triangle)$, $b$ is conjugate to $a$. It is natural to ask whether $a$ is conjugate to $b$. More generally, is the relation *is conjugate to* symmetric? We show next that the answer is always 'yes'; in fact, in any group, the relation *is conjugate to* is an equivalence relation.

A relation is an *equivalence relation* if it is reflexive, symmetric and transitive. The proof of Theorem 2.2 reminds you of the definitions of these three properties. Equivalence relations were introduced in Unit I3.

**Theorem 2.2** In any group $G$, the relation *is conjugate to*, denoted by $\sim$, is an equivalence relation on the set of elements of $G$.

**Proof** In the 'reminders' on the left-hand side of this proof we use $\sim$ to denote the relation *is conjugate to* on $G$. Thus $x \sim y$ means that $y = gxg^{-1}$, for some $g \in G$.

We show that the relation *is conjugate to* on $G$ is reflexive, symmetric and transitive.

E1 REFLEXIVE $[x \sim x?]$

For all $x \in G$, we have $x = exe^{-1}$. Thus $e$ conjugates $x$ to $x$, so $x$ is conjugate to $x$.

The identity element $e$ conjugates each element $x$ to itself.

E2 SYMMETRIC $[x \sim y \Rightarrow y \sim x?]$

Suppose that $x, y \in G$ and that $x$ is conjugate to $y$; then there exists an element $g \in G$ such that

$$y = gxg^{-1}.$$

Multiplying both sides of this equation on the left by $g^{-1}$ and on the right by $g$, we get

$$\begin{aligned} g^{-1}yg &= g^{-1}(gxg^{-1})g \\ &= (g^{-1}g)x(g^{-1}g) \quad \text{(associativity)} \\ &= exe \quad \text{(inverses)} \\ &= x \quad \text{(identity)}. \end{aligned}$$

If $g$ conjugates $x$ to $y$, then $g^{-1}$ conjugates $y$ to $x$.

Now $(g^{-1})^{-1} = g$, so we have $g^{-1}y(g^{-1})^{-1} = x$. Thus $g^{-1}$ conjugates $y$ to $x$, so $y$ is conjugate to $x$.

E3 TRANSITIVE $[x \sim y$ and $y \sim z \Rightarrow x \sim z?]$

Suppose that $x, y, z \in G$ and that $x$ is conjugate to $y$ and $y$ is conjugate to $z$; then there exist elements $g$ and $h$ in $G$ such that

$$y = gxg^{-1} \quad \text{and} \quad z = hyh^{-1}.$$

Substituting $gxg^{-1}$ for $y$ in the second equation, we get

$$\begin{aligned} z &= h(gxg^{-1})h^{-1} \\ &= (hg)x(g^{-1}h^{-1}) \quad \text{(associativity)} \\ &= (hg)x(hg)^{-1} \quad (\text{since } (hg)^{-1} = g^{-1}h^{-1}). \end{aligned}$$

Unit GTA1, Property 4.4.

Thus $hg$ conjugates $x$ to $z$, so $x$ is conjugate to $z$.

If $g$ conjugates $x$ to $y$ and $h$ conjugates $y$ to $z$, then $hg$ conjugates $x$ to $z$.

Hence the relation is an equivalence relation because it satisfies the axioms E1, E2 and E3. ■

**Exercise 2.3**

(a) Write down an element $g \in S_4$ that conjugates $(1\ 2\ 3\ 4)$ to $(1\ 3\ 4\ 2)$. Verify that $g^{-1}$ conjugates $(1\ 3\ 4\ 2)$ to $(1\ 2\ 3\ 4)$.

(b) Write down an element $g \in S_5$ that conjugates $(1\ 2\ 3)(4\ 5)$ to $(1\ 3\ 5)(2\ 4)$ and an element $h \in S_4$ that conjugates $(1\ 3\ 5)(2\ 4)$ to $(1\ 2)(3\ 4\ 5)$. Verify that $h \circ g$ conjugates $(1\ 2\ 3)(4\ 5)$ to $(1\ 2)(3\ 4\ 5)$.

The symmetric property of conjugacy means that instead of saying that $y$ is a conjugate of $x$, we can simply say that $x$ and $y$ are *conjugate elements* in a group, meaning that each is a conjugate of the other.

Because it is an equivalence relation, conjugacy partitions the elements of a group into equivalence classes. The equivalence class containing a particular element $x$ consists of all the elements of the group that are conjugate to $x$: we call this set the *conjugacy class* of $x$.

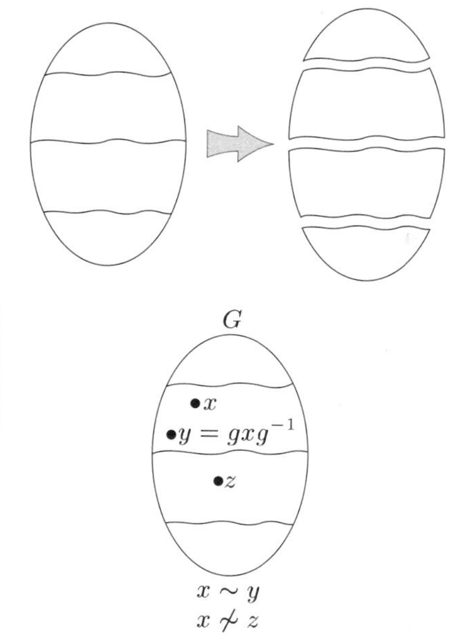


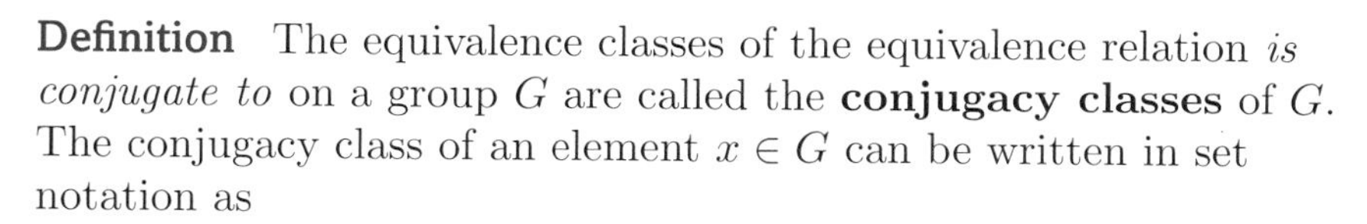

**Definition** The equivalence classes of the equivalence relation *is conjugate to* on a group $G$ are called the **conjugacy classes** of $G$. The conjugacy class of an element $x \in G$ can be written in set notation as

$$\{y \in G : y = gxg^{-1}, \text{ for some } g \in G\}$$

or as

$$\{gxg^{-1} : g \in G\}.$$

Thus if two elements are conjugate, then they are in the same conjugacy class in $G$; if they are not conjugate, then they are in different conjugacy classes. Each group element belongs to one and only one conjugacy class.

**Example 2.2** Determine the conjugacy classes of the group $S(\triangle)$.

**Solution** In Example 2.1 we saw that the only elements which are conjugate to $a$ are $a$ and $b$. Consequently $\{a, b\}$ is one conjugacy class of $S(\triangle)$. We now work out the conjugacy class containing the reflection $r$. We need to work out six conjugates, just as we did for the rotation $a$:

$$\begin{aligned}
e \circ r \circ e^{-1} &= e \circ (r \circ e) = e \circ r = r,\\
a \circ r \circ a^{-1} &= a \circ (r \circ b) = a \circ t = s,\\
b \circ r \circ b^{-1} &= b \circ (r \circ a) = b \circ s = t,\\
r \circ r \circ r^{-1} &= r \circ (r \circ r) = r \circ e = r,\\
s \circ r \circ s^{-1} &= s \circ (r \circ s) = s \circ a = t,\\
t \circ r \circ t^{-1} &= t \circ (r \circ t) = t \circ b = s.
\end{aligned}$$

| $\circ$ | $e$ | $a$ | $b$ | $r$ | $s$ | $t$ |
|---|---|---|---|---|---|---|
| $e$ | $e$ | $a$ | $b$ | $r$ | $s$ | $t$ |
| $a$ | $a$ | $b$ | $e$ | $t$ | $r$ | $s$ |
| $b$ | $b$ | $e$ | $a$ | $s$ | $t$ | $r$ |
| $r$ | $r$ | $s$ | $t$ | $e$ | $a$ | $b$ |
| $s$ | $s$ | $t$ | $r$ | $b$ | $e$ | $a$ |
| $t$ | $t$ | $r$ | $s$ | $a$ | $b$ | $e$ |

$S(\triangle)$

Thus $r$ is conjugate only to $r$, $s$ and $t$, so its conjugacy class is $\{r, s, t\}$.

We have now found two conjugacy classes of $S(\triangle)$, namely $\{a, b\}$ and $\{r, s, t\}$. Between them, these two classes contain five of the six elements of $S(\triangle)$, leaving just the identity element $e$. Since the conjugacy classes partition the group, $\{e\}$ must form a conjugacy class on its own, so the partition of $S(\triangle)$ into conjugacy classes is

$$\{e\}, \quad \{a, b\}, \quad \{r, s, t\}. \quad \blacksquare$$

Notice that the partition in Example 2.2 brings together elements of similar geometric type:

| | |
|---|---|
| the identity element | $\{e\}$, |
| rotations through $2\pi/3$ and $4\pi/3$ | $\{a, b\}$, |
| three reflections | $\{r, s, t\}$. |

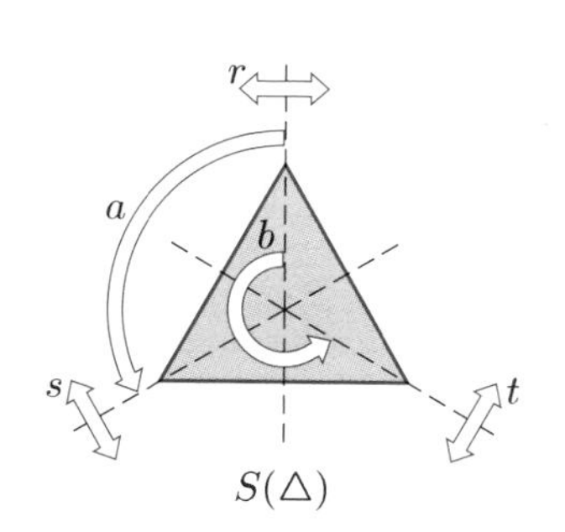

$S(\triangle)$

**Exercise 2.4** Determine the conjugacy classes of the group $(\mathbb{Z}_7^*, \times_7)$.

## 2.3 Some basic results

In Example 2.2 we observed that the identity element is conjugate only to itself in the group $S(\triangle)$. This property is true in general.

**Theorem 2.3** Let $G$ be a group with identity element $e$. Then $\{e\}$ is a conjugacy class; that is, $e$ is conjugate to itself alone.

**Proof** The identity element $e$ is conjugate to those elements of the form $geg^{-1}$, where $g \in G$. But, for each $g \in G$, $geg^{-1} = gg^{-1} = e$. So the conjugacy class of $e$ has the single member $e$. ■

In some groups there are many elements other than the identity that are conjugate only to themselves. For example, in Exercise 2.4 we found that each element of $\mathbb{Z}_7^*$ forms a conjugacy class on its own, and this happens in any Abelian group.

**Theorem 2.4** In an Abelian group, each conjugacy class contains a single element.

**Proof** Let $G$ be an Abelian group and let $x$ be any element of $G$. The conjugacy class containing $x$ is the set

$$\{gxg^{-1} : g \in G\}.$$

But, for any $g \in G$, we have $gx = xg$, so

$$\begin{aligned} gxg^{-1} &= (gx)g^{-1} \quad \text{(associativity)} \\ &= (xg)g^{-1} \quad (gx = xg) \\ &= x(gg^{-1}) \quad \text{(associativity)} \\ &= xe \quad \text{(inverses)} \\ &= x \quad \text{(identity)}. \end{aligned}$$

Hence the conjugacy class of $x$ is

$$\{gxg^{-1} : g \in G\} = \{x\}. \quad ■$$

In the final result of this section we show that, in any group, conjugate elements necessarily have the same order. We have already seen much evidence for this. For example, in $S_n$ conjugate elements have the same cycle structure and therefore the same order. Also, in $S(\triangle)$ the three reflections $r$, $s$ and $t$ are all conjugate to each other and all have order 2, and the two rotations $a$ and $b$ are conjugate elements and both have order 3.

**Exercise 2.5** Prove that if $y = gxg^{-1}$ then:

(a) $y^2 = gx^2g^{-1}$;

(b) $y^3 = gx^3g^{-1}$;

(c) $y^4 = gx^4g^{-1}$.

A clear pattern emerges from Exercise 2.5; whenever $g$ conjugates $x$ to $y$, it also conjugates each power of $x$ to the corresponding power of $y$.

**Example 2.3** Show that if $g$ conjugates $x$ to $y$, then $g$ conjugates $x^n$ to $y^n$, for each positive integer $n$.

In fact, this statement is true for *any* integer $n$ (negative and zero as well as positive).

**Solution** We prove this result using mathematical induction. Suppose that $g$ conjugates $x$ to $y$.

Mathematical induction is explained in Unit I2.

Let $P(n)$ be the statement $y^n = gx^ng^{-1}$.

The statement $P(1)$ is $y = gxg^{-1}$, which is true.

To complete the proof, we need to show that

$$P(k) \Rightarrow P(k+1), \quad \text{for each positive integer } k.$$

We let $k$ be a positive integer and assume that $P(k)$ is true; that is,

$$y^k = gx^kg^{-1}.$$

Using this assumption, we must now prove that $P(k+1)$ is true. We have

$$\begin{aligned} y^{k+1} &= y^k y \quad (\text{definition of } y^{k+1}) \\ &= (gx^kg^{-1})(gxg^{-1}) \quad (\text{assumptions}) \\ &= gx^k(g^{-1}g)xg^{-1} \quad (\text{associativity}) \\ &= gx^kexg^{-1} \quad (\text{inverses}) \\ &= gx^{k+1}g^{-1} \quad (\text{identity}). \end{aligned}$$

Thus $P(k+1)$ is true. So we have shown that

$$P(k) \Rightarrow P(k+1), \quad \text{for each positive integer } k.$$

Hence, by mathematical induction, it follows that $P(n)$ is true for all positive integers $n$, so $g$ conjugates $x^n$ to $y^n$, for each positive integer $n$. ■

In Example 2.3 we have done much of the work in proving the following result.

**Theorem 2.5** Let $x$ and $y$ be conjugate elements in a group $G$; then $x$ and $y$ have the same order.

**Proof** Since $x$ and $y$ are conjugate elements, there exists an element $g \in G$ such that $y = gxg^{-1}$.

Now suppose that $x$ has finite order $s$; then $x^s = e$. It follows from Example 2.3 that

*Reminder*: An element $x$ has finite order $k$ if $k$ is the *least* positive integer such that $x^k = e$.

$$\begin{aligned} y^s &= gx^sg^{-1} \\ &= geg^{-1} = e. \end{aligned}$$

Since $y^s = e$, the element $y$ has finite order and the order of $y$ is at most $s$. So, if we let the order of $y$ be $r$, we have $r \le s$.

The reverse inequality follows from the symmetry of the situation. From $y = gxg^{-1}$, we have $x = g^{-1}yg$. It follows from Example 2.3 that

The equation $x = g^{-1}yg$ tells us that $g^{-1}$ conjugates $y$ to $x$, so we can apply Example 2.3 to deduce that $g^{-1}$ conjugates $y^n$ to $x^n$, for each positive integer $n$.

$$\begin{aligned} x^r &= g^{-1}y^rg \\ &= g^{-1}eg = e. \end{aligned}$$

Since $x^r = e$, the order of $x$ is at most $r$, so $s \le r$.

Putting the two inequalities together, we get $r = s$, as required.

That takes care of the finite order case. If either $x$ or its conjugate $y$ has finite order, then the other must have the same finite order: thus we cannot have a pair of conjugate elements, one of finite order and the other of infinite order. Hence, if one of $x$ and $y$ has infinite order, then so has the other. ■

We have just proved that conjugate elements have the same order. However, the converse is not true: *elements of the same order are not necessarily conjugate.* For example, in the symmetric group $S_4$, the transposition (1 2) and the element (1 2)(3 4) both have order 2, but they are not conjugate because they have different cycle structures.

**Exercise 2.6** Find two elements in the group $\mathbb{Z}_6$ that have the same order but are not conjugate.

## 2.4 Conjugacy in $S(\square)$

So far, we have seen one example of conjugacy in the symmetry group of a figure. In $S(\triangle)$, the three reflections are conjugate to each other, as are the two non-trivial rotations, and the identity element is in a conjugacy class by itself. So, in $S(\triangle)$, it seems that elements are conjugate if and only if they have the same geometric type.

We now determine the conjugacy classes of the group $S(\square)$. We might expect that these will similarly correspond to geometric type, so before doing any calculations, let us try to predict what they are. We know that $\{e\}$ is one conjugacy class. We also know that within each conjugacy class the elements have the same order. Now $S(\square)$ has two elements of order 4, namely $a$ and $c$ (the anticlockwise rotations through $\pi/2$ and $3\pi/2$). It is reasonable to guess that $\{a, c\}$ is a conjugacy class of $S(\square)$. The remaining five elements all have order 2 and are of three geometric types:

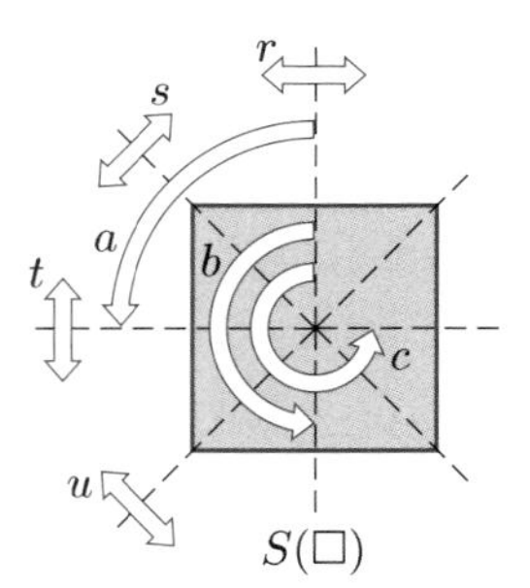

$S(\square)$

- $b$ — rotation through $\pi$,
- $s, u$ — reflections in diagonals,
- $r, t$ — reflections in axes through the midpoints of opposite sides.

Thus, if conjugacy does relate elements of the same geometric type in $S(\square)$, then we would expect $\{b\}$, $\{s, u\}$ and $\{r, t\}$ to be conjugacy classes.

Having made some predictions, we now check whether the above sets are indeed the conjugacy classes of $S(\square)$, by calculating the conjugates. We find the conjugacy class containing the element $s$ by calculating all eight conjugates of $s$:

$$e \circ s \circ e^{-1} = s,$$
$$a \circ s \circ a^{-1} = a \circ (s \circ c) = a \circ t = u,$$
$$b \circ s \circ b^{-1} = b \circ (s \circ b) = b \circ u = s,$$
$$c \circ s \circ c^{-1} = c \circ (s \circ a) = c \circ r = u,$$
$$r \circ s \circ r^{-1} = r \circ (s \circ r) = r \circ a = u,$$
$$s \circ s \circ s^{-1} = s,$$
$$t \circ s \circ t^{-1} = t \circ (s \circ t) = t \circ c = u,$$
$$u \circ s \circ u^{-1} = u \circ (s \circ u) = u \circ b = s.$$

| $\circ$ | $e$ | $a$ | $b$ | $c$ | $r$ | $s$ | $t$ | $u$ |
|---|---|---|---|---|---|---|---|---|
| $e$ | $e$ | $a$ | $b$ | $c$ | $r$ | $s$ | $t$ | $u$ |
| $a$ | $a$ | $b$ | $c$ | $e$ | $s$ | $t$ | $u$ | $r$ |
| $b$ | $b$ | $c$ | $e$ | $a$ | $t$ | $u$ | $r$ | $s$ |
| $c$ | $c$ | $e$ | $a$ | $b$ | $u$ | $r$ | $s$ | $t$ |
| $r$ | $r$ | $u$ | $t$ | $s$ | $e$ | $c$ | $b$ | $a$ |
| $s$ | $s$ | $r$ | $u$ | $t$ | $a$ | $e$ | $c$ | $b$ |
| $t$ | $t$ | $s$ | $r$ | $u$ | $b$ | $a$ | $e$ | $c$ |
| $u$ | $u$ | $t$ | $s$ | $r$ | $c$ | $b$ | $a$ | $e$ |

$S(\square)$

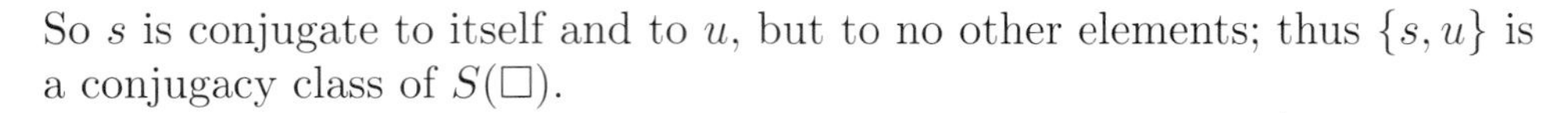

So $s$ is conjugate to itself and to $u$, but to no other elements; thus $\{s, u\}$ is a conjugacy class of $S(\square)$.

**Exercise 2.7** By calculating conjugates, show that, in $S(\square)$:

(a) the element $b$ is conjugate to itself alone;

(b) $a$ and $c$ are conjugate elements;

(c) $r$ and $t$ are conjugate elements.

We have now shown, in Exercise 2.7(a) and the discussion before the exercise, that three of the conjugacy classes of $S(\square)$ are $\{e\}$, $\{s, u\}$ and $\{b\}$. We have also shown, in Exercise 2.7(b) and (c), that $a$ and $c$ lie in the same conjugacy class and that $r$ and $t$ lie in the same conjugacy class. We know that $a$, $c$, $r$ and $t$ do not all lie in the same conjugacy class because $a$ and $c$ have order 4 whereas $r$ and $t$ have order 2.

Hence the partition of $S(\square)$ into conjugacy classes is

$$\{e\}, \quad \{b\}, \quad \{a, c\}, \quad \{r, t\}, \quad \{s, u\}.$$

This partition does indeed relate elements of the same geometric type, as predicted.

## Geometric type

You may have wondered why we consider reflections in the diagonals of a square to be of a different geometric type to reflections in axes through midpoints of opposite sides. Although any two reflections are of the same geometric type when considered simply as isometries of the plane, here we are thinking of geometric type 'relative to' a figure in question, in this case the square.

A useful informal way to think about this idea pictorially is as follows. Two symmetries $x$ and $y$ of a geometric figure are of the same geometric type when there is a symmetry $k$ of the figure that transforms a diagram illustrating $x$ into a diagram illustrating $y$ (when we ignore any labels).

The symmetry $k$ can be expected to conjugate $x$ to $y$. There are often several such symmetries that conjugate $x$ to $y$.

For example, consider the elements $s$ and $u$ of $S(\square)$, which are both reflections in diagonals. These are of the same geometric type because the symmetry $a \in S(\square)$ (a rotation through $\pi/2$ anticlockwise), for example, transforms a diagram illustrating $s$ into a diagram illustrating $u$.

You can check using the group table of $S(\square)$ that $u = a \circ s \circ a^{-1}$, as expected. (The group table is given on page 20.)

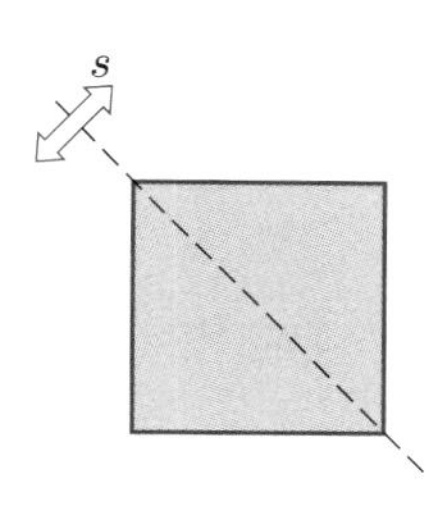


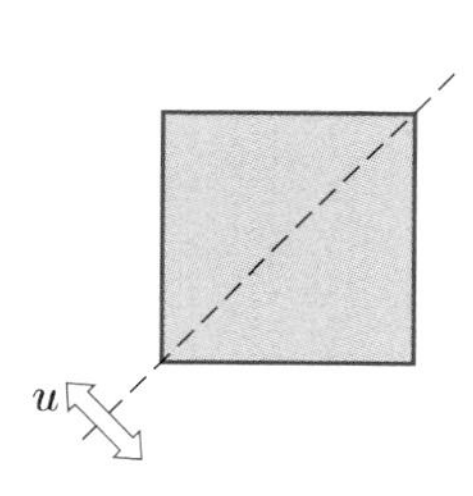


Similarly, the two rotations $a$ and $c$ are of the same geometric type because the reflection $r \in S(\square)$, for example, transforms a diagram illustrating $a$ into a diagram illustrating $c$. This is because $c$, a rotation of $3\pi/2$ anticlockwise, is the same as a rotation of $\pi/2$ clockwise.

You can check using the group table of $S(\square)$ that $c = r \circ a \circ r^{-1}$, as expected.

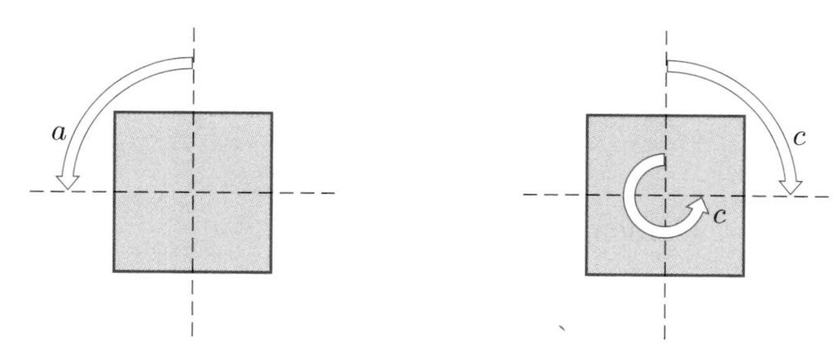


By way of contrast, consider the symmetries $s$ and $r$ (a reflection in a diagonal and a reflection in an axis through the midpoints of opposite sides, respectively). These are not of the same geometric type because there is no symmetry of the square that transforms a diagram illustrating $s$ into one illustrating $r$. This is because no symmetry of the square maps a vertex to a midpoint of a side. (See the following diagram.)

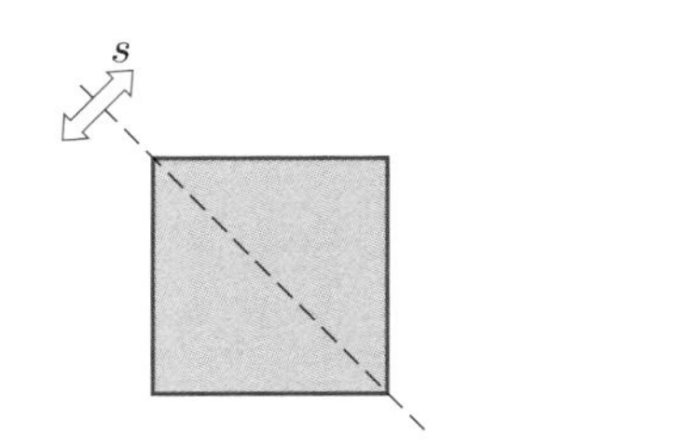


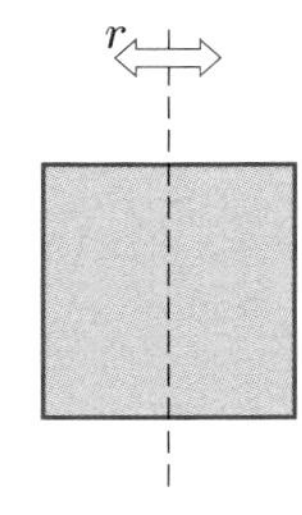


You can think about symmetries of solid figures, as well as plane ones, in this way, but you will have to picture three-dimensional diagrams.

# Further exercises

**Exercise 2.8** Find all the elements of $S_5$ that conjugate $(1\ 3\ 5\ 2\ 4)$ to $(1\ 4\ 2\ 5\ 3)$.

**Exercise 2.9** Determine the partition into conjugacy classes of the group $G$ defined by the following group table.

| | $e$ | $a$ | $b$ | $c$ | $w$ | $x$ | $y$ | $z$ |
|---|---|---|---|---|---|---|---|---|
| $e$ | $e$ | $a$ | $b$ | $c$ | $w$ | $x$ | $y$ | $z$ |
| $a$ | $a$ | $b$ | $c$ | $e$ | $x$ | $y$ | $z$ | $w$ |
| $b$ | $b$ | $c$ | $e$ | $a$ | $y$ | $z$ | $w$ | $x$ |
| $c$ | $c$ | $e$ | $a$ | $b$ | $z$ | $w$ | $x$ | $y$ |
| $w$ | $w$ | $z$ | $y$ | $x$ | $b$ | $a$ | $e$ | $c$ |
| $x$ | $x$ | $w$ | $z$ | $y$ | $c$ | $b$ | $a$ | $e$ |
| $y$ | $y$ | $x$ | $w$ | $z$ | $e$ | $c$ | $b$ | $a$ |
| $z$ | $z$ | $y$ | $x$ | $w$ | $a$ | $e$ | $c$ | $b$ |

**Exercise 2.10** Let $x$ be an element of a group $G$. Prove that the subset

$$C(x) = \{g \in G : gxg^{-1} = x\}$$

is a subgroup of $G$.

We can also write this subset $C(x)$ as

$$C(x) = \{g \in G : gx = xg\}.$$

The elements of $C(x)$ are said to **commute** with $x$, and $C(x)$ is called the **centraliser** of $x$.

**Exercise 2.11** Determine the conjugacy class containing $\pi$ in each of the following groups.

(a) $(\mathbb{R}, +)$ (b) $(\mathbb{R}^*, \times)$

# 3 Normal subgroups and conjugacy

After working through this section, you should be able to:

(a) explain the terms *left coset*, *right coset* and *normal subgroup*;

(b) use conjugacy to test whether a given subgroup of a group is normal;

(c) determine conjugate subgroups of a given subgroup;

(d) describe the connection between *normal* subgroups and *conjugate* subgroups;

(e) use conjugacy classes to find normal subgroups of a group.

In this section we explore the relationship between normal subgroups and conjugacy. Before doing so, we take a few pages to remind you of the definition of a normal subgroup and some associated ideas.

## 3.1 Cosets and normal subgroups (revision)

In this subsection we revise some important concepts from Unit GTA4. No new material is included. Each topic is covered only briefly. If you find that you need more detail on a particular topic, then you should read it again in Unit GTA4. We begin with *cosets*.

**Definition** Let $H$ be a subgroup of a group $G$ and let $g$ be an element of $G$. The (**left**) **coset** $gH$ is the set of elements of $G$ of the form $gh$, where $h \in H$. That is,

$$gH = \{gh : h \in H\}.$$

It is the set obtained by composing each element of $H$ with $g$ on the left.

In this definition we have used the convention of omitting the symbol $\circ$.

For an additive group $(G, +)$, the corresponding notation and definition are

$$g + H = \{g + h : h \in H\}.$$

For example, let us calculate all the cosets of the subgroup $H = \{e, r\}$ in the group $S(\square)$. The group $S(\square)$ has eight elements, so there are eight potential cosets:

$$\begin{aligned}
eH &= e\{e,r\} = \{e \circ e, e \circ r\} = \{e,r\},\\
aH &= a\{e,r\} = \{a \circ e, a \circ r\} = \{a,s\},\\
bH &= b\{e,r\} = \{b \circ e, b \circ r\} = \{b,t\},\\
cH &= c\{e,r\} = \{c \circ e, c \circ r\} = \{c,u\},\\
rH &= r\{e,r\} = \{r \circ e, r \circ r\} = \{r,e\},\\
sH &= s\{e,r\} = \{s \circ e, s \circ r\} = \{s,a\},\\
tH &= t\{e,r\} = \{t \circ e, t \circ r\} = \{t,b\},\\
uH &= u\{e,r\} = \{u \circ e, u \circ r\} = \{u,c\}.
\end{aligned}$$

| $\circ$ | $e$ | $a$ | $b$ | $c$ | $r$ | $s$ | $t$ | $u$ |
|---|---|---|---|---|---|---|---|---|
| $e$ | $e$ | $a$ | $b$ | $c$ | $r$ | $s$ | $t$ | $u$ |
| $a$ | $a$ | $b$ | $c$ | $e$ | $s$ | $t$ | $u$ | $r$ |
| $b$ | $b$ | $c$ | $e$ | $a$ | $t$ | $u$ | $r$ | $s$ |
| $c$ | $c$ | $e$ | $a$ | $b$ | $u$ | $r$ | $s$ | $t$ |
| $r$ | $r$ | $u$ | $t$ | $s$ | $e$ | $c$ | $b$ | $a$ |
| $s$ | $s$ | $r$ | $u$ | $t$ | $a$ | $e$ | $c$ | $b$ |
| $t$ | $t$ | $s$ | $r$ | $u$ | $b$ | $a$ | $e$ | $c$ |
| $u$ | $u$ | $t$ | $s$ | $r$ | $c$ | $b$ | $a$ | $e$ |

$S(\square)$

From this calculation we can see that there are only four *distinct* cosets of the subgroup $H = \{e, r\}$ in the group $S(\square)$:

$$\begin{aligned}
eH &= rH = \{e,r\},\\
aH &= sH = \{a,s\},\\
bH &= tH = \{b,t\},\\
cH &= uH = \{c,u\}.
\end{aligned}$$

This example illustrates some properties of cosets that are true in general.

**Properties of cosets**

1. For each element $g$ and each subgroup $H$ of a *finite* group, the coset $gH$ has the same number of elements as $H$.
2. For each element $g$ and each subgroup $H$, the element $g$ lies in the coset $gH$.
3. One of the cosets $gH$ is $H$ itself.
4. Any two cosets $g_1H$ and $g_2H$ are either the same set or are disjoint.
5. The cosets of a subgroup in a group *partition* the group; that is, each element of the group belongs to one and only one of the distinct cosets.

These properties were proved in Unit GTA4.

For any $h$ in the subgroup $H$, we have $hH = H$.

*Remark* It follows from property 5 that for each pair of elements $g_1, g_2$ and each subgroup $H$,

$$g_2 \in g_1H \text{ if and only if } g_2H = g_1H.$$

The properties above lead to the following strategy for partitioning a finite group into cosets, which is more efficient than the method used above to find cosets.

**Strategy 3.1 (Unit GTA4, Strategy 1.1)**

To partition a finite group $G$ into cosets of a given subgroup $H$.

1. Take $H$ as the first coset.
2. Choose any element $g$ not assigned to a coset and determine the coset $gH$ to which $g$ belongs.
3. Repeat step 2 until every element of $G$ has been assigned to a coset.

This strategy can also be used for infinite groups if there are only a finite number of cosets.

### Exercise 3.1

(a) Partition $S(\triangle)$ into cosets of the subgroup $\{e, t\}$.

(b) Show that $\{1, 6\}$ is a subgroup of $(\mathbb{Z}_7^*, \times_7)$ and partition $\mathbb{Z}_7^*$ into cosets of this subgroup.

(c) Show that $\{0, 4, 8\}$ is a subgroup of $(\mathbb{Z}_{12}, +_{12})$ and partition $\mathbb{Z}_{12}$ into cosets of this subgroup.

(d) Show that $\{\ldots, -10, -5, 0, 5, 10, \ldots\}$ is a subgroup of $(\mathbb{Z}, +)$ and partition $\mathbb{Z}$ into cosets of this subgroup.

| $\circ$ | $e$ | $a$ | $b$ | $r$ | $s$ | $t$ |
|---|---|---|---|---|---|---|
| $e$ | $e$ | $a$ | $b$ | $r$ | $s$ | $t$ |
| $a$ | $a$ | $b$ | $e$ | $t$ | $r$ | $s$ |
| $b$ | $b$ | $e$ | $a$ | $s$ | $t$ | $r$ |
| $r$ | $r$ | $s$ | $t$ | $e$ | $a$ | $b$ |
| $s$ | $s$ | $t$ | $r$ | $b$ | $e$ | $a$ |
| $t$ | $t$ | $r$ | $s$ | $a$ | $b$ | $e$ |

$S(\triangle)$

One reason for studying cosets is that they lead to a simple proof of Lagrange's Theorem, which states that the order of each subgroup of a finite group $G$ divides the order of $G$. However, cosets are also of fundamental importance in their own right and will be used frequently in this block.

The proof of Lagrange's Theorem is as follows. Suppose that a finite group $G$ of order $n$ has a subgroup $H$ of order $m$. Let the number of cosets of $H$ in $G$ be $k$. Each coset has $m$ elements, so the total number of elements in $G$ is $km$; that is, $n = km$. Hence $m$ divides $n$.

The number of distinct cosets of a subgroup $H$ in a group $G$ is called the *index* of $H$ in $G$. If $G$ is finite, then the index of $H$ in $G$ is given by $|G|/|H|$. For example, the index of the subgroup $H = \{e, r\}$ in the group $S(\square)$ is $8/2 = 4$.

The index of a subgroup $H$ of an *infinite* group may be finite; for example, it follows from Exercise 3.1(d) that the index of $\{\ldots, -10, -5, 0, 5, 10, \ldots\}$ in $(\mathbb{Z}, +)$ is 5.

A subgroup $H$ of an infinite group that does not have a finite index is said to have *infinite index*. For example, $H = \{\ldots, -10, -5, 0, 5, 10, \ldots\}$ is a subgroup of the group $(\mathbb{R}, +)$ and has infinite index in this group. Amongst its cosets are $1 + H$, $1.6 + H$ and $\pi + H$; each real number $r$ in the interval $[0, 5)$ corresponds to a distinct coset $r + H$ of $H$ in $\mathbb{R}$.

The cosets defined at the beginning of this subsection are *left cosets*. A *left* coset is formed by composing each element of a subgroup $H$ of a group $G$ with an element $g$ in $G$ on the *left*. We can equally well define *right cosets*, as follows.

**Definition** Let $H$ be a subgroup of a group $G$ and let $g$ be an element of $G$. The **right coset** $Hg$ is the set of elements of $G$ of the form $hg$, where $h \in H$. That is,

$$Hg = \{hg : h \in H\}.$$

It is the set obtained by composing each element of $H$ with $g$ on the right.

For an additive group $(G, +)$, the corresponding notation and definition are

$$H + g = \{h + g : h \in H\}.$$

However, additive groups are usually Abelian and so $H + g = g + H$ for all $g \in G$; that is, each right coset is equal to the corresponding left coset.

For example, the right cosets of the subgroup $H = \{e, r\}$ in the group $S(\square)$ are

$$\begin{aligned} H &= \{e, r\} = He = Hr, \\ Ha &= \{e \circ a, r \circ a\} = \{a, u\} = Hu, \\ Hb &= \{e \circ b, r \circ b\} = \{b, t\} = Ht, \\ Hc &= \{e \circ c, r \circ c\} = \{c, s\} = Hs. \end{aligned}$$

Right cosets have properties analogous to those of left cosets. In particular, the right cosets of a subgroup $H$ in a group $G$ partition $G$. Thus, given any group $G$ and subgroup $H$, we have *two* partitions of $G$—the *left partition*, formed by the left cosets, and the *right partition*, formed by the right cosets.

These two partitions of the group $G$ may be different. For example, for the group $G = S(\square)$ and the subgroup $H = \{e, r\}$, the left and right partitions can be depicted as follows.

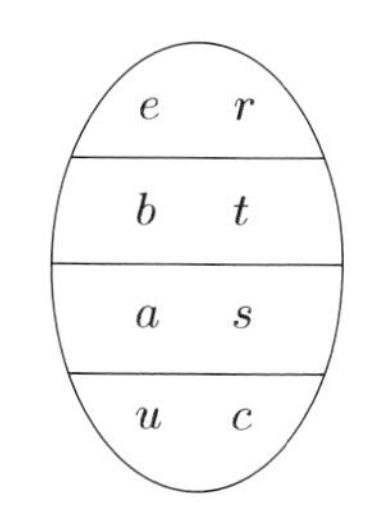

the partition into left cosets of $\{e, r\}$

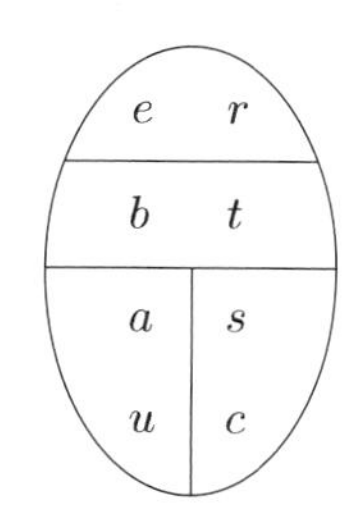

the partition into right cosets of $\{e, r\}$

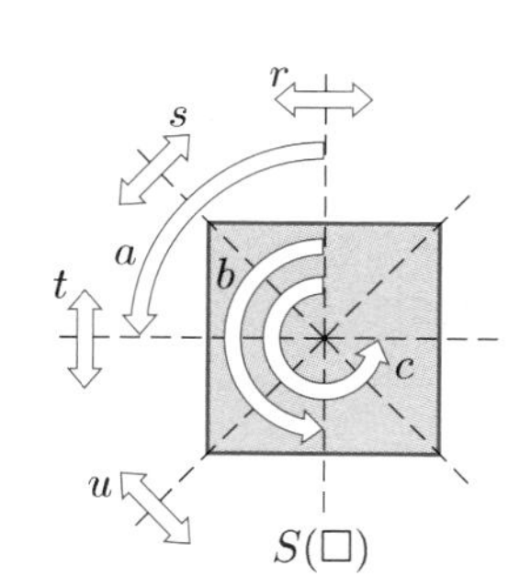

$S(\square)$

However, if we take the subgroup $H = \{e, b\}$, then the left and right partitions of $S(\square)$ coincide, as illustrated below.

The left and right cosets of $\{e, b\}$ can be found in a similar way to those of $\{e, r\}$; we omit the details here.

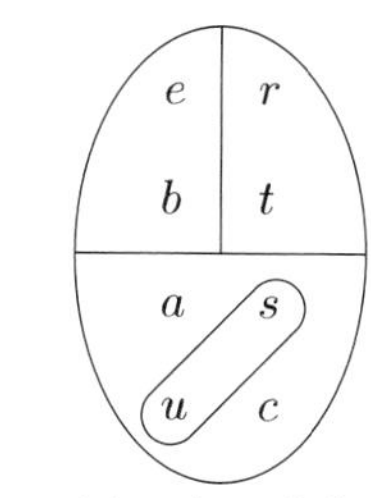

the partition into left or right cosets of $\{e, b\}$

Subgroups, such as this, for which the two partitions turn out to be the same, are of especial interest in the study of groups and so they are given a special name.

**Definition** Let $G$ be a group and let $N$ be a subgroup of $G$. Then $N$ is a **normal subgroup** of $G$ if the left and right partitions of $G$ into cosets of $N$ are the same—that is, if

$$gN = Ng, \quad \text{for each } g \in G.$$

We often use the letter $N$ to denote a normal subgroup.

**Exercise 3.2** Determine whether $\{e, t\}$ is a normal subgroup of $S(\triangle)$.

Exercise 3.1(a) asked you to calculate the left cosets of $\{e, t\}$ in $S(\triangle)$.

In every group $G$, the identity subgroup $\{e\}$ and the group $G$ itself are both normal subgroups. Two other useful facts about normal subgroups are given below.

**Facts about normal subgroups (Unit GTA4, Theorems 4.2 and 4.3)**

In an Abelian group, every subgroup is a normal subgroup.

Any subgroup of index 2 in a group is a normal subgroup.

The first of these facts holds because, in an Abelian group, each left coset is equal to the corresponding right coset, so the two partitions are the same.

For the second fact, note that the order of a subgroup of index 2 is exactly half the order of the group, so the left and right partitions each consist of the subgroup itself and a second coset containing all the remaining elements.

**Exercise 3.3**

(a) Show that $\{e, a, b\}$ is a normal subgroup of $S(\triangle)$.

(b) Show that $\{0, 4\}$ is a normal subgroup of $\mathbb{Z}_8$.

There are many ways in which normal subgroups can be distinguished from ordinary subgroups; many of these distinguishing features are closely related to conjugacy and we shall study several of these in the rest of this section.

## 3.2 Normal subgroups and conjugates

We now demonstrate one of the connections between normal subgroups and conjugacy.

Suppose that $N$ is a normal subgroup of $G$, and let $n$ and $g$ be any elements of $N$ and $G$, respectively. Then

$$gn \in gN \quad \text{(by the definition of coset)},$$

so

$$gn \in Ng \quad (\text{since } gN = Ng, \text{ because } N \text{ is normal}).$$

This says that $gn$ is an element of the right coset $Ng$, so

$$gn = n_1 g, \quad \text{for some element } n_1 \in N.$$

Multiplying both sides of this equation on the right by $g^{-1}$, we get

$$gng^{-1} = n_1 g g^{-1} = n_1 e = n_1,$$

so $gng^{-1} \in N$.

This tells us that if $N$ is a normal subgroup of $G$, then

> for any element $n \in N$ and any element $g \in G$, the conjugate $gng^{-1}$ always lies in $N$;

that is,

> a normal subgroup contains every conjugate of each of its elements.

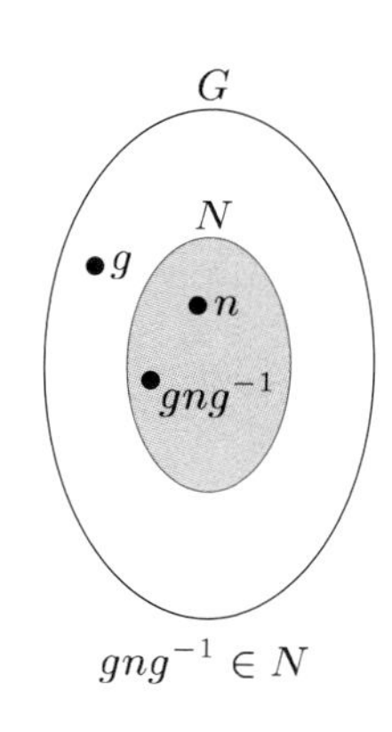


This connection between conjugacy and normality is more than just a property of normal subgroups because, conversely,

> any subgroup that contains every conjugate of each of its elements is a normal subgroup.

Hence we have the following theorem.

**Theorem 3.1** Let $G$ be a group and let $N$ be a subgroup of $G$. Then $N$ is a normal subgroup of $G$ if and only if

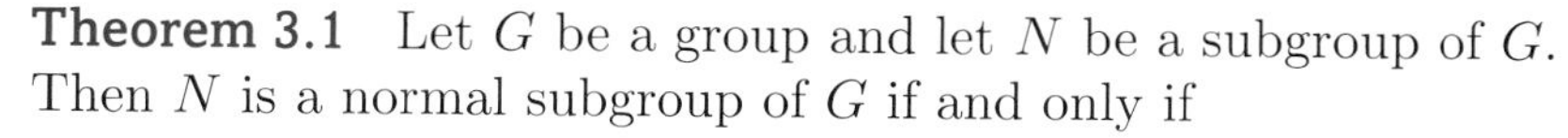

$$gng^{-1} \in N, \quad \text{for each } g \in G \text{ and each } n \in N.$$

We prove this theorem in Subsection 3.5.

Theorem 3.1 gives us an alternative way to determine whether a subgroup is normal; we say that it *characterises* normal subgroups.

Until now we have tested subgroups for normality by finding the left and right partitions of the group into cosets. This is feasible for small finite groups where we have a group table. But this approach has limited application; for example, it is often not useful for groups of large or infinite order. Theorem 3.1 gives us the following more versatile strategy.

**Strategy 3.2** To prove that a subgroup $N$ is a normal subgroup of a group $G$.

1. Take a general element $g \in G$ and a general element $n \in N$.
2. Show that the conjugate $gng^{-1}$ belongs to $N$.

To illustrate the use of Strategy 3.2, we give alternative proofs of two results that we met earlier. The first result (Example 3.1) is the first 'fact' on page 26; the second result (Example 3.2) is a consequence of the second fact on page 26.

**Example 3.1** Prove that, in an Abelian group $G$, any subgroup $H$ is normal.

Unit GTA4, Theorem 4.2.

**Solution** Let $g$ be any element of $G$ and let $h$ be any element of $H$. We need to show that $ghg^{-1} \in H$.

Since $G$ is Abelian, we have $gh = hg$, so

$$\begin{aligned} ghg^{-1} &= hgg^{-1} \quad \text{(commutativity)} \\ &= he \quad \text{(inverses)} \\ &= h \quad \text{(identity)}. \end{aligned}$$

Thus $ghg^{-1} \in H$. It follows that $H$ is a normal subgroup of $G$. ■

**Example 3.2** Prove that, for all $n \geq 2$, the alternating group $A_n$ is a normal subgroup of the symmetric group $S_n$.

Unit GTA4, corollary to Theorem 4.3.

**Solution** Let $g$ be any element of $S_n$ and let $h$ be any element of $A_n$. We need to show that $g \circ h \circ g^{-1} \in A_n$; that is, we need to show that $g \circ h \circ g^{-1}$ is an *even* permutation.

There are two cases to consider.

1. If $g$ is even, then $g^{-1}$ is even and hence $g \circ h \circ g^{-1}$ is

   $$\text{even} + \text{even} + \text{even} = \text{even};$$

   thus $g \circ h \circ g^{-1} \in A_n$.
2. If $g$ is odd, then $g^{-1}$ is odd and hence $g \circ h \circ g^{-1}$ is

   $$\text{odd} + \text{even} + \text{odd} = \text{even};$$

   thus $g \circ h \circ g^{-1} \in A_n$.

Thus, in each case, $g \circ h \circ g^{-1} \in A_n$. It follows that $A_n$ is a normal subgroup of $S_n$. ■

**Exercise 3.4** Use Strategy 3.2 to prove that, for any group $G$, the subgroups $\{e\}$ and $G$ are normal subgroups of $G$.

Earlier in the course, we met the following example of a group. The underlying set is the subset $X$ of $\mathbb{R}^2$ given by

Unit GTA2, Example 1.5.

$$X = \{(a, b) \in \mathbb{R}^2 : a \neq 0\},$$

and the binary operation $*$ on $X$ is defined by

$$(a, b) * (c, d) = (ac, ad + b).$$

We discovered that the identity element of this group is $(1, 0)$ and that the inverse of the element $(a, b)$ is $(1/a, -b/a)$.

**Exercise 3.5**

(a) Verify that, in $(X, *)$,

$$(a, b) * (1, 0) = (a, b) \quad \text{and} \quad (1/a, -b/a) * (a, b) = (1, 0).$$

(b) Determine the following conjugates in $(X, *)$:

$$(3, 2) * (1, 7) * (3, 2)^{-1} \quad \text{and} \quad (-1, 3) * (1, -2) * (-1, 3)^{-1}.$$

We also showed earlier that the subset

$$A = \{(1, b) : b \in \mathbb{R}\}$$

is a normal subgroup of the group $(X, *)$. We showed that it is normal by showing that the partitions of $X$ into left and right cosets of $A$ are the same.

We proved that $A$ is a subgroup of $(X, *)$ in Unit GTA2, Example 1.5(b), and that it is a normal subgoup in Unit GTA4, Subsection 5.3.

In the next example we give an alternative proof that this subgroup is normal, using the new strategy (Strategy 3.2) introduced in this subsection.

**Example 3.3** Prove that $A = \{(1, b) : b \in \mathbb{R}\}$ is a normal subgroup of $(X, *)$. (You may assume that $A$ is a subgroup of $(X, *)$.)

**Solution** Let $(c,d)$ be any element of $X$ and let $(1,b)$ be any element of $A$. We need to show that $(c,d)*(1,b)*(c,d)^{-1} \in A$.

Now $(c,d)^{-1} = (1/c, -d/c)$, so we have

$$\begin{aligned}(c,d)*(1,b)*(c,d)^{-1} &= ((c,d)*(1,b))*(1/c,-d/c)\\ &= (c, cb+d)*(1/c,-d/c)\\ &= (1, -d+cb+d)\\ &= (1, cb).\end{aligned}$$

The element $(1,cb)$ belongs to $A$, since its first coordinate is 1. Thus $A$ is a normal subgroup of $X$. ■

Exercise 3.5(b) provides supporting evidence that $A$ is normal in $X$—it shows two examples of conjugates of elements of $A$ which belong to $A$.

Strategy 3.2, for showing that a subgroup is normal, can be turned round to provide a useful strategy for showing that a subgroup is not normal: all we need to do is to find one counter-example.

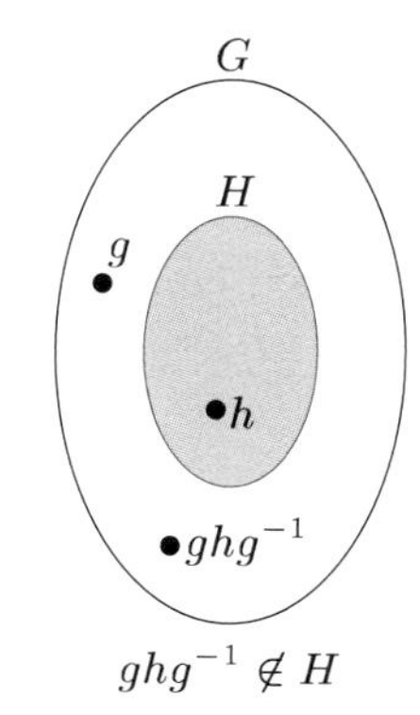


$ghg^{-1} \notin H$

> **Strategy 3.3** To prove that a subgroup $H$ is *not* a normal subgroup of a group $G$.
>
> Find *one* element $g \in G$ and *one* element $h \in H$ such that the conjugate $ghg^{-1}$ does not belong to $H$.

For example, to show that the subgroup $H = \{e, r\}$ is not a normal subgroup of $S(\square)$, we find (after some experimentation) that

$$a \in S(\square) \quad \text{and} \quad r \in H, \quad \text{but} \quad a \circ r \circ a^{-1} = t \notin H.$$

And that is all we need: $r \in H$, and $r$ has a conjugate which does not belong to $H$.

**Exercise 3.6** Use Strategy 3.3 to prove that the following subgroups are not normal subgroups of $S_4$:

(a) $H = \{e, (1\ 2), (3\ 4), (1\ 2)(3\ 4)\}$;

(b) $H = \{g \in S_4 : g(2) = 2\}$, the subgroup of all permutations which fix the symbol 2.

**Exercise 3.7** Let $(X, *)$ be the group discussed in Example 3.3.

(a) Show that the subgroup $C = \{(a, 0) : a \in \mathbb{R}, a \neq 0\}$ is not a normal subgroup of $X$.

(b) Show that the subset $K = \{(1, l) : l \in \mathbb{Z}\}$ of $X$ is a subgroup of $X$, and determine whether it is a normal subgroup of $X$.

We showed that the subset $C$ of $X$ is a subgroup in Unit GTA2, Exercise 1.12.

## 3.3 Conjugate subgroups

In this subsection we look at another connection between normal subgroups and conjugacy.

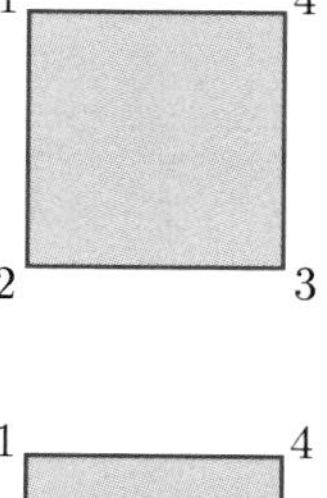


In Unit GTA3 we saw a way of finding new subgroups of a symmetric group $S_n$ from old ones. For example, consider the subgroup of $S_4$ obtained as follows. By labelling the four vertex locations of a square as 1, 2, 3 and 4, we can represent the group $S(\square)$ as a subgroup of $S_4$ in such a way that each symmetry in $S(\square)$ is given by the corresponding permutation of the vertex labels:

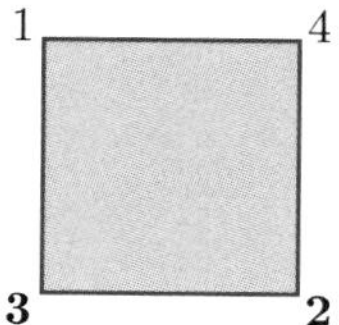


$$H = \{e, (1\ 2\ 3\ 4), (1\ 3)(2\ 4), (1\ 4\ 3\ 2), (1\ 2)(3\ 4), (2\ 4), (1\ 4)(2\ 3), (1\ 3)\}.$$

If we now relabel the vertex locations (still using the symbols 1, 2, 3 and 4), then we get a another subgroup $H'$ of $S_4$ representing $S(\square)$, which may or may not be the same as the original subgroup. For example, if we interchange the labels 2 and 3, the transposition $(2\ 3)$ is the permutation that renames the labels, and the permutations representing the elements of $S(\square)$ become

$$H' = \{e, (1\ 3\ 2\ 4), (1\ 2)(3\ 4), (1\ 4\ 2\ 3), (1\ 3)(2\ 4), (3\ 4), (1\ 4)(2\ 3), (1\ 2)\}.$$

The two subgroups $H$ and $H'$ of $S_4$ are *conjugate subgroups*. We established an algebraic relationship between them: if the renaming permutation $(2\ 3)$ is denoted by $g$, then

Unit GTA3, Section 3.

$$H' = gHg^{-1} = \{g \circ h \circ g^{-1} : h \in H\}.$$

We also discovered the following general result: if $H$ is *any* subgroup of $S_n$ and $g$ is *any* element of $S_n$, then $gHg^{-1}$ is also a subgroup of $S_n$. This idea is not restricted to permutation groups; we now extend it to groups in general.

The subgroup $gHg^{-1}$ of $S_n$ is formed by renaming each symbol in each permutation in $H$ using $g$.

**Notation** Let $H$ be a subgroup of a group $G$ and let $g$ be any element of $G$. Then

$$gHg^{-1} = \{ghg^{-1} : h \in H\}.$$

For example, consider the subgroup $H = \{e, t\}$ of $S(\triangle)$ and the element $a$ of $S(\triangle)$. We have

$$aHa^{-1} = \{a \circ e \circ a^{-1}, a \circ t \circ a^{-1}\} = \{e, r\}.$$

The group table of $S(\triangle)$ is given on page 24. In particular,

$$a \circ e \circ a^{-1} = a \circ a^{-1} = e,$$
$$a \circ t \circ a^{-1} = a \circ t \circ b$$
$$= (a \circ t) \circ b = s \circ b = r.$$

The following theorem generalises the result mentioned above, from permutation groups to all groups.

**Theorem 3.2** Let $H$ be a subgroup of a group $G$ and let $g$ be any element of $G$. Then the subset $gHg^{-1}$ is a subgroup of $G$.

**Proof** We show that the three subgroup properties hold.

SG1 CLOSURE Let $h_1$ and $h_2$ be any two elements of $H$. Then $gh_1g^{-1}$ and $gh_2g^{-1}$ are elements of $gHg^{-1}$, and

$$\begin{aligned}(gh_1g^{-1})(gh_2g^{-1}) &= gh_1(g^{-1}g)h_2g^{-1} \quad \text{(associativity)}\\ &= gh_1eh_2g^{-1} \quad \text{(inverses)}\\ &= g(h_1h_2)g^{-1} \in gHg^{-1} \quad \text{(closure).}\end{aligned}$$

The final step follows from the closure property for the subgroup $H$; as $h_1$ and $h_2$ belong to $H$, so too does the product $h_1h_2$.

SG2 IDENTITY The identity element $e$ can be written as $geg^{-1}$, which is an element of $gHg^{-1}$, since $e \in H$. Therefore $e \in gHg^{-1}$.

SG3 INVERSES Let $h$ be any element of $H$. Then $ghg^{-1}$ is an element of $gHg^{-1}$ and

$$\begin{aligned}(ghg^{-1})^{-1} &= (g^{-1})^{-1}h^{-1}g^{-1} \quad \text{(inverses)}\\ &= gh^{-1}g^{-1} \in gHg^{-1} \quad \text{(inverses in } H\text{).}\end{aligned}$$

By Property 4.4 in Unit GTA1, if $a$, $b$ and $c$ are elements of a group, then $(abc)^{-1} = (bc)^{-1}a^{-1} = c^{-1}b^{-1}a^{-1}$.

Hence $gHg^{-1}$ satisfies the three subgroup properties and so is a subgroup of $G$. ■

Two subgroups of a group which are related by conjugation (as in Theorem 3.2) are called *conjugate subgroups*.

> **Definition** Two subgroups $H$ and $H'$ of a group $G$ are **conjugate subgroups** in $G$ if there exists an element $g \in G$ such that
>
> $$H' = gHg^{-1}.$$

**Exercise 3.8** In the group $S(\square)$, determine the subgroup $gHg^{-1}$ in each of the following cases:

(a) $g = a$ and $H = \{e, s\}$; (b) $g = r$ and $H = \{e, b, s, u\}$.

The group table of $S(\square)$ is on page 23.

**Exercise 3.9** Consider the following subgroup $K$ of $S_4$:

$$K = \{e, (1\ 2)(3\ 4), (1\ 3)(2\ 4), (1\ 4)(2\ 3)\}.$$

$K$ is isomorphic to the Klein group $K_4$.

(a) Determine the following conjugate subgroups of $K$:

$$(1\ 2\ 4)K(1\ 2\ 4)^{-1} \quad \text{and} \quad (1\ 2\ 3\ 4)K(1\ 2\ 3\ 4)^{-1}.$$

(b) Write down all the subgroups of $S_4$ which are conjugate to $K$.

Hint: Remember that conjugation preserves cycle structure.

Exercise 3.9 highlights an interesting property of the subgroup

$$K = \{e, (1\ 2)(3\ 4), (1\ 3)(2\ 4), (1\ 4)(2\ 3)\}$$

of $S_4$; it is **self-conjugate**—that is, it is not conjugate to any subgroup of $S_4$ other than itself. Expressing this algebraically, we have

$$gKg^{-1} = K, \quad \text{for each element } g \in S_4.$$

There is a strong connection between self-conjugate subgroups and normal subgroups—they are the same! This provides a third characterisation of normality:

a subgroup is normal if and only if it is self-conjugate.

The first two characterisations are the definition of a normal subgroup and Theorem 3.1.

We state this result formally in the following theorem.

> **Theorem 3.3** Let $G$ be a group and let $N$ be a subgroup of $G$. Then $N$ is a normal subgroup of $G$ if and only if
>
> $$gNg^{-1} = N, \quad \text{for each } g \in G.$$

We prove this theorem in Subsection 3.5.

## 3.4 Normal subgroups and conjugacy classes

The fact that the normal subgroups are precisely the self-conjugate ones is interesting, but one that we shall have little cause to call upon. However, there is another closely related connection between normality and conjugacy which will prove to be useful in this course. Recall that the conjugacy class of an element $x$ in a group $G$ is the subset of all elements of $G$ that are conjugate to $x$:

$$\{gxg^{-1} : g \in G\}.$$

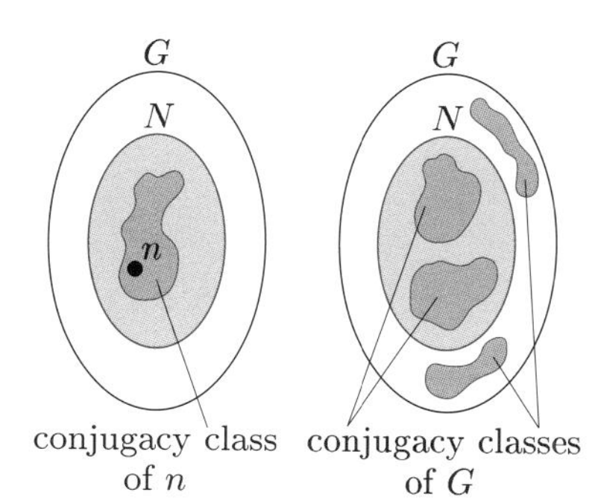


Now suppose that $N$ is a normal subgroup of $G$ and that $n$ is any element of $N$. We know from Theorem 3.1 that every conjugate of $n$ belongs to $N$; that is, the whole of the conjugacy class of $n$ is in $N$.

Thus a normal subgroup $N$ of $G$ contains the entire conjugacy class of each of its elements:

> a conjugacy class cannot lie partly inside and partly outside a normal subgroup.

Each conjugacy class of $G$ is either wholly inside $N$ or wholly outside $N$.

It follows that

> a normal subgroup is a union of conjugacy classes.

A 'union of conjugacy classes' can be a trivial union containing just one class.

The converse of the statement above is also true:

> any subgroup of $G$ which is a union of conjugacy classes of $G$ is a normal subgroup.

Thus we have the following fourth characterisation of normal subgroups.

**Theorem 3.4** Let $G$ be a group and let $N$ be a subgroup of $G$. Then $N$ is a normal subgroup of $G$ if and only if

> $N$ is a union of conjugacy classes of $G$.

We prove this theorem in Subsection 3.5.

In the remainder of this subsection we look at examples that illustrate the use of Theorem 3.4.

**Example 3.4** Find all the normal subgroups of $S(\square)$.

**Solution** In Subsection 2.4 we found that $S(\square)$ has the following five conjugacy classes:

$$\{e\}, \quad \{a,c\}, \quad \{b\}, \quad \{r,t\}, \quad \{s,u\}.$$

Suppose that we have a subgroup $H$ of $S(\square)$. Theorem 3.4 provides a simple test for determining whether $H$ is normal: we just look to see whether $H$ is a union of these conjugacy classes. For example, the subgroup $H$ consisting of the four direct symmetries $\{e,a,b,c\}$ is normal in $S(\square)$ because $H$ is a union of three conjugacy classes:

$$H = \{e\} \cup \{a,c\} \cup \{b\}.$$

On the other hand, the subgroup $\{e,r\}$ is not a union of conjugacy classes and so is not a normal subgroup of $S(\square)$.

The group $S(\square)$ has ten subgroups.

See Exercise 1.6.

| Subgroup | Order |
|---|---|
| $S(\square)$ | 8 |
| $\{e,a,b,c\}, \{e,b,r,t\}, \{e,b,s,u\}$ | 4 |
| $\{e,b\}, \{e,r\}, \{e,s\}, \{e,t\}, \{e,u\}$ | 2 |
| $\{e\}$ | 1 |

Six of these subgroups are normal subgroups.

| Subgroup | Union of conjugacy classes |
|---|---|
| $S(\square)$ | $\{e\} \cup \{a,c\} \cup \{b\} \cup \{r,t\} \cup \{s,u\}$ |
| $\{e,a,b,c\}$ | $\{e\} \cup \{a,c\} \cup \{b\}$ |
| $\{e,b,r,t\}$ | $\{e\} \cup \{b\} \cup \{r,t\}$ |
| $\{e,b,s,u\}$ | $\{e\} \cup \{b\} \cup \{s,u\}$ |
| $\{e,b\}$ | $\{e\} \cup \{b\}$ |
| $\{e\}$ | $\{e\}$ |

The remaining four subgroups $\{e, r\}$, $\{e, s\}$, $\{e, t\}$ and $\{e, u\}$ are not normal, since none of them can be expressed as a union of conjugacy classes. ■

Example 3.4 illustrates that it is not difficult to test whether a subgroup is normal, *once we know the conjugacy classes.*

Let us now try the same exercise on the group $S_4$. We know all the conjugacy classes of $S_4$, because two elements in $S_4$ are conjugate in $S_4$ if and only if they have the *same cycle structure.* We also know all the subgroups of $S_4$, but instead of considering each of these in turn we shall take another approach. This approach illustrates that it is possible to find the normal subgroups of a fairly small group such as $S_4$, knowing only the conjugacy classes and some elementary facts about subgroups.

We found the subgroups of $S_4$ in Unit GTA3, Section 4.

**Example 3.5** Determine all the normal subgroups of $S_4$.

**Solution** The group $S_4$ has five conjugacy classes, one for each of the five types of cycle structure. These conjugacy classes are as follows.

Unit GTA3, Section 4.

| Conjugacy classes | Number of elements |
|---|---|
| $C_1 = \{e\}$ | 1 identity element |
| $C_2 = \{(- \ -)\}$ | 6 transpositions |
| $C_3 = \{(- \ - \ -)\}$ | 8 3-cycles |
| $C_4 = \{(- \ - \ - \ -)\}$ | 6 4-cycles |
| $C_5 = \{(- \ -)(- \ -)\}$ | 3 products of 2-cycles |

Which unions of these classes are subgroups? We can narrow the field using two facts.

- Each subgroup must contain the identity element $e$.
- By Lagrange's Theorem, the order of any subgroup of $S_4$ must divide 24, the order of $S_4$.

So we need to consider only unions of conjugacy classes which include class $C_1$ and which contain, in total, 1, 2, 3, 4, 6, 8, 12 or 24 elements. So we can dismiss, for example,

$$C_1 \cup C_2 \quad \text{and} \quad C_1 \cup C_3 \cup C_4,$$

as these contain $1 + 6 = 7$ and $1 + 8 + 6 = 15$ elements, respectively. Similarly, we can dismiss $C_2 \cup C_4$, which has 12 elements but does not include the identity element $e$.

In order to draw up a list of candidates, we need to find all the ways of adding up some of the numbers

$$1, 6, 8, 6 \text{ and } 3 \text{ (the sizes of the conjugacy classes)},$$

always including 1, to give a total of 1, 2, 3, 4, 6, 8, 12 or 24. It does not take long to check that there are only four ways of doing this:

$$1, \ 1 + 3 = 4, \quad 1 + 8 + 3 = 12, \quad 1 + 6 + 8 + 6 + 3 = 24.$$

The checking can be reduced by noting that any even total must include both the numbers 1 and 3.

So the only unions of conjugacy classes that include $C_1$ and have the right number of elements are

$$\begin{array}{ll} C_1 & \text{(1 element)}, \\ C_1 \cup C_5 & \text{(4 elements)}, \\ C_1 \cup C_3 \cup C_5 & \text{(12 elements)}, \\ C_1 \cup C_2 \cup C_3 \cup C_4 \cup C_5 & \text{(24 elements)}. \end{array}$$

These are the only candidates for normal subgroups.

By Theorem 3.4, any of these sets which is a subgroup is automatically normal. But which of them are subgroups? We have seen earlier in the course that all four are subgroups. The first, third and fourth sets are, respectively,

$\{e\}$ the identity subgroup,
$A_4$ the alternating group,
$S_4$ the whole group.

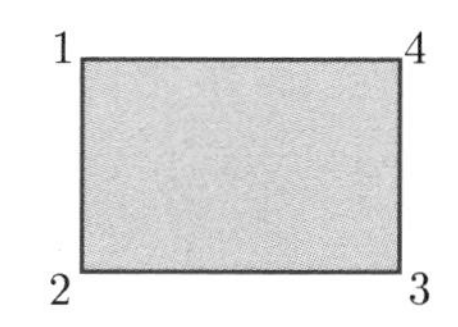


The second set represents the symmetry group of a rectangle with vertex locations labelled 1, 2, 3 and 4. Thus these four subgroups are the only normal subgroups of $S_4$. ■

We summarise the method that we used in Example 3.5 as a general strategy.

**Strategy 3.4** To find all the normal subgroups of a finite group $G$, when the partition of $G$ into conjugacy classes is known.

1. Look at all the possible unions of conjugacy classes that include the class $\{e\}$.
2. Consider only those unions for which the total number of elements divides $|G|$, the order of the group $G$.
3. Determine whether each union of conjugacy classes is a subgroup of $G$: any union that is a subgroup is a normal subgroup of $G$.

**Exercise 3.10** The conjugacy classes of $S(\triangle)$ are

$\{e\}$ the identity element,
$\{a, b\}$ the rotations through $2\pi/3$ and $4\pi/3$,
$\{r, s, t\}$ the three reflections.

Determine all the normal subgroups of $S(\triangle)$.

The subgroups of $S(\triangle)$ were given in Subsection 1.4.

**Exercise 3.11** The group $A_5$ has five conjugacy classes, as follows:

the identity element,
20 3-cycles, such as $(1\ 2\ 3)$,
15 products of two transpositions, such as $(1\ 2)(3\ 4)$,
12 5-cycles conjugate to $(1\ 2\ 3\ 4\ 5)$,
12 5-cycles conjugate to $(1\ 2\ 3\ 5\ 4)$.

Determine all the normal subgroups of $A_5$.

The 24 5-cycles split into two conjugacy classes in $A_5$.

## 3.5 Characterisations of normality

We have now seen four properties that characterise a normal subgroup. Each of them gives an alternative method for checking whether or not a subgroup is normal. We can summarise this more formally as follows.

A subgroup $N$ of a group $G$ is **normal** if and only if it satisfies any one of the following equivalent properties.

Property A: $gN = Ng$, for each $g \in G$. — Definition
Property B: $gng^{-1} \in N$, for each $g \in G$ and each $n \in N$. — Theorem 3.1
Property C: $gNg^{-1} = N$, for each $g \in G$. — Theorem 3.3
Property D: $N$ is a union of conjugacy classes of $G$. — Theorem 3.4

We used Property A in the basic definition of a normal subgroup, but any of the other three properties could have been used in its place. We can use any of the four properties when we wish to prove that a subgroup is normal, or show that it is not normal.

Property A is useful when we have information concerning the left and right partitions into cosets.

Property B is useful in many general situations.

Property C is helpful when we have knowledge about conjugate subgroups.

Property D is particularly useful when the conjugacy classes are known.

As yet, we have not provided a proof that the four properties are equivalent; we need to do this to justify the use of whichever property seems most helpful in a particular situation. The remainder of this section will remedy this omission.

Once we have proved the equivalence of the four properties, we have also proved Theorems 3.1, 3.3 and 3.4.

## Outline of the proof

We prove five implications, which we abbreviate as

A $\Rightarrow$ C, C $\Rightarrow$ A, B $\Rightarrow$ C, C $\Rightarrow$ D, D $\Rightarrow$ B.

A

$\Updownarrow$

C

$\Nearrow$ $\Searrow$

B $\Leftarrow$ D

For example, C $\Rightarrow$ D means that

if a subgroup $N$ of a group $G$ satisfies Property C, then it also satisfies Property D.

It follows from these five implications that any one of the four properties is equivalent to any other. For example, A $\Leftrightarrow$ B follows from

A $\Rightarrow$ C, C $\Rightarrow$ D, D $\Rightarrow$ B (which together give A $\Rightarrow$ B)

and

B $\Rightarrow$ C, C $\Rightarrow$ A (which together give B $\Rightarrow$ A).

We now state the theorem that we need to prove, and give the proof.

We could have proved just four implications; for example,
A $\Rightarrow$ B, B $\Rightarrow$ C,
C $\Rightarrow$ D, D $\Rightarrow$ A.
However the five implications that we have chosen are more straightforward to prove.

**Theorem 3.5** Let $N$ be a subgroup of a group $G$. The following four properties are equivalent.

Property A: $gN = Ng$, for each $g \in G$.
Property B: $gng^{-1} \in N$, for each $g \in G$ and each $n \in N$.
Property C: $gNg^{-1} = N$, for each $g \in G$.
Property D: $N$ is a union of conjugacy classes of $G$.

**Proof**

If you are short of time, omit this proof.

A $\Rightarrow$ C Suppose that $gN = Ng$, for each $g \in G$. Let $g \in G$; we have to prove that $gNg^{-1} = N$. Now

$$\begin{aligned}
&x \in gNg^{-1}\\
&\Leftrightarrow x = gng^{-1} \text{ for some } n \in N\\
&\Leftrightarrow x = n_1gg^{-1} \text{ for some } n_1 \in N \quad (\text{since } gN = Ng)\\
&\Leftrightarrow x = n_1 \text{ for some } n_1 \in N\\
&\Leftrightarrow x \in N,
\end{aligned}$$

so $gNg^{-1} = N$, as required.

The forward implications ($\Rightarrow$) prove that $gNg^{-1} \subseteq N$, and the backward implications ($\Leftarrow$) prove that $gNg^{-1} \supseteq N$.

C ⇒ A Suppose that $gNg^{-1} = N$, for each $g \in G$. Let $g \in G$; we have to prove that $gN = Ng$. Now

$$\begin{aligned} & x \in gN \\ & \Leftrightarrow x = gn \text{ for some } n \in N \\ & \Leftrightarrow x = gng^{-1}g \text{ for some } n \in N \\ & \Leftrightarrow x = n_1 g \text{ for some } n_1 \in N \quad (\text{since } gNg^{-1} = N) \\ & \Leftrightarrow x \in Ng, \end{aligned}$$

The forward implications (⇒) prove that $gN \subseteq Ng$, and the backward implications (⇐) prove that $gN \supseteq Ng$.

so $gN = Ng$, as required.

B ⇒ C Suppose that Property B holds; that is, $gng^{-1} \in N$, for each $g \in G$ and each $n \in N$. Let $g \in G$; we have to prove that $gNg^{-1} = N$.

First we prove that $N \subseteq gNg^{-1}$. Let $n \in N$. Now $g^{-1}$ is an element of $G$, so by Property B,

$$g^{-1}ng = g^{-1}n(g^{-1})^{-1} \in N,$$

and hence

$$n = (gg^{-1})n(gg^{-1}) = g(g^{-1}ng)g^{-1} \in gNg^{-1}.$$

Thus $N \subseteq gNg^{-1}$, as required.

It follows immediately from Property B that $gNg^{-1} \subseteq N$, so $gNg^{-1} = N$, as required.

C ⇒ D Suppose that $gNg^{-1} = N$, for each $g \in G$. Let $n$ be any element of $N$ and let $gng^{-1}$ be any conjugate of $n$ in $G$. Then $gng^{-1} \in gNg^{-1} = N$. Thus $N$ contains every conjugate in $G$ of each of its elements; that is, it is a union of conjugacy classes of $G$.

D ⇒ B Suppose that $N$ is a union of conjugacy classes of $G$. Then, for each $g \in G$ and each $n \in N$, the element $gng^{-1}$ lies in the conjugacy class of $n$ and so $gng^{-1} \in N$. ■

## Further exercises

**Exercise 3.12** Consider the group $G$ whose table is given in Exercise 2.9. For each of the following subgroups of $G$, determine both its left and its right coset partitions, and hence state whether it is a normal subgroup of $G$.

(a) $\{e, b\}$ (b) $\{e, w, b, y\}$

**Exercise 3.13** In the group $S(\square)$, find all the subgroups that are conjugate to $\{e, r\}$.

**Exercise 3.14**

(a) Let $H$ be a cyclic subgroup of a group $G$, generated by the element $h \in G$; that is, $H = \langle h \rangle$.

Show that $gHg^{-1}$ is the cyclic subgroup of $G$ generated by the element $ghg^{-1}$; that is $gHg^{-1} = \langle ghg^{-1} \rangle$.

(b) Find all the subgroups of $S_4$ that are conjugate to the subgroup

$$\{e, (1\ 2\ 3\ 4), (1\ 3)(2\ 4), (1\ 4\ 3\ 2)\}.$$

**Exercise 3.15** Let $X = \{(a, b) \in \mathbb{R}^2 : a \neq 0\}$ be the group with binary operation $*$ defined by $(a, b) * (c, d) = (ac, ad + b)$ and let $C = \{(a, 0) : a \in \mathbb{R}^*\}$.

Then $C$ is a subgroup of $(X, *)$, but it is not a normal subgroup.

We showed that the subgroup $C$ is not a normal subgroup of $X$ in Exercise 3.7(a).

Determine the following conjugate subgroups of $C$:

$$(1, 2)C(1, 2)^{-1} \quad \text{and} \quad (2, 1)C(2, 1)^{-1}.$$

**Exercise 3.16** In Exercise 3.7(b) we discovered that the set

$$K = \{(1, k) : k \in \mathbb{Z}\}$$

is a subgroup of $(X, *)$, but is not a normal subgroup.

Determine the following conjugate subgroups of $K$:

$$(\tfrac{1}{2}, \tfrac{1}{2})K(\tfrac{1}{2}, \tfrac{1}{2})^{-1} \quad \text{and} \quad (\tfrac{1}{3}, 0)K(\tfrac{1}{3}, 0)^{-1}.$$

# 4 Conjugacy in symmetry groups

After working through this section, you should be able to:

(a) appreciate that conjugate elements in symmetry groups must have similar *fixed point sets*;

(b) use the *Fixed Point Theorem* to help determine conjugacy classes in symmetry groups.

## 4.1 Geometric classification and fixed point sets

### Geometric type and conjugacy classes

The elements of the symmetry group of any plane or solid figure may be classified by geometric type. For example, the eight elements of the group $S(\square)$ can be classified as follows:

We discussed what we mean by 'geometric type' at the end of Subsection 2.4.

| | |
|---|---|
| the identity element | $\{e\}$, |
| rotations through $\pi/2$ and $3\pi/2$ | $\{a, c\}$, |
| rotation through $\pi$ | $\{b\}$, |
| reflections in the diagonals | $\{s, u\}$, |
| reflections in the axes through the midpoints of the sides | $\{r, t\}$. |

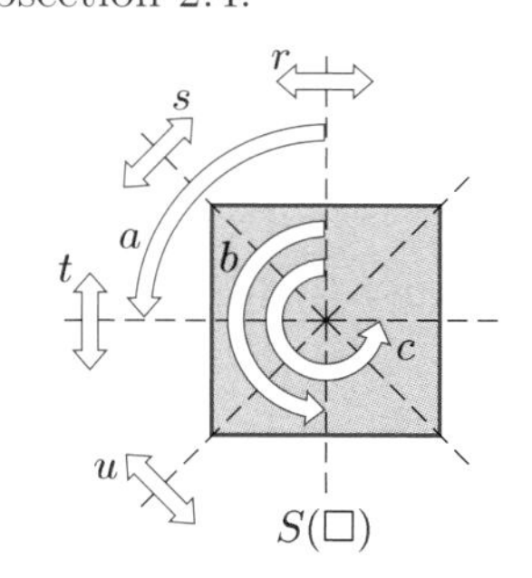

$S(\square)$

Conjugacy gives us another way of classifying the elements of a group—into conjugacy classes. In Subsection 2.4 we found that $S(\square)$ has five conjugacy classes—the five classes listed above. So, in $S(\square)$, conjugacy relates elements of similar geometric type.

The same thing happens with the group $S(\triangle)$; the three conjugacy classes correspond to the three classes of similar geometric type:

| | |
|---|---|
| the identity element | $\{e\}$, |
| rotations through $2\pi/3$ and $4\pi/3$ | $\{a, b\}$, |
| three reflections | $\{r, s, t\}$. |

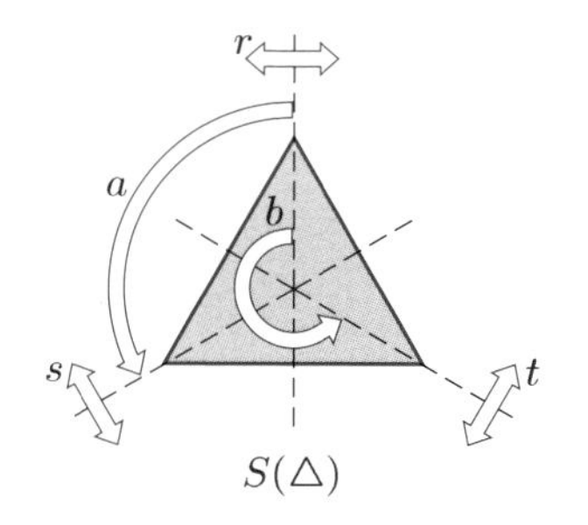

$S(\triangle)$

In the video programme we explore this connection more deeply, looking at the relationship between conjugacy and 'similar geometric type' in more complicated symmetry groups.

## Fixed point sets

The programme also uncovers a key result concerning the fixed point sets of conjugate elements in a symmetry group. By the *fixed point set* of a symmetry we mean the set of points of the figure which are fixed—that is, not moved—by the symmetry.

> **Definition** Let $f$ be a symmetry of a figure $F$. Then the **fixed point set** of $f$ is
>
> $$\{x \in F : f(x) = x\},$$
>
> and is denoted by $\mathrm{Fix}(f)$.

For example, a rotational symmetry of a plane figure fixes at most a single point, namely the centre of rotation if this lies in the figure. A reflection of a plane figure fixes all the points of the figure that lie on the axis of reflection.

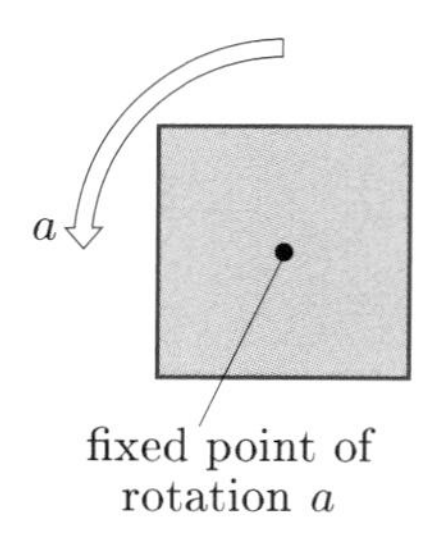


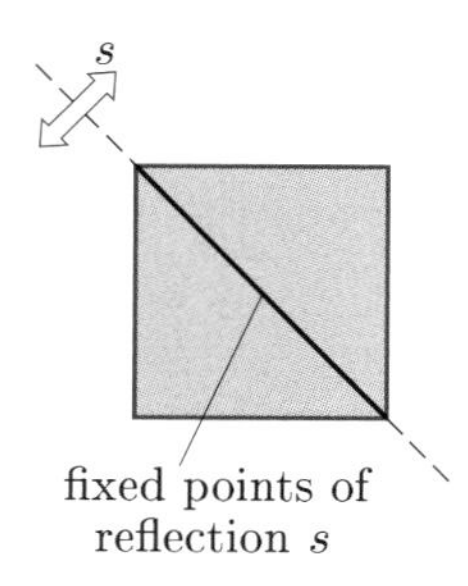


Similarly, a rotation of a solid figure fixes all the points of the figure that lie on the axis of rotation. A reflection of a solid figure fixes all the points of the figure that lie in the plane of reflection.

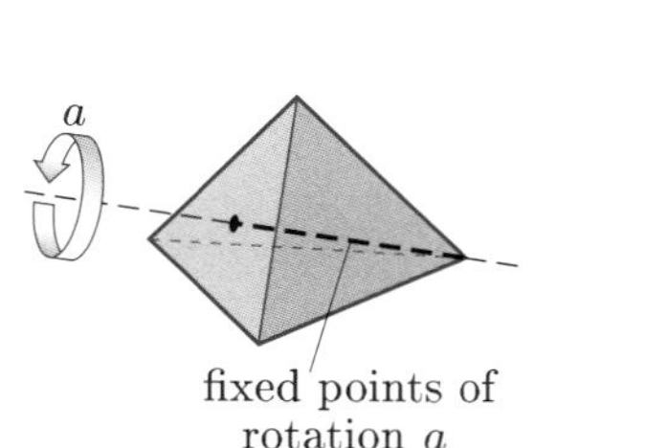


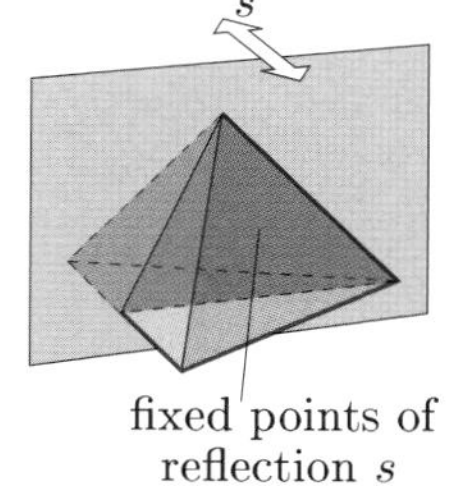


**Exercise 4.1** Consider the double tetrahedron shown in the margin. Write down the fixed point set of each of the following symmetries:

(a) the reflection in the plane through vertices 3, 4 and 5;

(b) the reflection in the plane through vertices 1, 2 and 3;

(c) the rotation (1 2 3).

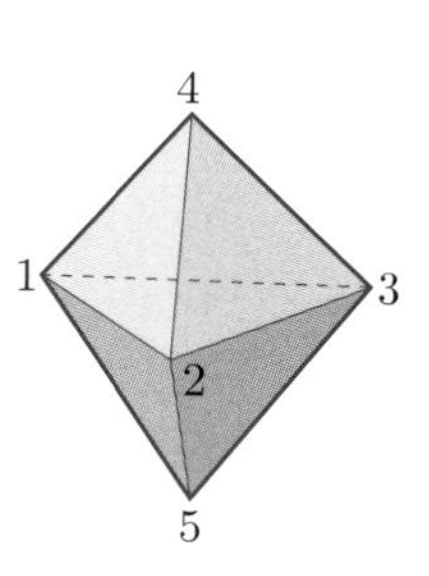


**Watch the video programme 'Conjugacy and fixed points'.**

Video

## 4.2 Review of the programme

Earlier we found that, for each of the groups $S(\triangle)$ and $S(\square)$, the partition by geometric type agrees with the partition into conjugacy classes. The programme poses the question of whether this is also true of the symmetry group of the double tetrahedron.

To answer this question, we first classify the elements of the symmetry group by geometric type. In addition to the identity element, there are two types of rotation.

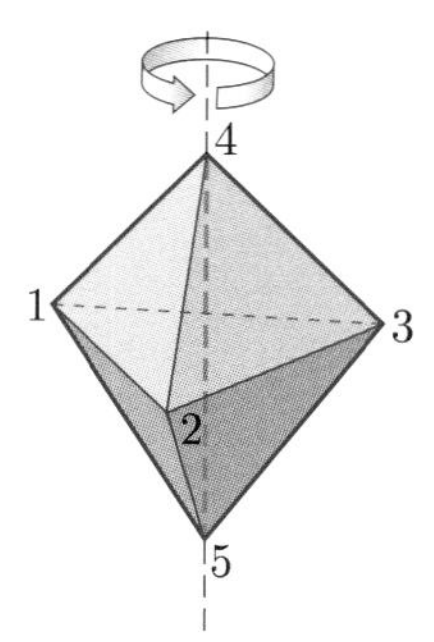


rotations through
$2\pi/3$ and $4\pi/3$

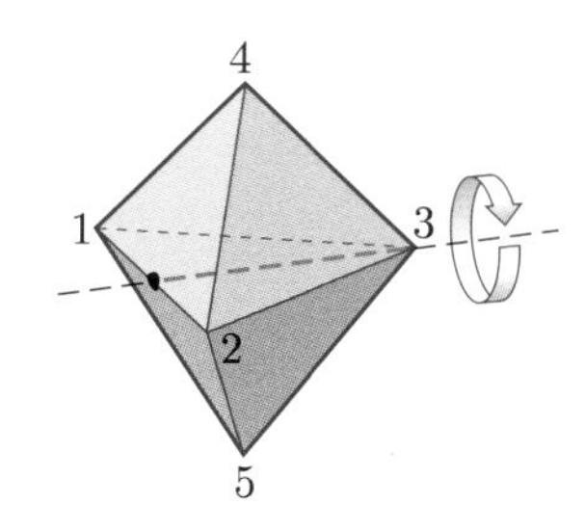


rotation through $\pi$
(three such axes)

This accounts for the subgroup of direct symmetries, of order 6.

There are two types of reflection.

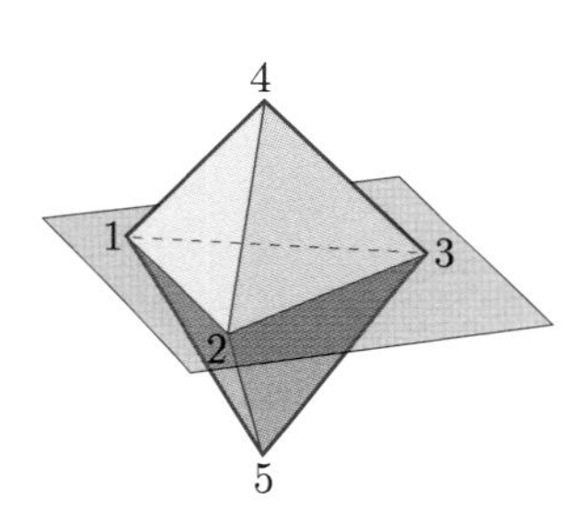


reflection in the horizontal
plane of symmetry

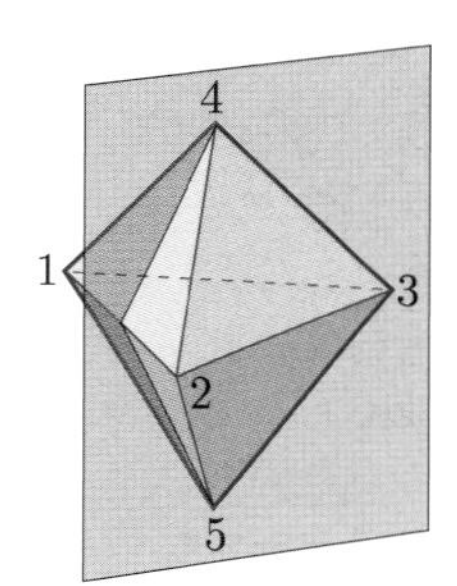


reflection in a vertical plane
of symmetry (three such planes)

The two remaining elements are indirect symmetries which are composites of the above reflections and rotations; for example, a reflection in the plane through vertices 1, 2 and 3, followed by a rotation through $2\pi/3$ or $4\pi/3$ about the axis through vertices 4 and 5.

There are the same number of indirect symmetries as direct symmetries, so the group has order 12.

This classifies the twelve elements of the symmetry group into six geometric types:

the identity (one symmetry);

the two types of rotation (two and three symmetries, respectively);

the two types of reflection (one symmetry and three symmetries, respectively);

the remaining symmetries, which are composites of those mentioned already (two symmetries).

We now find the conjugacy classes so that we can see whether the partition into conjugacy classes is the same as the partition by geometric type. Let us represent each of the twelve symmetries by the corresponding permutation of the five vertices, labelled as shown in the diagrams above. Then the symmetry group of the double tetrahedron is represented as a permutation group $G$, a subgroup of $S_5$ of order 12.

To find the conjugacy classes, it is helpful to begin by partitioning the twelve elements according to their cycle structure in $G$, as shown in the following table.

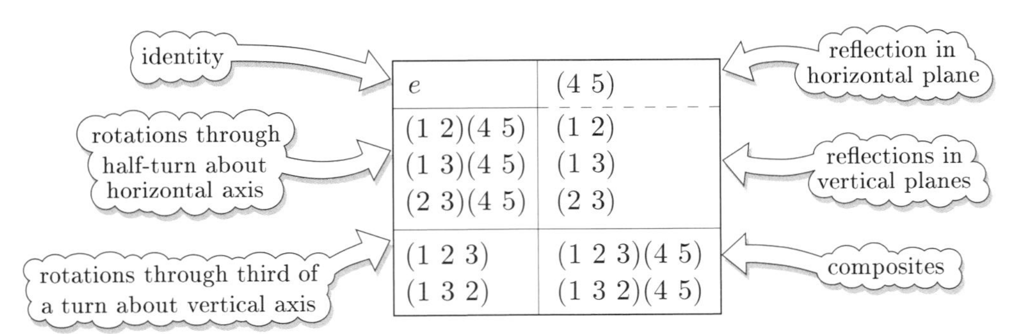


| | |
|---|---|
| $e$ | $(4\ 5)$ |
| $(1\ 2)(4\ 5)$<br>$(1\ 3)(4\ 5)$<br>$(2\ 3)(4\ 5)$ | $(1\ 2)$<br>$(1\ 3)$<br>$(2\ 3)$ |
| $(1\ 2\ 3)$<br>$(1\ 3\ 2)$ | $(1\ 2\ 3)(4\ 5)$<br>$(1\ 3\ 2)(4\ 5)$ |

The four elements $(4\ 5)$, $(1\ 2)$, $(1\ 3)$ and $(2\ 3)$ all lie in the same class of the partition by cycle structure. Unlike the other classes in this partition, this class contains elements of different geometric type, as indicated by the dotted line.

It is helpful to do this because whenever we represent the elements of a symmetry group as permutations, the partition into conjugacy classes can always be obtained by further 'splitting' some (or none) of the classes of the partition by cycle structure.

This is because if a symmetry group $G$ is represented as a subgroup of $S_n$, then any two elements that are conjugate in $G$ are also conjugate in $S_n$ and therefore have the same cycle structure.

Thus we can obtain the conjugacy classes of $G$ by starting with the partition by cycle structure and determining, for each subset in this partition, whether all the elements in that subset are conjugate to each other, or whether the subset splits into two or more conjugacy classes.

If the partition into conjugacy classes turns out to be the same as the partition by geometric type, then the only further split will be as indicated by the dotted line in the table above. This would give us two elements with the same cycle structure, $(1\ 2)$ and $(4\ 5)$, which are not conjugate in $G$. Can this happen?

It is indeed possible: we know that $(1\ 2)$ and $(4\ 5)$ are conjugate in $S_5$, but this does *not* mean that they are conjugate in $G$. This is because, although we know that there is at least one element $g$ in the group $S_5$ such that $(1\ 2) = g \circ (4\ 5) \circ g^{-1}$, there may not be any such element $g$ in the subgroup $G$ of $S_5$.

We have already met an example of non-conjugate elements with the same cycle structure. In $S(\square)$ with the elements represented as permutations of the vertex labels, the rotation $b$ has the same cycle structure as the reflection $t$, but $b$ and $t$ are not conjugate in $S(\square)$. (See Subsection 2.4.)

In the programme we prove the following result concerning the fixed point sets of conjugate symmetries. We use this theorem to help us complete the determination of the conjugacy classes of $G$.

**Theorem 4.1 Fixed Point Theorem**

Let $g$ and $k$ be elements of a symmetry group $G$. If $L$ is the fixed point set of $g$, then $k(L)$ is the fixed point set of the conjugate element $kgk^{-1}$.

We write $kgk^{-1}$ rather than $k \circ g \circ k^{-1}$ for ease of presentation. We usually omit the operation $\circ$ in composites in the rest of this section. Thus if $f$ and $g$ are functions (such as permutations), then $fg$ denotes the *composite* $f \circ g$. Be careful not to confuse this notation with the notation used in the analysis blocks where $fg$ denotes the *product* of real functions $f$ and $g$.

To illustrate how the theorem can be used to help determine conjugacy classes in the symmetry group of the double tetrahedron, consider the symmetry $s = (1\ 2)$, which is the reflection in the plane passing through the vertices 3, 4 and 5, shown in the following diagram. Its fixed point set is the part of this plane lying within the double tetrahedron.

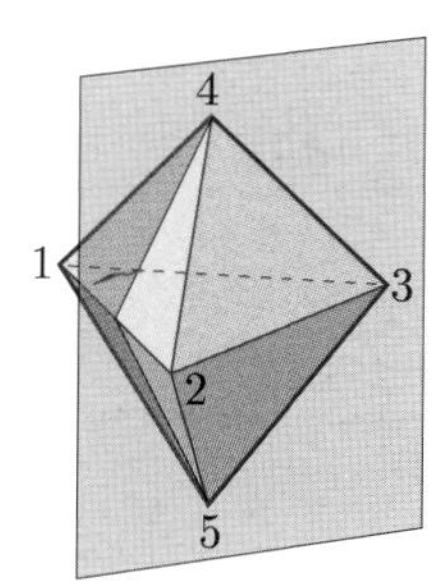


The Fixed Point Theorem tells us that any conjugate $ksk^{-1}$ of $s$ in $G$ is a symmetry whose fixed point set is the image under $k$ of the fixed point set of $s$. Now, symmetries of the double tetrahedron can map the plane through vertices 3, 4 and 5 to only three possible positions, namely to itself, to the plane through vertices 1, 4 and 5, and to the plane through vertices 2, 4 and 5. For example,

the fixed plane of $s$ is mapped to itself by $k = e$,

the fixed plane of $s$ is mapped to the plane through vertices 1, 4 and 5 by $k = (1\ 2\ 3)$,

the fixed plane of $s$ is mapped to the plane through vertices 2, 4 and 5 by $k = (1\ 3\ 2)$.

There are symmetries other than those given here that also map the fixed plane of $s$ to the planes given here.

The Fixed Point Theorem allows us to conclude that the only possible conjugates of $s$ are symmetries which have one of these three planes as a fixed point set. There are only three such symmetries, namely the three reflections in these three planes; that is, $s = (1\ 2)$ itself, $(1\ 3)$ and $(2\ 3)$.

We now have to determine whether each of these three reflections is indeed a conjugate of $s$. It seems reasonable to expect that the three symmetries $k$ described above would conjugate $s$ to these three reflections. We now check that conjugating $s = (1\ 2)$ by the identity, by $(1\ 2\ 3)$ and by $(1\ 3\ 2)$ in turn does indeed give $(1\ 2)$, $(2\ 3)$ and $(1\ 3)$, respectively.

There are two alternative ways in which we can check this. We can simply find the conjugates using the usual method for finding conjugates of permutations. Alternatively, we can argue using the Fixed Point Theorem. For example, the theorem tells us that if we conjugate $s = (1\ 2)$ by $k = (1\ 2\ 3)$, then the result is a symmetry whose fixed point set is the image under $k$ of the fixed plane of $s$. We have already worked out above that this image is the plane through vertices 1, 4 and 5. There is only one symmetry of the double tetrahedron whose fixed point set is this plane, namely the reflection $(2\ 3)$. Therefore the conjugate of $s = (1\ 2)$ by $k = (1\ 2\ 3)$ is $(2\ 3)$.

For example, we can conjugate $s = (1\ 2)$ by $k = (1\ 2\ 3)$ using the renaming method as follows.

$$\begin{array}{cc} & (1\ 2) \\ k & \downarrow\ \downarrow \\ & (2\ 3) \end{array}$$

Thus

$$(1\ 2\ 3)(1\ 2)(1\ 2\ 3)^{-1} = (2\ 3).$$

We can check in a similar way that the conjugate of $s = (1\ 2)$ by $k = (1\ 3\ 2)$ is $(1\ 3)$, and we know that the conjugate of $(1\ 2)$ by the identity is $(1\ 2)$. We conclude that the conjugacy class of $s$ is $\{(1\ 2), (1\ 3), (2\ 3)\}$.

The other conjugacy classes can be found in a similar way.

*Remark* The above approach to finding the conjugacy class of a given element $s$ of a symmetry group can be summarised as follows.

1. Find each symmetry $t$ for which there is a symmetry $k$ that maps $\text{Fix}(s)$ to $\text{Fix}(t)$. Each such symmetry $t$ *may* be a conjugate of $s$. Any other symmetry is not a conjugate of $s$.
2. To test whether each such symmetry $t$ is a conjugate of $s$, try checking whether $t = ksk^{-1}$, where $k$ is a symmetry that maps $\text{Fix}(s)$ to $\text{Fix}(t)$.

If $t \neq ksk^{-1}$, then $t$ may or may not be a conjugate of $s$.

## Post-programme work

Although the programme was concerned only with symmetry groups, the Fixed Point Theorem is true for any group whose elements are functions of some kind. For example, above we used a permutation group to represent a symmetry group, but we can also consider a permutation group simply in terms of the effects its elements have on the symbols permuted. The fixed point set of each permutation is then just the set of symbols that it fixes.

**Exercise 4.2** Let $g = (1\ 2\ 4)(5\ 7)$ in $S_7$. For each of the following elements $k \in S_7$, write down the conjugate $kgk^{-1}$ and verify that $k$ maps $\{3, 6\}$, the fixed point set of $g$, to the fixed point set of $kgk^{-1}$.

(a) $k = (2\ 3\ 5\ 6)$ (b) $k = (1\ 3)(4\ 7)$

We end this subsection with a theorem that is sometimes useful when determining the conjugacy classes of a symmetry group.

**Theorem 4.2** A direct symmetry cannot be conjugate to an indirect symmetry in a symmetry group.

**Proof** We use the fact that the composite of two direct symmetries or two indirect symmetries is a direct symmetry, whereas the composite of a direct symmetry and an indirect symmetry is an indirect symmetry. We also use the facts that the inverse of a direct symmetry is direct and that the inverse of an indirect symmetry is indirect.

Let $g$ be a direct symmetry in a symmetry group and let $k$ be any element of the group. If $k$ is direct, then $kgk^{-1}$ is the composite of three direct symmetries and is therefore direct. If $k$ is indirect, then $kgk^{-1}$ is the composite of a direct symmetry and two indirect symmetries and is therefore again direct. Therefore every conjugate of $g$ is direct, which proves the theorem. ■

# 4.3 Conjugacy in $S(⬡)$

In this subsection we revise much of what we have done in this unit by applying our ideas about conjugacy to the group $S(⬡)$—the symmetry group of a regular hexagon. The group $S(⬡)$ has order 12, comprising a rotational subgroup of order 6 (the distinct powers of $a$, the anticlockwise rotation through $\pi/3$), together with the reflections $q_1$, $q_2$, $q_3$, $q_4$, $q_5$ and $q_6$ in the lines of symmetry $l_1$, $l_2$, $l_3$, $l_4$, $l_5$ and $l_6$, respectively, as illustrated in the following figures.

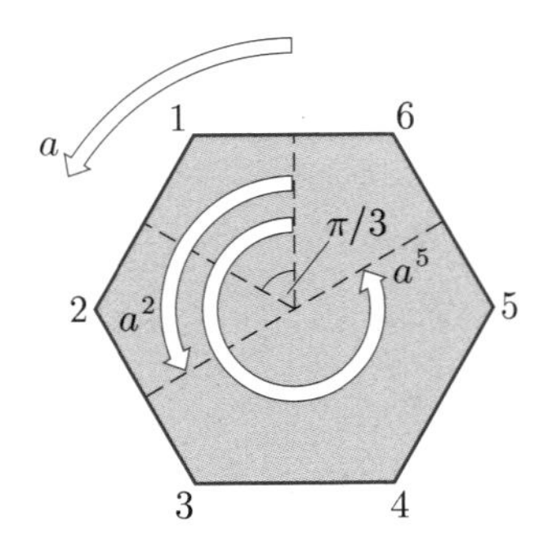


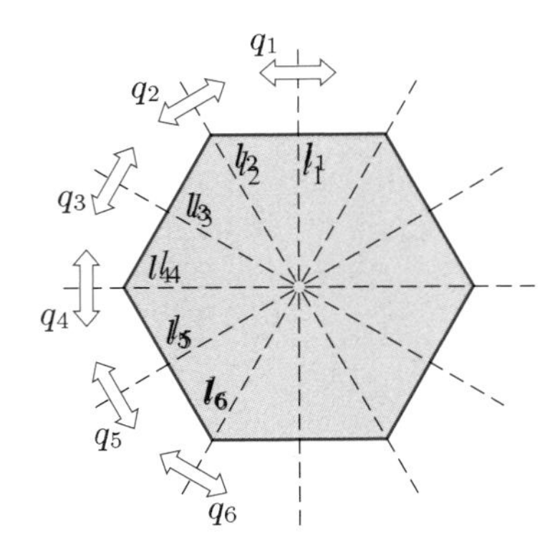

**Exercise 4.3** Predict the conjugacy classes of $S(\hexagon)$ by partitioning the twelve elements according to geometric type.

We shall now attempt to confirm that the conjugacy classes predicted in Exercise 4.3 are correct. We begin by representing the elements of $S(\hexagon)$ as permutations.

By labelling the vertices as shown in the figure, we can write $S(\hexagon)$ as a subgroup of $S_6$. For instance, the rotation $a$ is the permutation $(1\ 2\ 3\ 4\ 5\ 6)$ and the reflection $q_4$ is $(1\ 3)(4\ 6)$.

**Exercise 4.4** Express the twelve elements of $S(\hexagon)$ as permutations of the vertex labels of the hexagon. Partition the twelve elements by cycle structure.

We obtain the conjugacy classes of $S(\hexagon)$ by starting with its partition by cycle structure; we then determine, for each subset in that partition, whether all the elements in the subset are conjugate to each other, or whether the subset splits into two or more conjugacy classes.

Consider first the symmetries with cycle structure $(-\ -)(-\ -)(-\ -)$: this subset contains the rotation $a^3$ (through $\pi$), and the reflections $q_1$, $q_3$ and $q_5$. We predicted that $a^3$ is not in the same conjugacy class as $q_1$, $q_3$ and $q_5$ because it is of a different geometric type, so we expect this set to split into more than one conjugacy class. In fact, $a^3$ cannot be conjugate to any of $q_1$, $q_3$ and $q_5$ because $a^3$ is a direct symmetry and reflections are indirect symmetries.

See Theorem 4.2.

Thus this subset splits at least into $\{a^3\}$ and $\{q_1, q_3, q_5\}$. It remains to establish whether the set $\{q_1, q_3, q_5\}$ splits further, or whether this set is a conjugacy class. You are asked to establish this in the next exercise.

**Exercise 4.5** Determine the fixed point set of the reflection $q_1$. To where can this fixed point set be mapped by the elements of $S(\hexagon)$? Use step 2 of the remark on page 41 to determine the conjugacy class of $q_1$.

We found in Exercise 4.5 that $\{q_1, q_3, q_5\}$ is a conjugacy class of $S(\hexagon)$. We can show in a similar way that $\{q_2, q_4, q_6\}$ is another conjugacy class; we omit the details here.

To complete the classification into conjugacy classes, it remains to decide whether the rotations $a$ and $a^5$ are conjugate and whether $a^2$ and $a^4$ are conjugate.

The approach of the remark on page 41 does not help us to do this. The fixed point set of each of the rotations $a$, $a^2$, $a^4$ and $a^5$ is the central point of the hexagon. Hence for each pair of these rotations there is a symmetry of the hexagon that maps the fixed point set of one of the pair to the fixed point set of the other, but it is not true that each pair of these rotations is a conjugate pair. We therefore have to think more carefully when choosing symmetries that we would expect to conjugate $a$ to $a^5$ or $a^2$ to $a^4$.

For example, $a$ and $a^2$ are not conjugate.

**Exercise 4.6** By finding suitable conjugating elements, show that the two elements in each of the following classes are conjugate to each other.

(a) $\{a, a^5\}$ (b) $\{a^2, a^4\}$

The informal explanation of geometric type in Subsection 2.4 may help you to predict suitable conjugating elements.

We now know the partition of $S(\hexagon)$ into conjugacy classes.

| Conjugacy class | Cycle structure | Number of elements |
|---|---|---|
| $C_1 = \{e\}$ | (−)(−)(−)(−)(−)(−) | 1 |
| $C_2 = \{a, a^5\}$ | (− − − − − −) | 2 |
| $C_3 = \{a^2, a^4\}$ | (− − −)(− − −) | 2 |
| $C_4 = \{a^3\}$ | (− −)(− −)(− −) | 1 |
| $C_5 = \{q_1, q_3, q_5\}$ | (− −)(− −)(− −) | 3 |
| $C_6 = \{q_2, q_4, q_6\}$ | (− −)(− −)(−)(−) | 3 |

The cycle structure given here is that of the corresponding permutation of the vertices.

The partition into conjugacy classes agrees with the partition by geometric type found in Exercise 4.3, as expected.

We are now ready for a final exercise. Which subgroups of $S(\hexagon)$ are normal? Strategy 3.4 gives a method for determining the normal subgroups of a finite group whose conjugacy classes are known. Following this strategy, we now look for unions of conjugacy classes, including $\{e\}$, in which the total number of elements divides 12, the order of $S(\hexagon)$. Any such union which is a subgroup of $S(\hexagon)$ must be a normal subgroup.

**Exercise 4.7** Use Strategy 3.4 to determine all the normal subgroups of $S(\hexagon)$.

## 4.4 Proof of the Fixed Point Theorem

We now prove our main result.

**Theorem 4.1 Fixed Point Theorem**

Let $g$ and $k$ be elements of a group $G$ of functions. If $L$ is the fixed point set of $g$, then $k(L)$ is the fixed point set of the conjugate element $kgk^{-1}$.

If you are short of time, omit this proof.

**Proof** Let $L$ be the fixed point set of $g$. We have to show that two sets are equal: $k(L)$ and the fixed point set of $kgk^{-1}$.

Throughout this proof we use the fact that if $f_1$ and $f_2$ are functions, then

$$(f_2 \circ f_1)(x) = f_2(f_1(x))$$

for all $x$ for which $f_2(f_1(x))$ is defined. (This is just the definition of $f_2 \circ f_1$.) We are omitting the symbol $\circ$ to simplify the notation, so this rule is written as

$$f_2 f_1(x) = f_2(f_1(x)).$$

First suppose that $x \in k(L)$. Then $k^{-1}(x) \in L$. Hence $k^{-1}(x)$ is fixed by $g$, so $g(k^{-1}(x)) = k^{-1}(x)$. Taking the image of each side of this equation under $k$ gives

$$k(g(k^{-1}(x))) = k(k^{-1}(x));$$

that is, $kgk^{-1}(x) = x$. Thus $x$ is in the fixed point set of $kgk^{-1}$. This shows that $k(L)$ is a subset of the fixed point set of $kgk^{-1}$.

Now suppose that $x$ is in the fixed point set of $kgk^{-1}$, so $kgk^{-1}(x) = x$. Taking the image of each side of this equation under $k^{-1}$ gives

$$k^{-1}(kgk^{-1}(x)) = k^{-1}(x);$$

that is, $g(k^{-1}(x)) = k^{-1}(x)$.

Thus $k^{-1}(x)$ is fixed by $g$, so $k^{-1}(x) \in L$. Hence $x \in k(L)$. This shows that the fixed point set of $kgk^{-1}$ is a subset of $k(L)$.

It follows that $k(L)$ is equal to the fixed point set of $kgk^{-1}$, as required. ■

## Further exercise

**Exercise 4.8** The group $G$ of direct symmetries of the square prism shown below has order 8, with the five axes of rotational symmetry indicated. The six faces of the prism are labelled as shown.

Here you are asked to consider conjugacy in the group of direct symmetries of the figure, not in the whole symmetry group as in earlier examples and exercises.

Axis 1 passes through faces 1 and 2, axis 3 passes through faces 3 and 5, and axis 5 passes through faces 4 and 6.

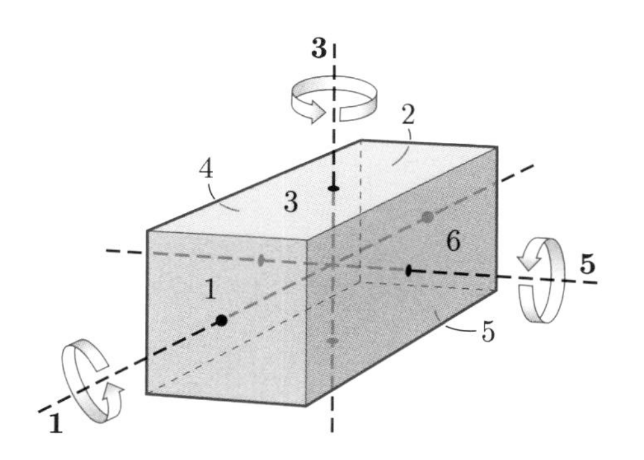


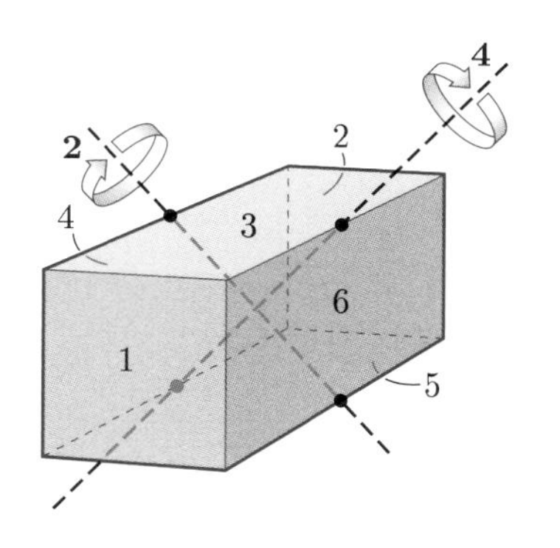


(a) Classify the eight elements of $G$ according to their geometric type.

(b) Represent each of the eight elements of $G$ as a permutation of the faces $\{1, 2, 3, 4, 5, 6\}$. Compare the classification of $G$ by cycle structure with your answer to part (a).

(c) Find the conjugacy classes of $G$ by checking whether elements with the same cycle structure in part (b) are conjugate in $G$.

# 5 Matrix groups

After working through this section, you should be able to:

(a) determine whether a given set of $2 \times 2$ matrices forms a group under matrix multiplication;

(b) calculate conjugate elements and conjugate subgroups in matrix groups;

(c) calculate cosets of a given subgroup of a given matrix group;

(d) work with the cosets of a given subgroup that is infinite and/or has infinite index.

In this section we study groups of matrices whose entries are real numbers: we shall see that these provide us with a rich source of examples of *infinite groups*.

All the definitions and results in group theory that we have met so far apply to infinite groups as well as to finite groups, with the exception of Lagrange's Theorem, which applies only to finite groups. In particular, the cosets of any subgroup form a partition of the group.

Although the idea is the same in theory, partitioning an infinite group into cosets can create new situations in practice. A subgroup of an infinite group can have infinite index; that is, infinitely many cosets. If this is the case, then we cannot list the subsets in the partition and so we need another way of describing the infinite set of distinct cosets. Later in this section we look at this problem in the context of groups of matrices.

## 5.1 Properties of matrices (revision)

In this section we consider the infinite groups of matrices that we encountered in the Linear Algebra Block. We consider the set of invertible $2 \times 2$ matrices with real entries and the binary operation of matrix multiplication. We explore conjugate subgroups and normal subgroups in this setting.

We begin by reviewing some important properties of matrices.

The $2 \times 2$ *identity matrix* for matrix multiplication is $\mathbf{I} = \begin{pmatrix} 1 & 0 \\ 0 & 1 \end{pmatrix}$.

Thus, for each $2 \times 2$ matrix $\mathbf{A}$,

$$\mathbf{AI} = \mathbf{A} = \mathbf{IA}.$$

A $2 \times 2$ matrix $\mathbf{A}$ is *invertible* if there exists a $2 \times 2$ matrix $\mathbf{B}$ such that

$$\mathbf{AB} = \mathbf{I} = \mathbf{BA}.$$

For any given invertible matrix $\mathbf{A}$, there exists exactly one matrix $\mathbf{B}$ with the above property. This matrix is denoted by $\mathbf{A}^{-1}$ and is called the *inverse* of $\mathbf{A}$. Thus, for any invertible matrix $\mathbf{A}$,

$$\mathbf{AA}^{-1} = \mathbf{I} = \mathbf{A}^{-1}\mathbf{A}.$$

We can determine whether a $2 \times 2$ matrix $\mathbf{A} = \begin{pmatrix} a & b \\ c & d \end{pmatrix}$ is invertible by calculating its *determinant*, which is

$$\det(\mathbf{A}) = ad - bc.$$

A matrix $\mathbf{A}$ is invertible if and only if $\det(\mathbf{A}) \neq 0$.

Determinants have the following multiplicative property. For all $2 \times 2$ matrices $\mathbf{A}$ and $\mathbf{B}$,

$$\det(\mathbf{AB}) = \det(\mathbf{A})\det(\mathbf{B}).$$

In particular, for any invertible $2 \times 2$ matrix $\mathbf{A}$,

$$\det(\mathbf{AA}^{-1}) = \det(\mathbf{A})\det(\mathbf{A}^{-1}).$$

Since $\det(\mathbf{AA}^{-1}) = \det \mathbf{I} = 1$, this gives the following further property of determinants. For any invertible $2 \times 2$ matrix $\mathbf{A}$,

$$\det(\mathbf{A}^{-1}) = 1/\det(\mathbf{A}).$$

We shall need to calculate matrix inverses; for an invertible $2 \times 2$ matrix this is done as follows.

$$\text{If } \mathbf{A} = \begin{pmatrix} a & b \\ c & d \end{pmatrix}, \quad \text{then } \mathbf{A}^{-1} = \frac{1}{ad - bc}\begin{pmatrix} d & -b \\ -c & a \end{pmatrix}, \quad \text{where } ad - bc \neq 0.$$

Thus to find $\mathbf{A}^{-1}$ from $\mathbf{A}$, carry out the following steps.

1. Interchange the two entries on the leading diagonal ($a$ and $d$).
2. Change the signs of the other entries ($b$ and $c$);
3. Divide each entry by $\det(\mathbf{A}) = ad - bc$.

**Exercise 5.1** Decide whether each of the following matrices is invertible, and write down the inverse if it exists.

(a) $\begin{pmatrix} 2 & 1 \\ 0 & 1 \end{pmatrix}$ (b) $\begin{pmatrix} 0 & -1 \\ 1 & 0 \end{pmatrix}$ (c) $\begin{pmatrix} 1 & 3 \\ 0 & 2 \end{pmatrix}$

(d) $\begin{pmatrix} 3 & 1 \\ 6 & 2 \end{pmatrix}$ (e) $\begin{pmatrix} 2 & -2 \\ 1 & -1 \end{pmatrix}$ (f) $\begin{pmatrix} a & b \\ 0 & d \end{pmatrix}$

## 5.2 Examples of matrix groups

The groups that we consider here are all subgroups of one group, which we call $M$: it is the group of all invertible $2 \times 2$ matrices with real entries under matrix multiplication. In the first example we confirm that $M$ is a group.

**Example 5.1** Let

$$M = \left\{ \begin{pmatrix} a & b \\ c & d \end{pmatrix} : a, b, c, d \in \mathbb{R},\ ad - bc \neq 0 \right\}.$$

Show that $M$ is a group under matrix multiplication.

**Solution** We show that the four group axioms hold.

G1 CLOSURE Let $\mathbf{A}$ and $\mathbf{B}$ be any elements of $M$. Then $\mathbf{AB}$ is a $2 \times 2$ matrix. Also $\det(\mathbf{A}) \neq 0$ and $\det(\mathbf{B}) \neq 0$, so, since

$$\det(\mathbf{AB}) = \det(\mathbf{A})\det(\mathbf{B}),$$

it follows that $\det(\mathbf{AB}) \neq 0$. Hence $\mathbf{AB} \in M$, so $M$ is closed under matrix multiplication.

G2 IDENTITY The $2 \times 2$ identity matrix $\mathbf{I}$ has determinant $1 \neq 0$, so $\mathbf{I} \in M$ and we have

$$\mathbf{AI} = \mathbf{A} = \mathbf{IA}, \quad \text{for each } \mathbf{A} \in M.$$

So $\mathbf{I}$ is an identity element in $M$.

G3 INVERSES If $\mathbf{A}$ is any element of $M$, then $\det(\mathbf{A}) \neq 0$. Thus $\mathbf{A}^{-1}$ exists and $\det(\mathbf{A}^{-1}) = 1/\det(\mathbf{A}) \neq 0$, so $\mathbf{A}^{-1} \in M$ and we have

$$\mathbf{AA}^{-1} = \mathbf{I} = \mathbf{A}^{-1}\mathbf{A}, \quad \text{for each } \mathbf{A} \in M.$$

So each element $\mathbf{A} \in M$ has an inverse element $\mathbf{A}^{-1} \in M$.

G4 ASSOCIATIVITY Matrix multiplication is associative.

Hence $(M, \times)$ satisfies the four group axioms and so is a group. ■

*Remark* Since $(M, \times)$ is a group, inverses in $M$ have the following properties:

Unit GTA1, Properties 4.3 and 4.4.

$$(\mathbf{A}^{-1})^{-1} = \mathbf{A}, \quad \text{for each } \mathbf{A} \in M,$$
$$(\mathbf{AB})^{-1} = \mathbf{B}^{-1}\mathbf{A}^{-1}, \quad \text{for each } \mathbf{A}, \mathbf{B} \in M.$$

We are now ready to explore the many subgroups of $M$.

**Listen to the audio as you work through the frames.**

Audio

## 1. Is $U = \left\{ \begin{pmatrix} a & b \\ 0 & d \end{pmatrix} : ad \neq 0 \right\}$ a subgroup of M?

SG1 CLOSURE Let $\begin{pmatrix} a & b \\ 0 & d \end{pmatrix}, \begin{pmatrix} x & y \\ 0 & z \end{pmatrix} \in U$, so that

$ad \neq 0,\ xz \neq 0$; then

$$\begin{pmatrix} a & b \\ 0 & d \end{pmatrix}\begin{pmatrix} x & y \\ 0 & z \end{pmatrix} = \begin{pmatrix} ax & ay + bz \\ 0 & dz \end{pmatrix} \in U,$$

because $ax \times dz = ad \times xz \neq 0$.

SG2 IDENTITY $\mathbf{I} = \begin{pmatrix} 1 & 0 \\ 0 & 1 \end{pmatrix} \in U$, because $\det(\mathbf{I}) = 1 \neq 0$.

SG3 INVERSES $\begin{pmatrix} a & b \\ 0 & d \end{pmatrix}^{-1} = \frac{1}{ad}\begin{pmatrix} d & -b \\ 0 & a \end{pmatrix} \in U$,

because

determinant $= \frac{d}{ad} \times \frac{a}{ad} = \frac{1}{ad} \neq 0$.

$ad \neq 0$

Hence U is a subgroup of M.

## 2. Is $W = \left\{ \begin{pmatrix} a & 1 \\ 0 & d \end{pmatrix} : ad \neq 0 \right\}$ a subgroup of M?

SG2 fails, because $\mathbf{I} = \begin{pmatrix} 1 & 0 \\ 0 & 1 \end{pmatrix} \notin W$, so

W is not a subgroup of M.

## 3. Is $V = \left\{ \begin{pmatrix} a & b \\ c & d \end{pmatrix} : ad - bc = 1 \right\}$ a subgroup of M?

SG1 CLOSURE Let $\mathbf{A}, \mathbf{B} \in V$, so that $\det(\mathbf{A}) = \det(\mathbf{B}) = 1$;

then

$$\det(\mathbf{AB}) = \det(\mathbf{A}) \times \det(\mathbf{B}) = 1 \times 1 = 1,$$

so $\mathbf{AB} \in V$.

SG2 IDENTITY $\mathbf{I} = \begin{pmatrix} 1 & 0 \\ 0 & 1 \end{pmatrix}$; $\det(\mathbf{I}) = 1$, so $\mathbf{I} \in V$.

SG3 INVERSES For $\mathbf{A} \in V$, $\det(\mathbf{A}) = 1$, and

$\det(\mathbf{A}^{-1}) = 1/\det(\mathbf{A}) = 1/1 = 1$,

so $\mathbf{A}^{-1} \in V$.

Hence V is a subgroup of M.

## 4. Exercise 5.2

Show that:

(a) $H = \left\{ \begin{pmatrix} a & 0 \\ 0 & d \end{pmatrix} : ad = 1 \right\}$ is a subgroup of V;

(b) $N = \left\{ \begin{pmatrix} a & b \\ 0 & a \end{pmatrix} : a \neq 0 \right\}$ is a subgroup of U;

(c) $X = \left\{ \begin{pmatrix} a & b \\ c & 1 \end{pmatrix} : a - bc \neq 0 \right\}$ is not a subgroup of M.

## 5. Conjugate subgroups

Let H be a subgroup of a group G.

For any $g \in G$, define

$$gHg^{-1} = \{ghg^{-1} : h \in H\};$$

then $gHg^{-1}$ is a subgroup of G.

H and $gHg^{-1}$ are **conjugate subgroups**

## 6. Conjugating H in the group M

Let $H = \left\{\begin{pmatrix} a & 0 \\ 0 & d\end{pmatrix} : ad = 1\right\}$, $\mathbf{g} = \begin{pmatrix} 2 & 1 \\ 0 & 1\end{pmatrix} \in M$; then

$$\mathbf{g}H\mathbf{g}^{-1} = \left\{\begin{pmatrix} 2 & 1 \\ 0 & 1\end{pmatrix}\begin{pmatrix} a & 0 \\ 0 & d\end{pmatrix}\begin{pmatrix} 2 & 1 \\ 0 & 1\end{pmatrix}^{-1} : ad = 1\right\}$$

(g, h, $g^{-1}$)

$$= \left\{\begin{pmatrix} 2a & d \\ 0 & d\end{pmatrix}\begin{pmatrix} \frac{1}{2} & -\frac{1}{2} \\ 0 & 1\end{pmatrix} : ad = 1\right\}$$

$$= \left\{\begin{pmatrix} a & d-a \\ 0 & d\end{pmatrix} : ad = 1\right\}.$$

$d-a$ can be **non-zero**

So $\mathbf{g}H\mathbf{g}^{-1}$ is a **different** subgroup of M.

for this $\mathbf{g}$, $\mathbf{g}H\mathbf{g}^{-1} \neq H$

## 7. Conjugating U in the group M

Let $U = \left\{\begin{pmatrix} a & b \\ 0 & d\end{pmatrix} : ad \neq 0\right\}$, $\mathbf{g} = \begin{pmatrix} 0 & -1 \\ 1 & 0\end{pmatrix} \in M$; then

$$\mathbf{g}U\mathbf{g}^{-1} = \left\{\begin{pmatrix} 0 & -1 \\ 1 & 0\end{pmatrix}\begin{pmatrix} a & b \\ 0 & d\end{pmatrix}\begin{pmatrix} 0 & -1 \\ 1 & 0\end{pmatrix}^{-1} : ad \neq 0\right\}$$

(g, u, $g^{-1}$)

$$= \left\{\begin{pmatrix} 0 & -d \\ a & b\end{pmatrix}\begin{pmatrix} 0 & 1 \\ -1 & 0\end{pmatrix} : ad \neq 0\right\}$$

$$= \left\{\begin{pmatrix} d & \mathbf{0} \\ -b & a\end{pmatrix} : ad \neq 0\right\}$$

**lower** triangular matrices

So $\mathbf{g}U\mathbf{g}^{-1}$ is a **different** subgroup of M.

for this $\mathbf{g}$, $\mathbf{g}U\mathbf{g}^{-1} \neq U$

## 8. Exercise 5.3

Determine the following subgroups in M:

(a) $\begin{pmatrix} 1 & 2 \\ 0 & 1\end{pmatrix} H \begin{pmatrix} 1 & 2 \\ 0 & 1\end{pmatrix}^{-1}$;

(b) $\begin{pmatrix} 1 & 0 \\ 1 & 1\end{pmatrix} H \begin{pmatrix} 1 & 0 \\ 1 & 1\end{pmatrix}^{-1}$;

(c) $\begin{pmatrix} 1 & 1 \\ 0 & 1\end{pmatrix} U \begin{pmatrix} 1 & 1 \\ 0 & 1\end{pmatrix}^{-1}$.

Do you get any **new** subgroups?

## 9. Conjugate subgroups of N in U

Let $N = \left\{\begin{pmatrix} a & b \\ 0 & a \end{pmatrix} : a \neq 0\right\}$, $g = \begin{pmatrix} 1 & 3 \\ 0 & 2 \end{pmatrix} \in U$; then

$$\begin{pmatrix} 1 & 3 \\ 0 & 2 \end{pmatrix} N \begin{pmatrix} 1 & 3 \\ 0 & 2 \end{pmatrix}^{-1} = \left\{\begin{pmatrix} 1 & 3 \\ 0 & 2 \end{pmatrix}\begin{pmatrix} a & b \\ 0 & a \end{pmatrix}\begin{pmatrix} 1 & 3 \\ 0 & 2 \end{pmatrix}^{-1} : a \neq 0\right\}$$

$$= \left\{\begin{pmatrix} a & b+3a \\ 0 & 2a \end{pmatrix}\begin{pmatrix} 1 & -\frac{3}{2} \\ 0 & \frac{1}{2} \end{pmatrix} : a \neq 0\right\}$$

$$= \left\{\begin{pmatrix} a & \frac{b}{2} \\ 0 & a \end{pmatrix} : a \neq 0\right\} = N;$$

(g) ($b \in \mathbb{R}$) ($\frac{b}{2}$ can take ANY real value)

$$\begin{pmatrix} 2 & -3 \\ 0 & -1 \end{pmatrix} N \begin{pmatrix} 2 & -3 \\ 0 & -1 \end{pmatrix}^{-1} = \left\{\begin{pmatrix} 2 & -3 \\ 0 & -1 \end{pmatrix}\begin{pmatrix} a & b \\ 0 & a \end{pmatrix}\begin{pmatrix} 2 & -3 \\ 0 & -1 \end{pmatrix}^{-1} : a \neq 0\right\}$$

$$= \left\{\begin{pmatrix} 2a & 2b-3a \\ 0 & -a \end{pmatrix}\begin{pmatrix} \frac{1}{2} & -\frac{3}{2} \\ 0 & -1 \end{pmatrix} : a \neq 0\right\}$$

$$= \left\{\begin{pmatrix} a & -2b \\ 0 & a \end{pmatrix} : a \neq 0\right\} = N.$$

(g) ($-2b$ can take ANY real value)

In general,

$$\begin{pmatrix} x & y \\ 0 & z \end{pmatrix} N \begin{pmatrix} x & y \\ 0 & z \end{pmatrix}^{-1} = \left\{\begin{pmatrix} x & y \\ 0 & z \end{pmatrix}\begin{pmatrix} a & b \\ 0 & a \end{pmatrix}\begin{pmatrix} x & y \\ 0 & z \end{pmatrix}^{-1} : a \neq 0, xz \neq 0\right\}$$

$$= \left\{\begin{pmatrix} xa & xb+ya \\ 0 & za \end{pmatrix}\begin{pmatrix} \frac{1}{x} & -\frac{y}{xz} \\ 0 & \frac{1}{z} \end{pmatrix} : a \neq 0, xz \neq 0\right\}$$

$$= \left\{\begin{pmatrix} a & \frac{xb}{z} \\ 0 & a \end{pmatrix} : a \neq 0, xz \neq 0\right\} = N.$$

So N is a **normal subgroup** of U.

(for ALL $g \in U$, $gNg^{-1} = N$)

## 10. Strategies 3.2 and 3.3 for normal subgroups

**GUESS** behaviour ........... **CHECK** definition.

**To show that N is a normal subgroup of G,**

take general elements $g \in G$, $n \in N$,

and show that $gng^{-1} \in N$.

(need general proof, as in Frame 9)

**To show that N is NOT a normal subgroup of G,**

find ONE $g \in G$ and ONE $n \in N$

such that $gng^{-1} \notin N$.

(need ONE counter-example, as in Frames 6, 7)

## 11. Exercise 5.4

Use the strategies above to determine whether

(a) $D = \left\{\begin{pmatrix} a & 0 \\ 0 & d \end{pmatrix} : ad \neq 0\right\}$ is a normal subgroup of M;

(b) $N = \left\{\begin{pmatrix} a & b \\ 0 & a \end{pmatrix} : a \neq 0\right\}$ is a normal subgroup of M;

(c) $Y = \left\{\begin{pmatrix} 1 & b \\ 0 & 1 \end{pmatrix} : b \in \mathbb{R}\right\}$ is a normal subgroup of U.

(You need not check the subgroup properties.)

## 5.3 Cosets in matrix groups

We now look briefly at cosets in the context of matrix groups.

We work with the group $U$ of upper triangular invertible $2 \times 2$ matrices under matrix multiplication:

$$U = \left\{ \begin{pmatrix} a & b \\ 0 & d \end{pmatrix} : a, b, d \in \mathbb{R},\ ad \neq 0 \right\}.$$

See Frame 1.

First we consider cosets of the following (normal) subgroup $N$ of $U$:

$$N = \left\{ \begin{pmatrix} a & b \\ 0 & a \end{pmatrix} : a, b \in \mathbb{R},\ a \neq 0 \right\}.$$

See Frames 4 and 9. We have included the condition $a, b \in \mathbb{R}$ after the colon because it aids clarity to do so in this subsection. In Subsection 5.2 we often omitted conditions like this and just assumed that the variables take all real values satisfying the other specified conditions.

We begin by looking at some particular cosets of $N$ in $U$. For example, consider the coset $\begin{pmatrix} 3 & 4 \\ 0 & 5 \end{pmatrix} N$. The subgroup $N$ contains the particular elements

$$\begin{pmatrix} 2 & 1 \\ 0 & 2 \end{pmatrix} \quad \text{and} \quad \begin{pmatrix} \pi & 17 \\ 0 & \pi \end{pmatrix},$$

so the coset $\begin{pmatrix} 3 & 4 \\ 0 & 5 \end{pmatrix} N$ contains the particular elements

$$\begin{pmatrix} 3 & 4 \\ 0 & 5 \end{pmatrix} \begin{pmatrix} 2 & 1 \\ 0 & 2 \end{pmatrix} = \begin{pmatrix} 6 & 11 \\ 0 & 10 \end{pmatrix}$$

and

$$\begin{pmatrix} 3 & 4 \\ 0 & 5 \end{pmatrix} \begin{pmatrix} \pi & 17 \\ 0 & \pi \end{pmatrix} = \begin{pmatrix} 3\pi & 51 + 4\pi \\ 0 & 5\pi \end{pmatrix}.$$

How can we describe the set of matrices in the coset $\begin{pmatrix} 3 & 4 \\ 0 & 5 \end{pmatrix} N$?

By definition,

$$\begin{aligned} \begin{pmatrix} 3 & 4 \\ 0 & 5 \end{pmatrix} N &= \left\{ \begin{pmatrix} 3 & 4 \\ 0 & 5 \end{pmatrix} \mathbf{A} : \mathbf{A} \in N \right\} \\ &= \left\{ \begin{pmatrix} 3 & 4 \\ 0 & 5 \end{pmatrix} \begin{pmatrix} a & b \\ 0 & a \end{pmatrix} : a, b \in \mathbb{R},\ a \neq 0 \right\} \\ &= \left\{ \begin{pmatrix} 3a & 3b + 4a \\ 0 & 5a \end{pmatrix} : a \in \mathbb{R}^*,\ b \in \mathbb{R} \right\}. \end{aligned}$$

We have written the conditions

$a, b \in \mathbb{R},\ a \neq 0$

slightly more simply as

$a \in \mathbb{R}^*,\ b \in \mathbb{R}$.

This describes the coset, but we can simplify this description. For any particular value of $a \in \mathbb{R}^*$, as $b$ takes all values in $\mathbb{R}$, so does $3b + 4a$. So instead of specifying that the top right entry of the matrix is $3b + 4a$ where $b \in \mathbb{R}$, we can specify that it is simply $y$, say, where $y \in \mathbb{R}$. So we obtain

$$\begin{pmatrix} 3 & 4 \\ 0 & 5 \end{pmatrix} N = \left\{ \begin{pmatrix} 3a & y \\ 0 & 5a \end{pmatrix} : a \in \mathbb{R}^*,\ y \in \mathbb{R} \right\}.$$

We can make a further small simplification. As $a$ takes all values in $\mathbb{R}^*$, so does $3a$. So instead of specifying that the top left entry of the matrix is $3a$ where $a \in \mathbb{R}^*$, we can put $3a = x$, say, and specify that the entry is $x$ where $x \in \mathbb{R}^*$. However the bottom right entry of the matrix is also expressed in terms of $a$, so we have to express it in terms of $x$. Substituting $a = x/3$ gives $5a = \frac{5}{3}x$. Thus we can describe the coset as

$$\begin{pmatrix} 3 & 4 \\ 0 & 5 \end{pmatrix} N = \left\{ \begin{pmatrix} x & y \\ 0 & \frac{5}{3}x \end{pmatrix} : x \in \mathbb{R}^*,\ y \in \mathbb{R} \right\}.$$

**Exercise 5.5** Find a similar expression for each of the following cosets of $N$ in $U$.

(a) $\begin{pmatrix} -5 & -3 \\ 0 & 2 \end{pmatrix} N$ (b) $\begin{pmatrix} 3 & 5 \\ 0 & 3 \end{pmatrix} N$

So far, we have found expressions for *particular* cosets. How can we describe a *general* coset of $N$ in $U$?

Consider a general coset

$$\begin{pmatrix} p & q \\ 0 & s \end{pmatrix} N, \quad \text{where } p, q, s \in \mathbb{R} \text{ and } ps \neq 0.$$

The matrix $\begin{pmatrix} p & q \\ 0 & s \end{pmatrix}$, where $p, q, s \in \mathbb{R}$ and $ps \neq 0$, is a general element of $U$.

By definition,

$$\begin{aligned}\begin{pmatrix} p & q \\ 0 & s \end{pmatrix} N &= \left\{ \begin{pmatrix} p & q \\ 0 & s \end{pmatrix} \mathbf{A} : \mathbf{A} \in N \right\} \\ &= \left\{ \begin{pmatrix} p & q \\ 0 & s \end{pmatrix} \begin{pmatrix} a & b \\ 0 & a \end{pmatrix} : a, b \in \mathbb{R},\ a \neq 0 \right\} \\ &= \left\{ \begin{pmatrix} pa & pb + qa \\ 0 & sa \end{pmatrix} : a \in \mathbb{R}^*,\ b \in \mathbb{R} \right\}.\end{aligned}$$

As with the particular examples that we have looked at, we can simplify this description. For any particular value of $a \in \mathbb{R}^*$, as $b$ takes all values in $\mathbb{R}$, so does $pb + qa$, so we can specify that the top right entry of the matrix is simply $y$, say, where $y \in \mathbb{R}$. Similarly, we can specify that the top left and bottom right entries are $x$ and $(s/p)x$, respectively, where $x \in \mathbb{R}^*$. Thus we can describe the coset as

$$\begin{pmatrix} p & q \\ 0 & s \end{pmatrix} N = \left\{ \begin{pmatrix} x & y \\ 0 & (s/p)x \end{pmatrix} : x \in \mathbb{R}^*,\ y \in \mathbb{R} \right\}. \tag{5.1}$$

This is a useful way to describe a general coset $\begin{pmatrix} p & q \\ 0 & s \end{pmatrix} N$ of $N$ in $U$.

We now find a way to describe the *set of cosets* of $N$ in $U$. One obvious way to describe this set is as

$$\left\{ \begin{pmatrix} p & q \\ 0 & s \end{pmatrix} N : \begin{pmatrix} p & q \\ 0 & s \end{pmatrix} \in U \right\};$$

that is, as

$$\left\{ \begin{pmatrix} p & q \\ 0 & s \end{pmatrix} N : p, s \in \mathbb{R}^*, q \in \mathbb{R} \right\}.$$

However, this description has the disadvantage that different choices of the triple of values $p$, $q$ and $s$ give the same coset $\begin{pmatrix} p & q \\ 0 & s \end{pmatrix} N$. Let us try to find a simpler description. We begin by choosing a 'simple' element from the general coset $\begin{pmatrix} p & q \\ 0 & s \end{pmatrix} N$. We can take $x = 1$ and $y = 0$ in equation (5.1) to give us the element

That is, the set notation specifies each distinct coset more than once.

$$\begin{pmatrix} 1 & 0 \\ 0 & s/p \end{pmatrix} \in \begin{pmatrix} p & q \\ 0 & s \end{pmatrix} N.$$

Hence

$$\begin{pmatrix} 1 & 0 \\ 0 & s/p \end{pmatrix} N = \begin{pmatrix} p & q \\ 0 & s \end{pmatrix} N,$$

Recall that if $H$ is a subgroup of a group $G$ and $k$ is any element of the coset $gH$, then $kH = gH$.

so the set of cosets of $N$ in $U$ can be described more simply as

$$\left\{ \begin{pmatrix} 1 & 0 \\ 0 & s/p \end{pmatrix} N : p, s \in \mathbb{R}^* \right\}.$$

The condition $q \in \mathbb{R}$ is no longer needed because $q$ does not now appear on the left of the colon.

We can simplify this description further. As $s$ and $p$ take all values in $\mathbb{R}^*$, so does $s/p$, so we can put $s/p = r$, where $r \in \mathbb{R}^*$. Hence the set of cosets can be described as

$$\left\{ \begin{pmatrix} 1 & 0 \\ 0 & r \end{pmatrix} N : r \in \mathbb{R}^* \right\}. \tag{5.2}$$

This description is a good one because, for each coset of $N$ in $U$, there is a *unique* value of $r$ such that the coset is $\begin{pmatrix} 1 & 0 \\ 0 & r \end{pmatrix} N$, as we now prove.

In other words, different values of $r$ give different cosets.

We use the standard method for proving uniqueness: we assume that $r_1$ and $r_2$ correspond to the same coset, and deduce that they must be equal.

If $r_1$ and $r_2$ are elements of $\mathbb{R}^*$ such that

$$\begin{pmatrix} 1 & 0 \\ 0 & r_1 \end{pmatrix} N = \begin{pmatrix} 1 & 0 \\ 0 & r_2 \end{pmatrix} N,$$

then

$$\begin{pmatrix} 1 & 0 \\ 0 & r_1 \end{pmatrix} \in \begin{pmatrix} 1 & 0 \\ 0 & r_2 \end{pmatrix} N.$$

Now, by equation (5.1),

$$\begin{pmatrix} 1 & 0 \\ 0 & r_2 \end{pmatrix} N = \left\{ \begin{pmatrix} x & y \\ 0 & r_2 x \end{pmatrix} : x \in \mathbb{R}^*,\ y \in \mathbb{R} \right\},$$

so

$$\begin{pmatrix} 1 & 0 \\ 0 & r_1 \end{pmatrix} = \begin{pmatrix} x & y \\ 0 & r_2 x \end{pmatrix} \quad \text{for some } x \in \mathbb{R}^* \text{ and } y \in \mathbb{R}.$$

Equating corresponding entries in these two matrices shows that $x = 1$ and hence that $r_1 = r_2$, as required.

**Exercise 5.6** Consider the following subgroup $Y$ of $U$:

$$Y = \left\{ \begin{pmatrix} 1 & b \\ 0 & 1 \end{pmatrix} : b \in \mathbb{R} \right\}.$$

See Frame 11.

(a) Find an expression for the particular coset

$$\begin{pmatrix} 3 & 4 \\ 0 & 5 \end{pmatrix} Y.$$

(b) Find an expression for the general coset

$$\begin{pmatrix} p & q \\ 0 & s \end{pmatrix} Y.$$

(c) Describe the set of cosets of $Y$ in $U$ in a similar way to expression (5.2). (That is, your description should use set notation, and each distinct coset should be specified only once in this set notation.)

# Further exercises

In these exercises, $M$ is the group of all invertible $2 \times 2$ matrices with real entries, under matrix multiplication.

**Exercise 5.7** Decide whether each of the following subsets of $M$ is a subgroup of $M$, and justify your answer.

$$A = \left\{ \begin{pmatrix} a & 0 \\ c & a \end{pmatrix} : a, c \in \mathbb{R}, a \neq 0 \right\}$$

$$B = \left\{ \begin{pmatrix} a & 0 \\ 1 & 1/a \end{pmatrix} : a \in \mathbb{R}^* \right\}$$

$$C = \left\{ \begin{pmatrix} 1+n & n \\ -n & 1-n \end{pmatrix} : n \in \mathbb{Z} \right\}$$

**Exercise 5.8** The set $H = \left\{ \begin{pmatrix} a & 0 \\ 0 & 1/a \end{pmatrix} : a \in \mathbb{R}^* \right\}$ is a subgroup of $M$.

Find the conjugate subgroup $gHg^{-1}$ for the following $g$.

(a) $g = \begin{pmatrix} 1 & 1 \\ 0 & 1 \end{pmatrix}$ (b) $g = \begin{pmatrix} 0 & 1 \\ 1 & 2 \end{pmatrix}$

**Exercise 5.9** For the subgroup $C$ of $M$ in Exercise 5.7, find the conjugate subgroup $gCg^{-1}$ for the following $g$.

(a) $g = \begin{pmatrix} 1 & 2 \\ 0 & 1 \end{pmatrix}$ (b) $g = \begin{pmatrix} 1 & 0 \\ 3 & 1 \end{pmatrix}$

**Exercise 5.10** Show that the subgroup $A$ of $M$ in Exercise 5.7 is a normal subgroup of the group $L$ of invertible lower triangular $2 \times 2$ matrices under matrix multiplication.

Earlier we showed that the set $U$ of invertible upper triangular $2 \times 2$ matrices is a group under matrix multiplication. The proof that $L$ is a group is similar; we omit the details.

**Exercise 5.11** The group (under matrix multiplication) of invertible upper triangular $2 \times 2$ matrices

$$U = \left\{ \begin{pmatrix} a & b \\ 0 & d \end{pmatrix} : ad \neq 0 \right\}$$

has a normal subgroup

See Frame 11.

$$Y = \left\{ \begin{pmatrix} 1 & b \\ 0 & 1 \end{pmatrix} : b \in \mathbb{R} \right\}.$$

In Exercise 5.6 we found that the set $U/Y$ of cosets of $Y$ in $U$ may be written in the form

$$\left\{ \begin{pmatrix} p & 0 \\ 0 & s \end{pmatrix} Y : p, s \in \mathbb{R}^* \right\}.$$

Complete the following formula for the binary operation on $U/Y$:

$$\begin{pmatrix} p_1 & 0 \\ 0 & s_1 \end{pmatrix} Y \cdot \begin{pmatrix} p_2 & 0 \\ 0 & s_2 \end{pmatrix} Y = \begin{pmatrix} ? & 0 \\ 0 & ? \end{pmatrix} Y.$$

# Solutions to the exercises

**1.1** **(a)** $(\{0,2,4,6\}, \times_8)$ is not a group.

The operation $\times_8$ is closed and associative on the set $\{0,2,4,6\}$.

However, the set contains no identity element, so axiom G2 fails.

(Axiom G3 is without meaning here—if there is no identity element, then there is no notion of inverses.)

**(b)** $(\{1,2,3,4\}, \times_5)$ is a group, with the following group table.

| $\times_5$ | 1 | 2 | 3 | 4 |
|---|---|---|---|---|
| 1 | 1 | 2 | 3 | 4 |
| 2 | 2 | 4 | 1 | 3 |
| 3 | 3 | 1 | 4 | 2 |
| 4 | 4 | 3 | 2 | 1 |

**1.2** **(a)** $(1\ 2\ 7\ 5)(3\ 8\ 4) \circ (1\ 3\ 6\ 7\ 5)$
$= (1\ 8\ 4\ 3\ 6\ 5\ 2\ 7)$

**(b)** $(1\ 3\ 7)(2\ 5\ 4) \circ (2\ 4)(3\ 8)(5\ 6)$
$= (1\ 3\ 8\ 7)(2)(4\ 5\ 6)$
$= (1\ 3\ 8\ 7)(4\ 5\ 6)$ (more usual form)

**1.3** **(a)** $((1\ 7\ 5\ 2)(3\ 8\ 4))^{-1}$
$= (2\ 5\ 7\ 1)(4\ 8\ 3)$
$= (1\ 2\ 5\ 7)(3\ 4\ 8)$ (more usual form)

**(b)** $((1\ 4)(2\ 3)(6\ 8))^{-1}$
$= (4\ 1)(3\ 2)(8\ 6)$
$= (1\ 4)(2\ 3)(6\ 8)$ (more usual form)

**1.4** **(a)** $(1\ 5\ 8)(2\ 7\ 3\ 4)$ is even + odd = odd.

**(b)** $(1\ 8)(2\ 7)(3\ 5\ 4\ 6)$ is odd + odd + odd = odd.

**1.5** **(a)** $a \circ s = r$

**(b)** $b^{-1} = a$

(We look along the row labelled $b$ until we find $e$, then note that it is in the column labelled $a$.)

**(c)** Using the associativity property and working from the left, we get

$$b \circ r \circ a = (b \circ r) \circ a = s \circ a = t;$$

alternatively, working from the right, we get

$$b \circ r \circ a = b \circ (r \circ a) = b \circ s = t.$$

**1.6** **(a)** The subgroup of order 1 is $\{e\}$.

**(b)** The five subgroups of order 2 are

$$\{e,b\}, \quad \{e,r\}, \quad \{e,s\}, \quad \{e,t\}, \quad \{e,u\}.$$

**(c)** The three subgroups of order 4 are

$$\{e,a,b,c\}, \quad \{e,b,r,t\}, \quad \{e,b,s,u\}.$$

The first of these is the group of rotations (direct symmetries) of the square; it can be spotted in the top left-hand corner of the group table for $S(\square)$. The subgroups $\{e,b,r,t\}$ and $\{e,b,s,u\}$ may be obtained by considering the symmetries of the following figures.

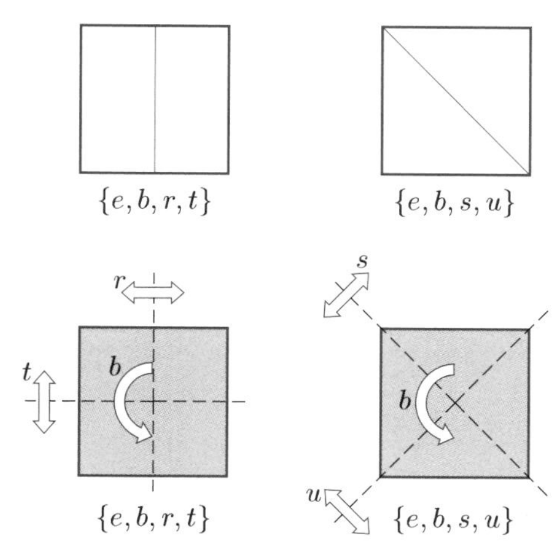


**(d)** The subgroup of order 8 is $S(\square)$ itself.

**1.7** **(a)** In $S(\square)$,

$$a^2 = a \circ a = b, \quad a^3 = b \circ a = c, \quad a^4 = c \circ a = e,$$

so $a$ has order 4. Also $b^2 = e$, so $b$ has order 2; and $r^2 = e$, so $r$ has order 2.

**(b)** In $\mathbb{Z}_6$, the binary operation is *additive*, so the order of an element is the least positive *multiple* of the element that is equal to the identity element, 0. Below we write multiples as *sums*.

The order of the element 0 is 1.

$1 +_6 1 = 2,$

$1 +_6 1 +_6 1 = 3,$

$1 +_6 1 +_6 1 +_6 1 = 4,$

$1 +_6 1 +_6 1 +_6 1 +_6 1 = 5,$

$1 +_6 1 +_6 1 +_6 1 +_6 1 +_6 1 = 0,$

so the element 1 has order 6.

$2 +_6 2 = 4, \quad 2 +_6 2 +_6 2 = 4 +_6 2 = 0,$

so the element 2 has order 3.

$3 +_6 3 = 0,$

so the element 3 has order 2.

$4 +_6 4 = 2, \quad 4 +_6 4 +_6 4 = 2 +_6 4 = 0$

so the element 4 has order 3.

$5 +_6 5 = 4,$

$5 +_6 5 +_6 5 = 4 +_6 5 = 3,$

$5 +_6 5 +_6 5 +_6 5 = 3 +_6 5 = 2,$

$5 +_6 5 +_6 5 +_6 5 +_6 5 = 2 +_6 5 = 1,$

$5 +_6 5 +_6 5 +_6 5 +_6 5 +_6 5 = 1 +_6 5 = 0,$

so the element 5 has order 6.

**1.8** In Exercise 1.7(b), when finding the orders of the elements of $\mathbb{Z}_6$, we did all the calculations needed to find the subgroup generated by each of these elements. Thus

$$\begin{aligned}
\langle 0\rangle &= \{0\},\\
\langle 1\rangle &= \{0,1,2,3,4,5\} = \mathbb{Z}_6,\\
\langle 2\rangle &= \{0,2,4\},\\
\langle 3\rangle &= \{0,3\},\\
\langle 4\rangle &= \{0,2,4\},\\
\langle 5\rangle &= \{0,1,2,3,4,5\} = \mathbb{Z}_6.
\end{aligned}$$

(Here the elements of the subgroups are listed in the natural order, rather than the order in which they are generated.)

**1.9** **(a)** The group $S(\square)$ is non-cyclic because it has order 8 but contains no element of order 8:

the identity element has order 1,

the four reflections have order 2,

rotation $b$ has order 2,

rotations $a$ and $c$ have order 4.

**(b)** The group $S^+(\square)$ is cyclic because it has order 4 and contains two elements ($a$ and $c$) of order 4; each of these elements is a generator of the group.

**(c)** The group $\mathbb{Z}_5$ is cyclic because it has order 5 and contains four elements (1, 2, 3 and 4) of order 5; each of these elements is a generator of the group.

**1.10** **(a)** In $S(\square)$, the elements $r$, $s$, $t$, $u$ and $b$ have order 2, so each of these generates a cyclic subgroup of order 2:

$$\{e,r\},\quad \{e,s\},\quad \{e,t\},\quad \{e,u\},\quad \{e,b\}.$$

The rotations $a$ and $c$ have order 4, and each generates the cyclic subgroup $\{e,a,b,c\}$ of order 4. (The elements $a$ and $c$ generate the *same* subgroup because $c = a^{-1}$.)

The identity element $e$ generates the subgroup $\{e\}$.

*Remark* In addition to these seven cyclic subgroups, $S(\square)$ has three further subgroups, which are non-cyclic. These are the group $S(\square)$ itself, and $\{e,b,r,t\}$ and $\{e,b,s,u\}$, the two non-cyclic subgroups of order 4, which are in the solution to Exercise 1.6(c).

**(b)** In the additive group $\mathbb{Z}_9$,

$$\begin{aligned}
\langle 0\rangle &= \{0\},\\
\langle 1\rangle &= \mathbb{Z}_9 = \langle -_9 1\rangle = \langle 8\rangle,\\
\langle 2\rangle &= \mathbb{Z}_9 = \langle -_9 2\rangle = \langle 7\rangle,\\
\langle 3\rangle &= \{0,3,6\} = \langle -_9 3\rangle = \langle 6\rangle,\\
\langle 4\rangle &= \mathbb{Z}_9 = \langle -_9 4\rangle = \langle 5\rangle.
\end{aligned}$$

Thus $\mathbb{Z}_9$ has three distinct cyclic subgroups.

**(c)** In the multiplicative group $\mathbb{Z}_7^*$, we have $2 \times_7 4 = 1$, so 2 and 4 are inverses, as are 3 and 5. In $\mathbb{Z}_7^*$,

$$\begin{aligned}
\langle 1\rangle &= \{1\},\\
\langle 2\rangle &= \{1,2,4\} = \langle 2^{-1}\rangle = \langle 4\rangle,\\
\langle 3\rangle &= \{1,3,2,6,4,5\} = \langle 3^{-1}\rangle = \langle 5\rangle,\\
\langle 6\rangle &= \{1,6\}.
\end{aligned}$$

Thus $\mathbb{Z}_7^*$ has four distinct cyclic subgroups.

**(d)** In $S_3$,

$$\begin{aligned}
\langle e\rangle &= \{e\},\\
\langle (1\ 2)\rangle &= \{e,(1\ 2)\},\\
\langle (1\ 3)\rangle &= \{e,(1\ 3)\},\\
\langle (2\ 3)\rangle &= \{e,(2\ 3)\},\\
\langle (1\ 2\ 3)\rangle &= \{e,(1\ 2\ 3),(1\ 3\ 2)\}\\
&= \langle (1\ 2\ 3)^{-1}\rangle = \langle (1\ 3\ 2)\rangle.
\end{aligned}$$

Thus $S_3$ has five distinct cyclic subgroups.

**2.1** **(a)** In $S_5$, $(1\ 3\ 5)$ conjugates $(1\ 2\ 4\ 3\ 5)$ to

$$\begin{aligned}
&(1\ 3\ 5)\circ(1\ 2\ 4\ 3\ 5)\circ(1\ 3\ 5)^{-1}\\
&= (1\ 3\ 5)\circ(1\ 2\ 4\ 3\ 5)\circ(1\ 5\ 3)\\
&= (1\ 3\ 2\ 4\ 5).
\end{aligned}$$

It is quicker and easier to use the renaming method. We use the conjugating element $(1\ 3\ 5)$ to rename the symbols in $(1\ 2\ 4\ 3\ 5)$:

$$\begin{array}{ll}
 & (1\ 2\ 4\ 3\ 5)\\
(1\ 3\ 5) & \ \downarrow\ \downarrow\ \downarrow\ \downarrow\ \downarrow\\
 & (3\ 2\ 4\ 5\ 1) = (1\ 3\ 2\ 4\ 5).
\end{array}$$

**(b)** Using the renaming method, we get

$$\begin{array}{ll}
 & (1\ 5\ 2)\\
(1\ 3)(2\ 4\ 5) & \ \downarrow\ \downarrow\ \downarrow\\
 & (3\ 2\ 4) = (2\ 4\ 3),
\end{array}$$

so

$$(1\ 3)(2\ 4\ 5)\circ(1\ 5\ 2)\circ((1\ 3)(2\ 4\ 5))^{-1} = (2\ 4\ 3).$$

**2.2** The permutation $(2\ 3\ 5)(4\ 6)$ can be written in the form $(-\ -\ -)(-\ -)$ in six different ways because each cycle can start at any symbol.

Using the usual way of writing $(2\ 3\ 5)(4\ 6)$, we obtain an element $g$ which renames $(1\ 4\ 3)(2\ 6)$ as $(2\ 3\ 5)(4\ 6)$ as follows:

$$\begin{array}{ll}
 & (1\ 4\ 3)\ (2\ 6)\ (5)\\
g & \ \downarrow\ \downarrow\ \downarrow\quad \downarrow\ \downarrow\quad \downarrow\\
 & (2\ 3\ 5)\ (4\ 6)\ (1)
\end{array}, \text{ which gives } g = (1\ 2\ 4\ 3\ 5).$$

Another way of writing the permutation $(2\ 3\ 5)(4\ 6)$ is $(3\ 5\ 2)(6\ 4)$. Using this expression, we get another conjugating element $g$, as follows:

$$\begin{array}{ll}
 & (1\ 4\ 3)\ (2\ 6)\ (5)\\
g & \ \downarrow\ \downarrow\ \downarrow\quad \downarrow\ \downarrow\quad \downarrow\\
 & (3\ 5\ 2)\ (6\ 4)\ (1)
\end{array}, \text{ which gives } g = (1\ 3\ 2\ 6\ 4\ 5).$$

The remaining four ways of writing $(2\ 3\ 5)(4\ 6)$ give conjugating elements $g$ as follows:

$(2\ 3\ 5)(6\ 4)$ gives $g = (1\ 2\ 6\ 4\ 3\ 5)$,
$(3\ 5\ 2)(4\ 6)$ gives $g = (1\ 3\ 2\ 4\ 5)$,
$(5\ 2\ 3)(4\ 6)$ gives $g = (1\ 5)(2\ 4)$,
$(5\ 2\ 3)(6\ 4)$ gives $g = (1\ 5)(2\ 6\ 4)$.

Thus the four new conjugating elements are

$(1\ 2\ 4\ 3\ 5)$, $(1\ 3\ 2\ 6\ 4\ 5)$,
$(1\ 2\ 6\ 4\ 3\ 5)$, $(1\ 5)(2\ 6\ 4)$.

**2.3 (a)** We wish to rename the cycle as follows:

$$\begin{array}{ll} & (1\ 2\ 3\ 4) \\ g & \ \downarrow\ \downarrow\ \downarrow\ \downarrow \\ & (1\ 3\ 4\ 2) \end{array}, \text{ which gives } g = (2\ 3\ 4).$$

Then

$$\begin{aligned} &g^{-1} \circ (1\ 3\ 4\ 2) \circ (g^{-1})^{-1} \\ &= (2\ 4\ 3) \circ (1\ 3\ 4\ 2) \circ (2\ 3\ 4) \\ &= (1\ 2\ 3\ 4). \end{aligned}$$

(If we were to reverse the arrows in the renaming diagram above, then we would obtain $g^{-1}$ as the conjugating permutation; this demonstrates why $g^{-1}$ conjugates $(1\ 3\ 4\ 2)$ back to $(1\ 2\ 3\ 4)$.)

There are other possible answers for $g$. The remaining three ways of writing $(1\ 3\ 4\ 2)$ give conjugating elements $g$ as follows:

$(3\ 4\ 2\ 1)$ gives $g = (1\ 3\ 2\ 4)$,
$(4\ 2\ 1\ 3)$ gives $g = (1\ 4\ 3)$,
$(2\ 1\ 3\ 4)$ gives $g = (1\ 2)$.

**(b)** The permutations $g$ and $h$ rename the symbols as follows:

$$\begin{array}{ll} & (1\ 2\ 3)(4\ 5) \\ g & \ \downarrow\ \downarrow\ \downarrow\ \ \downarrow\ \downarrow \\ & (1\ 3\ 5)(2\ 4) \end{array}, \text{ which gives } g = (2\ 3\ 5\ 4),$$

and

$$\begin{array}{ll} & (1\ 3\ 5)(2\ 4) \\ h & \ \downarrow\ \downarrow\ \downarrow\ \ \downarrow\ \downarrow \\ & (3\ 4\ 5)(1\ 2) \end{array}, \text{ which gives } h = (1\ 3\ 4\ 2).$$

Thus

$$h \circ g = (1\ 3\ 4\ 2) \circ (2\ 3\ 5\ 4) = (1\ 3\ 5\ 2\ 4)$$

and

$$\begin{aligned} &(h \circ g) \circ (1\ 2\ 3)(4\ 5) \circ (h \circ g)^{-1} \\ &= (1\ 3\ 5\ 2\ 4) \circ (1\ 2\ 3)(4\ 5) \circ (1\ 4\ 2\ 5\ 3) \\ &= (1\ 2)(3\ 4\ 5). \end{aligned}$$

(The two renaming diagrams above show that $h \circ g$ has the following effect:

$$\begin{array}{ll} & (1\ 2\ 3)(4\ \ 5) \\ h \circ g & \ \downarrow\ \downarrow\ \downarrow\ \ \downarrow\ \ \downarrow \\ & (3\ 4\ 5)(1\ \ 2) \end{array};$$

this demonstrates why $h \circ g$ conjugates $(1\ 2\ 3)(4\ 5)$ to $(1\ 2)(3\ 4\ 5)$.)

There are many other possible answers for $h$ and $g$.

The remaining ways of writing $(1\ 3\ 5)(2\ 4)$ give conjugating elements $g$ as follows:

$(1\ 3\ 5)(4\ 2)$ gives $g = (2\ 3\ 5)$,
$(3\ 5\ 1)(2\ 4)$ gives $g = (1\ 3)(2\ 5\ 4)$,
$(3\ 5\ 1)(4\ 2)$ gives $g = (1\ 3)(2\ 5)$,
$(5\ 1\ 3)(2\ 4)$ gives $g = (1\ 5\ 4\ 2)$,
$(5\ 1\ 3)(4\ 2)$ gives $g = (1\ 5\ 2)$.

The remaining ways of writing $(1\ 2)(3\ 4\ 5)$ give conjugating elements $h$ as follows:

$(3\ 4\ 5)(2\ 1)$ gives $h = (1\ 3\ 4)$,
$(4\ 5\ 3)(1\ 2)$ gives $h = (1\ 4\ 2)(3\ 5)$,
$(4\ 5\ 3)(2\ 1)$ gives $h = (1\ 4)(3\ 5)$,
$(5\ 3\ 4)(1\ 2)$ gives $h = (1\ 5\ 4\ 2)$,
$(5\ 3\ 4)(2\ 1)$ gives $h = (1\ 5\ 4)$.

**2.4** $(\mathbb{Z}_7^*, \times_7)$ is the group with elements $\{1, 2, 3, 4, 5, 6\}$, under the operation of multiplication modulo 7.

To determine the conjugacy class of the element 3, say, we could calculate all the conjugates of 3:

$$\begin{aligned} 1 \times_7 3 \times_7 1^{-1} &= 1 \times_7 3 \times_7 1 = 3, \\ 2 \times_7 3 \times_7 2^{-1} &= 2 \times_7 3 \times_7 4 = 3, \\ 3 \times_7 3 \times_7 3^{-1} &= 3 \times_7 3 \times_7 5 = 3, \end{aligned}$$

and so on. In each case, the conjugate of 3 is 3.

You can probably spot what is going on. Because the operation $\times_7$ is commutative, the calculation of any conjugate is straightforward; if $g$ and $x$ are any two elements of $\mathbb{Z}_7^*$, then

$$\begin{aligned} g \times_7 x \times_7 g^{-1} &= x \times_7 g \times_7 g^{-1} \quad \text{(commutativity)} \\ &= x \times_7 1 \quad \text{(inverses)} \\ &= x \quad \text{(identity)}. \end{aligned}$$

So each element is conjugate to itself alone.

Hence there are six conjugacy classes, each consisting of a single element:

$\{1\}, \{2\}, \{3\}, \{4\}, \{5\}, \{6\}$.

**2.5** Let $y = gxg^{-1}$.

**(a)**
$$\begin{aligned} y^2 &= (gxg^{-1})(gxg^{-1}) \\ &= gx(g^{-1}g)xg^{-1} \quad \text{(associativity)} \\ &= gxexg^{-1} \quad \text{(inverses)} \\ &= gx^2g^{-1} \quad \text{(identity)} \end{aligned}$$

**(b)**
$$\begin{aligned} y^3 = y^2y &= (gx^2g^{-1})(gxg^{-1}) \quad \text{(by part (a))} \\ &= gx^2(g^{-1}g)xg^{-1} \\ &= gx^2exg^{-1} \\ &= gx^3g^{-1} \end{aligned}$$

**(c)**
$$\begin{aligned} y^4 = y^3y &= (gx^3g^{-1})(gxg^{-1}) \quad \text{(by part (b))} \\ &= gx^3(g^{-1}g)xg^{-1} \\ &= gx^3exg^{-1} \\ &= gx^4g^{-1} \end{aligned}$$

**2.6** The group $\mathbb{Z}_6$ is Abelian, so each element is conjugate to itself alone. Thus any two elements of the same order have the required property.

The orders of the elements are as follows.

| Element | 0 | 1 | 2 | 3 | 4 | 5 |
|---|---|---|---|---|---|---|
| Order | 1 | 6 | 3 | 2 | 3 | 6 |

The elements 1 and 5 have the same order, but are not conjugate.

Similarly, the elements 2 and 4 have the same order, but are not conjugate.

**2.7 (a)** We check the eight conjugates of $b$:

$$\begin{aligned} e \circ b \circ e^{-1} &= b, & r \circ b \circ r^{-1} &= b,\\ a \circ b \circ a^{-1} &= b, & s \circ b \circ s^{-1} &= b,\\ b \circ b \circ b^{-1} &= b, & t \circ b \circ t^{-1} &= b,\\ c \circ b \circ c^{-1} &= b, & u \circ b \circ u^{-1} &= b. \end{aligned}$$

Thus the only element conjugate to $b$ is $b$ itself.

*Remark* The equation $g \circ b \circ g^{-1} = b$ is equivalent to the equation $g \circ b = b \circ g$. Thus this exercise shows that $b$ commutes with each of the eight elements of $S(\square)$. (A definition of 'commutes' is given in the margin on page 22.)

**(b)** From the group table for $S(\square)$, we see that

$$r \circ a \circ r^{-1} = r \circ (a \circ r) = r \circ s = c,$$

so $a$ and $c$ are conjugate elements in $S(\square)$.

**(c)** From the group table for $S(\square)$, we see that

$$a \circ r \circ a^{-1} = a \circ (r \circ c) = a \circ s = t,$$

so $r$ and $t$ are conjugate elements in $S(\square)$.

**2.8** Using the five possible starting symbols for the 5-cycle $(1\ 4\ 2\ 5\ 3)$, we obtain

$$g \begin{array}{c} (1\ 3\ 5\ 2\ 4) \\ \downarrow\downarrow\downarrow\downarrow\downarrow \\ (1\ 4\ 2\ 5\ 3) \end{array}, \text{ which gives } g = (2\ 5)(3\ 4),$$

$$g \begin{array}{c} (1\ 3\ 5\ 2\ 4) \\ \downarrow\downarrow\downarrow\downarrow\downarrow \\ (4\ 2\ 5\ 3\ 1) \end{array}, \text{ which gives } g = (1\ 4)(2\ 3),$$

$$g \begin{array}{c} (1\ 3\ 5\ 2\ 4) \\ \downarrow\downarrow\downarrow\downarrow\downarrow \\ (2\ 5\ 3\ 1\ 4) \end{array}, \text{ which gives } g = (1\ 2)(3\ 5),$$

$$g \begin{array}{c} (1\ 3\ 5\ 2\ 4) \\ \downarrow\downarrow\downarrow\downarrow\downarrow \\ (5\ 3\ 1\ 4\ 2) \end{array}, \text{ which gives } g = (1\ 5)(2\ 4),$$

$$g \begin{array}{c} (1\ 3\ 5\ 2\ 4) \\ \downarrow\downarrow\downarrow\downarrow\downarrow \\ (3\ 1\ 4\ 2\ 5) \end{array}, \text{ which gives } g = (1\ 3)(4\ 5).$$

**2.9** The identity element $e$ is in a conjugacy class of its own.

The element $b$ has order 2 (since $b^2 = e$) and is the only element of order 2, so it must be in a conjugacy class of its own.

The remaining six elements all have order 4: the element $a$ is conjugate to itself and to $c$, but to no other element, as can be checked by working out the eight conjugates $gag^{-1}$.

Similarly, $w$ and $y$ are conjugate to each other, but to no other element, as are $x$ and $z$.

So the partition into conjugacy classes is

$$\{e\},\quad \{b\},\quad \{a, c\},\quad \{w, y\},\quad \{x, z\}.$$

**2.10** We show that the three subgroup properties hold.

SG1 Let $g_1, g_2 \in C(x)$; then $g_1 x g_1^{-1} = x$ and $g_2 x g_2^{-1} = x$. Now

$$\begin{aligned} &(g_1g_2)x(g_1g_2)^{-1}\\ &= (g_1g_2)x(g_2^{-1}g_1^{-1}) \quad \text{(inverse of product)}\\ &= g_1(g_2xg_2^{-1})g_1^{-1} \quad \text{(associativity)}\\ &= g_1xg_1^{-1} \quad (g_2 \in C(x))\\ &= x \quad (g_1 \in C(x)), \end{aligned}$$

so $g_1g_2 \in C(x)$ and property SG1 holds.

SG2 We have $exe^{-1} = x$, so $e \in C(x)$ and property SG2 holds.

SG3 Let $g \in C(x)$; then

$$gxg^{-1} = x.$$

Multiplying each side of this equation on the left by $g^{-1}$ and on the right by $g$, we get

$$g^{-1}(gxg^{-1})g = g^{-1}xg;$$

that is

$$x = g^{-1}xg = g^{-1}x(g^{-1})^{-1},$$

so $g^{-1} \in C(x)$ and property SG3 holds.

Hence $C(x)$ satisfies the three subgroup properties and so is a subgroup of $G$.

**2.11 (a)** The group $(\mathbb{R}, +)$ is Abelian, so each conjugacy class consists of a single element. In particular, $\pi$ is conjugate only to itself, so its conjugacy class is $\{\pi\}$.

**(b)** The group $(\mathbb{R}^*, \times)$ is also Abelian, so again the conjugacy class of $\pi$ is $\{\pi\}$.

(There is nothing special about the number $\pi$ or the particular numerical groups here: every number in an Abelian group of numbers is in a conjugacy class of its own.)

**3.1** **(a)** The cosets of $\{e, t\}$ in $S(\triangle)$ are

$$H = \{e, t\},$$
$$aH = \{a \circ e, a \circ t\} = \{a, s\},$$
$$bH = \{b \circ e, b \circ t\} = \{b, r\}.$$

**(b)** Since $6 \times_7 6 = 1$, we have $\langle 6 \rangle = \{1, 6\}$; that is, $H = \{1, 6\}$ is the cyclic subgroup generated by 6 (and is therefore, in particular, a subgroup).

The cosets of $\{1, 6\}$ in $\mathbb{Z}_7^*$ are

$$H = \{1, 6\},$$
$$2H = \{2 \times_7 1, 2 \times_7 6\} = \{2, 5\},$$
$$3H = \{3 \times_7 1, 3 \times_7 6\} = \{3, 4\}.$$

**(c)** Since $4 +_{12} 4 = 8$ and $4 +_{12} 4 +_{12} 4 = 0$, we have

$$\langle 4 \rangle = \{0, 4, 8\};$$

that is, $H = \{0, 4, 8\}$ is the subgroup generated by 4.

The cosets of $\{0, 4, 8\}$ in $\mathbb{Z}_{12}$ are

$$H = \{0, 4, 8\},$$
$$1 + H = \{1 +_{12} 0, 1 +_{12} 4, 1 +_{12} 8\} = \{1, 5, 9\},$$
$$2 + H = \{2 +_{12} 0, 2 +_{12} 4, 2 +_{12} 8\} = \{2, 6, 10\},$$
$$3 + H = \{3 +_{12} 0, 3 +_{12} 4, 3 +_{12} 8\} = \{3, 7, 11\}.$$

**(d)** The set $H = \{\ldots, -10, -5, 0, 5, 10, \ldots\}$ is the subgroup of $\mathbb{Z}$ generated by 5.

The cosets of $H$ in $\mathbb{Z}$ are

$$H = \{\ldots, -10, -5, 0, 5, 10, \ldots\},$$
$$1 + H = \{\ldots, -9, -4, 1, 6, 11, \ldots\},$$
$$2 + H = \{\ldots, -8, -3, 2, 7, 12, \ldots\},$$
$$3 + H = \{\ldots, -7, -2, 3, 8, 13, \ldots\},$$
$$4 + H = \{\ldots, -6, -1, 4, 9, 14, \ldots\}.$$

**3.2** **(a)** The left cosets of $H = \{e, t\}$ in $S(\triangle)$ were found in Exercise 3.1(a) to be

$$H = \{e, t\},$$
$$aH = \{a, s\},$$
$$bH = \{b, r\}.$$

The right cosets are

$$H = \{e, t\},$$
$$Ha = \{e \circ a, t \circ a\} = \{a, r\},$$
$$Hb = \{e \circ b, t \circ b\} = \{b, s\}.$$

The left and right partitions are different, so $H = \{e, t\}$ is not a normal subgroup of $S(\triangle)$.

**3.3** In each case, we have to show first that the given set is a *subgroup* and then that it is *normal*.

**(a)** The set $\{e, a, b\}$ is a subgroup of $S(\triangle)$ because it is the subgroup $S^+(\triangle)$ of rotations. It is normal because it has index 2.

**(b)** The set $\{0, 4\}$ is a subgroup of $\mathbb{Z}_8$ because we have $4 +_8 4 = 0$, so $\langle 4 \rangle = \{0, 4\}$. It is normal because $\mathbb{Z}_8$ is Abelian.

**3.4** First we consider the subgroup $N = \{e\}$. Let $g$ be any element of $G$, and let $n$ be any element of $\{e\}$ —that is, $n = e$. Then

$$gng^{-1} = geg^{-1} = e \in \{e\}.$$

It follows from Strategy 3.2 that $\{e\}$ is normal in $G$.

Next take $N = G$. Let $g$ be any element of $G$ and let $n$ be any element of the subgroup $G$. Then, since $g$, $n$ and $g^{-1}$ all belong to $G$, we have $gng^{-1} \in G$ by the closure property in the group $G$.

It follows from Strategy 3.2 that $G$ is normal in $G$.

**3.5** In $(X, *)$, we have the following.

**(a)** $(a, b) * (1, 0) = (a \times 1, (a \times 0) + b) = (a, b)$,

$$(1/a, -b/a) * (a, b) = ((1/a) \times a, ((1/a) \times b) + (-b/a)) = (1, 0).$$

**(b)** $(3, 2) * (1, 7) * (3, 2)^{-1}$

$$= ((3, 2) * (1, 7)) * (\tfrac{1}{3}, -\tfrac{2}{3})$$
$$= (3, 23) * (\tfrac{1}{3}, -\tfrac{2}{3})$$
$$= (1, 21),$$

$$(-1, 3) * (1, -2) * (-1, 3)^{-1}$$
$$= ((-1, 3) * (1, -2)) * (-1, 3)$$
$$= (-1, 5) * (-1, 3)$$
$$= (1, 2).$$

**3.6** **(a)** We choose, for example, $g = (1\ 3) \in S_4$ and $h = (1\ 2) \in H$. Then $g \circ h \circ g^{-1}$ is

$$(1\ 3) \circ (1\ 2) \circ (1\ 3)^{-1} = (2\ 3),$$

which does not belong to $H$. It follows from Strategy 3.3 that $H$ is not a normal subgroup of $S_4$.

**(b)** We choose, for example, $g = (1\ 2) \in S_4$ and $h = (1\ 3) \in H$. Then $g \circ h \circ g^{-1}$ is

$$(1\ 2) \circ (1\ 3) \circ (1\ 2)^{-1} = (2\ 3),$$

which does not belong to $H$. It follows from Strategy 3.3 that $H$ is not a normal subgroup of $S_4$.

**3.7** **(a)** We choose, for example, $(1, 1) \in X$ and $(2, 0) \in C$. The conjugate of $(2, 0)$ by $(1, 1)$ is

$$(1, 1) * (2, 0) * (1, 1)^{-1} = (2, 1) * (1, -1) = (2, -1).$$

Now $(2, -1) \notin C$ because the second coordinate is non-zero. It follows from Strategy 3.3 that $C$ is not a normal subgroup of $X$.

**(b)** First we show briefly that $K$ is a subgroup of $X$. We show that the three subgroup properties hold.

SG1 Let $(1, m)$ and $(1, n)$ be any two elements of $K$. Then

$$(1, m) * (1, n) = (1, n + m) \in K,$$

so $K$ is closed under $*$.

SG2 The identity element of $X$ is $(1, 0)$, and this is an element of $K$.

SG3 Let $(1, n)$ be any element of $K$. The inverse in $X$ of $(1, n)$ is $(1, -n)$, and this is an element of $K$, so $K$ contains the inverse of each of its elements.

Hence $K$ satisfies the three subgroup properties and so is a subgroup of $X$.

To investigate its normality, we need to calculate the conjugate $g * k * g^{-1}$ for $g \in X$ and $k \in K$.
So we put $g = (a, b)$ where $a \in \mathbb{R}$, $a \neq 0$, and $k = (1, l)$ where $l \in \mathbb{Z}$; then

$$\begin{aligned} g * k * g^{-1} &= ((a, b) * (1, l)) * (1/a, -b/a) \\ &= (a, al + b) * (1/a, -b/a) \\ &= (1, -b + al + b) \\ &= (1, al). \end{aligned}$$

Since $a$ need not be an integer, $al$ will not always be an integer: for example, if $a = \frac{1}{2}$ and $l = 3$, then $al = \frac{3}{2}$. Thus $(1, al)$ will not always be in $K$.

It follows from Strategy 3.3 that $K$ is not a normal subgroup of $X$. Briefly, this is shown by the fact that $(\frac{1}{2}, 0) \in X$ and $(1, 3) \in K$ but

$$(\tfrac{1}{2}, 0) * (1, 3) * (\tfrac{1}{2}, 0)^{-1} = (1, \tfrac{3}{2}) \notin K.$$

**3.8** From the group table for $S(\square)$, we obtain the following.

**(a)** $aHa^{-1} = \{a \circ e \circ a^{-1}, a \circ s \circ a^{-1}\} = \{e, u\}$

**(b)** $rHr^{-1}$
$= \{r \circ e \circ r^{-1}, r \circ b \circ r^{-1}, r \circ s \circ r^{-1}, r \circ u \circ r^{-1}\}$
$= \{e, b, s, u\}$.

**3.9 (a)** To determine $(1\ 2\ 4)K(1\ 2\ 4)^{-1}$, we use the conjugating element $(1\ 2\ 4)$ to rename the symbols wherever they occur in the four elements of $K$. For example, $(1\ 2\ 4)$ renames $(1\ 2)(3\ 4)$ as $(2\ 4)(3\ 1)$, so the conjugate of $(1\ 2)(3\ 4)$ by $(1\ 2\ 4)$ is $(1\ 3)(2\ 4)$.

This method gives

$(1\ 2\ 4)K(1\ 2\ 4)^{-1}$
$= \{e,\ (1\ 3)(2\ 4),\ (1\ 4)(2\ 3),\ (1\ 2)(3\ 4)\}$.

Similarly, using $(1\ 2\ 3\ 4)$ to rename the symbols in the elements of $K$, we obtain

$(1\ 2\ 3\ 4)K(1\ 2\ 3\ 4)^{-1}$
$= \{e,\ (1\ 4)(2\ 3),\ (1\ 3)(2\ 4),\ (1\ 2)(3\ 4)\}$.

**(b)** To obtain all the subgroups conjugate to $K$, it looks as though we need to determine $gKg^{-1}$ for each of the remaining 22 choices for $g$. However, if you calculate some more conjugates of $K$, you will find that the conjugate subgroup is always $K$ itself.

This is because the three non-identity elements of $K$ are the *only* elements in $S_4$ with that particular cycle structure. As conjugation *preserves* cycle structure, the three conjugates $g \circ (1\ 2)(3\ 4) \circ g^{-1}$, $g \circ (1\ 3)(2\ 4) \circ g^{-1}$ and $g \circ (1\ 4)(2\ 3) \circ g^{-1}$ must be the three elements $(1\ 2)(3\ 4)$, $(1\ 3)(2\ 4)$ and $(1\ 4)(2\ 3)$ in some order. Hence, for all $g \in S_4$, we get $gKg^{-1} = K$.

**3.10** We use Strategy 3.4. The subgroups $\{e\}$, $S(\Delta)$ and $\{e, a, b\}$ are normal because each is a union of conjugacy classes. The other subgroups of $S(\Delta)$ are the three subgroups of order 2, namely $\{e, r\}$, $\{e, s\}$ and $\{e, t\}$, each consisting of the identity element together with a reflection. None of these is normal because none is a union of conjugacy classes.

**3.11** The group $A_5$ has order 60. We are given that it has five conjugacy classes with 1, 20, 15, 12 and 12 elements. Applying Strategy 3.4, we look for unions of these conjugacy classes, including $\{e\}$, in which the total number of elements is a divisor of 60.

Looking at the numbers, we seek ways of adding 1 and some of the numbers 20, 15, 12 and 12 to get a total which is one of the numbers 1, 2, 3, 4, 5, 6, 10, 12, 15, 20, 30 or 60.

The smallest possible sum greater than 1 that can be achieved with the given numbers, including 1, is 13, so none of the totals 2, 3, 4, 5, 6, 10 and 12 is possible. The smallest possible sum greater than 13 that can be achieved is 16, so the total 15 is not possible. Continuing this reasoning reveals that the only totals from the list that can be achieved are 1 and 60.

We conclude that the only normal subgroups of $A_5$ are the identity subgroup $\{e\}$, of order 1, and the whole group $A_5$, of order 60.

**3.12 (a)** The left partition of $\{e, b\}$ is

$\{e, b\}$,
$a\{e, b\} = \{a, c\}$,
$w\{e, b\} = \{w, y\}$,
$x\{e, b\} = \{x, z\}$.

The right partition of $\{e, b\}$ is

$\{e, b\}$,
$\{e, b\}a = \{a, c\}$,
$\{e, b\}w = \{w, y\}$,
$\{e, b\}x = \{x, z\}$.

The left and right partitions are the same, so $\{e, b\}$ is a normal subgroup.

**(b)** The subgroup $\{e, w, b, y\}$ has index 2, so both the left partition and the right partition consist of the subgroup itself and a second coset comprising the other four elements:

$$\{e, w, b, y\}, \quad \{a, x, c, z\}.$$

Hence $\{e, w, b, y\}$ is a normal subgroup.

**3.13** In $S(\square)$, the reflection $r$ is conjugate only to itself and to the reflection $t$. (We established this in Subsection 2.4.) Hence, for all $g \in S(\square)$,

$$\begin{aligned} g\{e, r\}g^{-1} &= \{g \circ e \circ g^{-1}, g \circ r \circ g^{-1}\} \\ &= \{e, r\} \text{ or } \{e, t\}. \end{aligned}$$

Thus the subgroup $\{e, r\}$ is conjugate only to itself and the subgroup $\{e, t\}$.

**3.14 (a)** Since each element of $H$ is of the form $h^r$, for some integer $r$, each element of $gHg^{-1}$ is of the form $gh^rg^{-1}$. But, by Example 2.3, we know that

$$gh^rg^{-1} = (ghg^{-1})^r.$$

Thus each element of $gHg^{-1}$ is equal to $(ghg^{-1})^r$, for some integer $r$, so $ghg^{-1}$ generates $gHg^{-1}$.

**(b)** The subgroup

$$\{e, (1\ 2\ 3\ 4), (1\ 3)(2\ 4), (1\ 4\ 3\ 2)\}$$

of $S_4$ is cyclic, generated by $(1\ 2\ 3\ 4)$.

By part (a), if we conjugate this subgroup by any element $g \in S_4$, then the resulting subgroup is cyclic, generated by $g \circ (1\ 2\ 3\ 4) \circ g^{-1}$.

The conjugacy class of $(1\ 2\ 3\ 4)$ is the set of all 4-cycles in $S_4$. Thus the given subgroup is conjugate to each of the cyclic subgroups generated by a 4-cycle, namely

$$\{e, (1\ 2\ 3\ 4), (1\ 3)(2\ 4), (1\ 4\ 3\ 2)\},$$
$$\{e, (1\ 2\ 4\ 3), (1\ 4)(2\ 3), (1\ 3\ 4\ 2)\},$$
$$\{e, (1\ 3\ 2\ 4), (1\ 2)(3\ 4), (1\ 4\ 2\ 3)\}.$$

**3.15** In $X$, we have $(1, 2)^{-1} = (1, -2)$ and $(2, 1)^{-1} = (\frac{1}{2}, -\frac{1}{2})$. So

$$\begin{aligned} (1, 2)C(1, 2)^{-1} &= \{(1, 2) * (a, 0) * (1, 2)^{-1} : a \in \mathbb{R}^*\} \\ &= \{(a, 2) * (1, -2) : a \in \mathbb{R}^*\} \\ &= \{(a, -2a + 2) : a \in \mathbb{R}^*\}, \end{aligned}$$

$$\begin{aligned} (2, 1)C(2, 1)^{-1} &= \{(2, 1) * (a, 0) * (2, 1)^{-1} : a \in \mathbb{R}^*\} \\ &= \{(2a, 1) * (\tfrac{1}{2}, -\tfrac{1}{2}) : a \in \mathbb{R}^*\} \\ &= \{(a, -a + 1) : a \in \mathbb{R}^*\}. \end{aligned}$$

*Remark* Theorem 3.2 shows that each of these subsets is a subgroup of $(X, *)$.

**3.16** In $X$, we have $(\frac{1}{2}, \frac{1}{2})^{-1} = (2, -1)$ and $(\frac{1}{3}, 0)^{-1} = (3, 0)$. So

$$\begin{aligned} (\tfrac{1}{2}, \tfrac{1}{2})K(\tfrac{1}{2}, \tfrac{1}{2})^{-1} &= \{(\tfrac{1}{2}, \tfrac{1}{2}) * (1, k) * (2, -1) : k \in \mathbb{Z}\} \\ &= \{(\tfrac{1}{2}, \tfrac{1}{2}k + \tfrac{1}{2}) * (2, -1) : k \in \mathbb{Z}\} \\ &= \{(1, \tfrac{1}{2}k) : k \in \mathbb{Z}\}, \end{aligned}$$

$$\begin{aligned} (\tfrac{1}{3}, 0)K(\tfrac{1}{3}, 0)^{-1} &= \{(\tfrac{1}{3}, 0) * (1, k) * (3, 0) : k \in \mathbb{Z}\} \\ &= \{(\tfrac{1}{3}, \tfrac{1}{3}k) * (3, 0) : k \in \mathbb{Z}\} \\ &= \{(1, \tfrac{1}{3}k) : k \in \mathbb{Z}\}. \end{aligned}$$

*Remark* Theorem 3.2 shows that each of these subsets is a subgroup of $(X, *)$.

**4.1 (a)** The fixed point set of the reflection in the plane passing through vertices 3, 4 and 5 is the portion of this plane lying within the double tetrahedron.

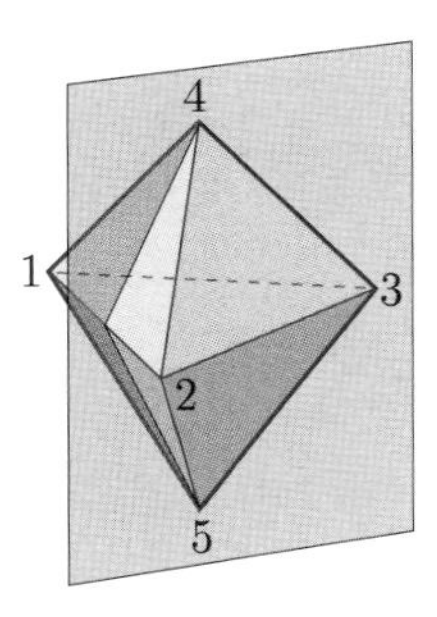


**(b)** The fixed point set of the reflection in the plane passing through vertices 1, 2 and 3 is the triangle with vertices 1, 2 and 3.

**(c)** The fixed point set of the rotation $(1\ 2\ 3)$ is the line segment joining vertices 4 and 5.

**4.2 (a)** $(2\ 3\ 5\ 6)g(2\ 3\ 5\ 6)^{-1} = (1\ 3\ 4)(6\ 7)$.
This permutation has fixed point set $\{5, 2\} = \{k(3), k(6)\}$.

**(b)** $(1\ 3)(4\ 7)g((1\ 3)(4\ 7))^{-1} = (2\ 7\ 3)(4\ 5)$.
This permutation has fixed point set $\{1, 6\} = \{k(3), k(6)\}$.

**4.3** We might anticipate that the six rotations split into four conjugacy classes:

| | |
|---|---|
| the identity element | $\{e\} = C_1$, |
| rotations through $\pi/3$ and $5\pi/3$ | $\{a, a^5\} = C_2$, |
| rotations through $2\pi/3$ and $4\pi/3$ | $\{a^2, a^4\} = C_3$, |
| rotation through $\pi$ | $\{a^3\} = C_4$. |

The reflections are of two distinct types:

| | |
|---|---|
| three reflections in diagonals | $\{q_2, q_4, q_6\} = C_5$, |
| three reflections in lines joining midpoints of opposite sides | $\{q_1, q_3, q_5\} = C_6$. |

On the grounds of geometric type, we expect these six sets to form the conjugacy classes of $S(\hexagon)$.

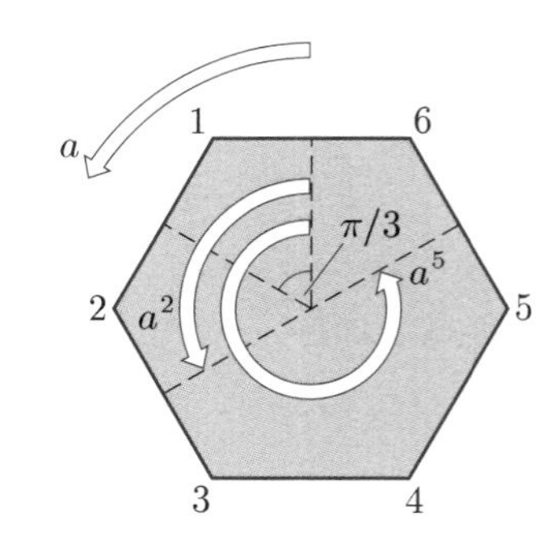


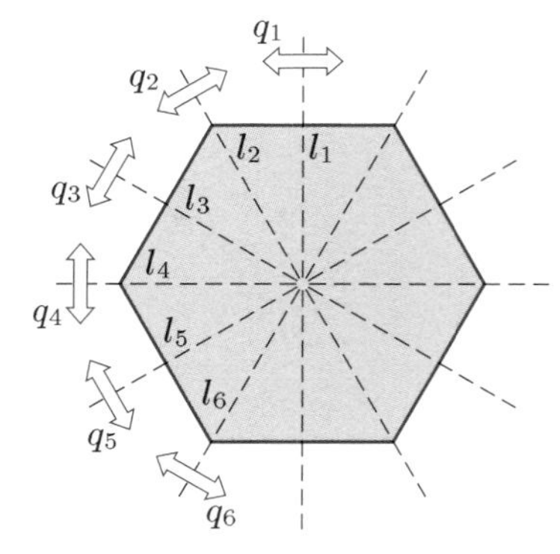


**4.4** The rotations are

$e$,
$a = (1\ 2\ 3\ 4\ 5\ 6)$,
$a^5 = (1\ 6\ 5\ 4\ 3\ 2)$,
$a^2 = (1\ 3\ 5)(2\ 4\ 6)$,
$a^4 = (1\ 5\ 3)(2\ 6\ 4)$,
$a^3 = (1\ 4)(2\ 5)(3\ 6)$.

The reflections are

$q_1 = (1\ 6)(2\ 5)(3\ 4)$,
$q_3 = (1\ 2)(3\ 6)(4\ 5)$,
$q_5 = (1\ 4)(2\ 3)(5\ 6)$,
$q_2 = (2\ 6)(3\ 5)$,
$q_4 = (1\ 3)(4\ 6)$,
$q_6 = (1\ 5)(2\ 4)$.

The partition by cycle structure is

$\{e\}$,
$\{a, a^5\}$,
$\{a^2, a^4\}$,
$\{a^3, q_1, q_3, q_5\}$,
$\{q_2, q_4, q_6\}$.

This partition almost agrees with our partition by geometric type; the only difference is that $a^3$, the rotation through $\pi$, has the same cycle structure as three of the reflections.

**4.5** See the diagram in the solution to Exercise 4.3. The fixed point set of $q_1$ is its axis of reflection, namely the line $l_1$ (to be precise, the portion of $l_1$ lying in the hexagon).

The symmetries of the hexagon map $l_1$ to $l_1$, to $l_3$ and to $l_5$, but to nowhere else. In fact, the identity element $e$ maps $l_1$ to itself, the rotation $a$ maps $l_1$ to $l_3$, and the rotation $a^2$ maps $l_1$ to $l_5$.

Now $l_1$, $l_3$ and $l_5$ are the fixed point sets of $q_1$, $q_3$ and $q_5$, respectively, and no other element of $S(\hexagon)$ has fixed point set $l_1$, $l_3$ or $l_5$. So the Fixed Point Theorem confirms that the only possible conjugates of $q_1$ are $q_1$, $q_3$ and $q_5$ (as we already know from the discussion before this exercise).

We now check that $q_1$, $q_3$ and $q_5$ are conjugates of $q_1$. We know that the conjugate of $q_1$ by $e$ is $q_1$. Also, by the Fixed Point Theorem, the conjugate of $q_1$ by $a$ is a symmetry with fixed point set $l_3$ (since $a$ maps $l_1$ to $l_3$), so it must be $q_3$, since $q_3$ is the only such symmetry in $S(\hexagon)$. Similarly the conjugate of $q_1$ by $a^2$ is $q_5$. Hence the conjugacy class of $q_1$ is $\{q_1, q_3, q_5\}$.

**4.6** Conjugating a rotation by any reflection gives a rotation through the same angle but in the opposite sense. (This is what we expect from the informal discussion of geometric type in Subsection 2.4.)

So, for example, we obtain the following.

(a) $q_1 a q_1^{-1} = a^{-1} = a^5$

(b) $q_1 a^2 q_1^{-1} = (a^2)^{-1} = a^4$

These equations can be confirmed by using the permutation representations of the symmetries.

**4.7** We are looking for unions of conjugacy classes, including $\{e\}$, which contain 1, 2, 3, 4, 6 or 12 elements and which are subgroups of $S(\hexagon)$.

Following Strategy 3.4, we first look for ways of adding to 1 some of the numbers 2, 2, 1, 3 and 3 to get a total which is a divisor of 12, the order of $S(\hexagon)$.

There are fourteen different unions of conjugacy classes containing $\{e\}$ for which the total number of elements is a divisor of 12, as given by the following sums:

| | |
|---|---|
| order 1 | $1$; |
| order 2 | $1+1$; |
| order 3 | $1+2$, $1+2$; |
| order 4 | $1+1+2$, $1+1+2$, $1+3$, $1+3$; |
| order 6 | $1+1+2+2$, $1+2+3$, $1+2+3$, $1+2+3$, $1+2+3$; |
| order 12 | $1+1+2+2+3+3$. |

(The sum $1+2$ is repeated because there are two conjugacy classes of size 2. Each sum $1+2$ corresponds to the union of $\{e\}$ with one of the conjugacy classes of size 2. Other repetitions occur for similar reasons.)

The final task is to determine which of the corresponding unions of conjugacy classes are subgroups; any which *is* a subgroup is necessarily a normal subgroup.

The following seven unions are subgroups and are therefore normal subgroups:

$\{e\} = C_1,$

$\{e, a^2, a^4\} = C_1 \cup C_3,$

$\{e, a^3\} = C_1 \cup C_4,$

$\{e, a, a^2, a^3, a^4, a^5\} = C_1 \cup C_2 \cup C_3 \cup C_4,$

$\{e, a^2, a^4, q_2, q_4, q_6\} = C_1 \cup C_3 \cup C_6,$

$\{e, a^2, a^4, q_1, q_3, q_5\} = C_1 \cup C_3 \cup C_5,$

$S(\bigcirc) = C_1 \cup C_2 \cup C_3 \cup C_4 \cup C_5 \cup C_6.$

(The first and last of the unions above are the subgroups consisting of the identity element alone and the whole group, respectively. The second, third and fourth unions are the cyclic subgroups generated by $a^2$, $a^3$ and $a$, respectively. You can check that each of the other two unions above is a subgroup either by drawing up a Cayley table and verifying the three subgroup properties, or by finding these subgroups of $S(\bigcirc)$ using the method for finding subgroups of symmetry groups that you saw in Unit GTA2, Strategy 1.3.)

The other unions of conjugacy classes are the following subsets, none of which is a subgroup—in each case, the closure axiom is violated:

$\{e, a, a^5\},$

$\{e, a, a^3, a^5\},$

$\{e, a^2, a^3, a^4\},$

$\{e, q_1, q_3, q_5\},$

$\{e, q_2, q_4, q_6\},$

$\{e, a, a^5, q_1, q_3, q_5\},$

$\{e, a, a^5, q_2, q_4, q_6\}.$

**4.8** (a) The four rotations about axis 1 are of three different geometric types:

the identity element,
rotation through $\pi$,
rotations through $\pi/2$ and $3\pi/2$.

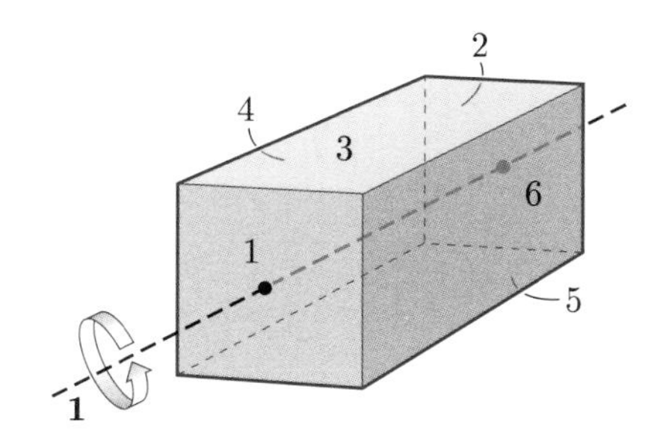


The remaining four rotations, each through $\pi$, are of two types:

rotations about axes 2 and 4 (axes through midpoints of opposite edges),

rotations about axes 3 and 5 (axes through midpoints of opposite faces).

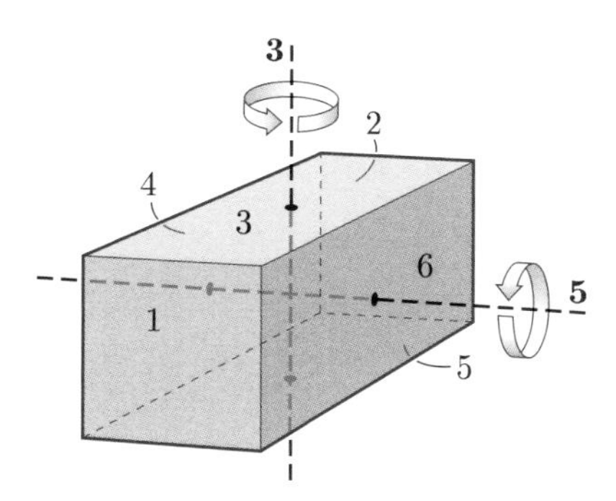


(b) The elements can be represented as follows:

the identity element is $e$,

the rotation through $\pi$ about axis 1 is (3 5)(4 6),

the rotations through $\pi/2$ and $3\pi/2$ about axis 1 are (3 4 5 6) and (3 6 5 4), respectively,

the rotations about axes 2 and 4 are (1 2)(3 4)(5 6) and (1 2)(3 6)(4 5), respectively,

the rotations about axes 3 and 5 are (1 2)(4 6) and (1 2)(3 5), respectively.

The cycle structures agree with the solution to part (a), except that the rotation through $\pi$ about axis 1 has the same cycle structure as the rotations about axes 3 and 5.

(c) The identity is conjugate to itself alone.

The rotation (3 5)(4 6) is not conjugate to either (1 2)(4 6) or (1 2)(3 5), by the Fixed Point Theorem. The fixed point set of (3 5)(4 6) is axis 1 (strictly, the portion of axis 1 lying in the prism), and the fixed point sets of (1 2)(4 6) and (1 2)(3 5) are axes 3 and 5, respectively, but there is no symmetry in $G$ mapping axis 1 to either axis 3 or axis 5.

(3 4 5 6) is conjugate to (3 6 5 4); for example, taking $g = (1\ 2)(4\ 6)$, we obtain

$$g(3\ 4\ 5\ 6)g^{-1} = (3\ 6\ 5\ 4).$$

The rotation (3 4 5 6) maps axis 2, the fixed point set of (1 2)(3 4)(5 6), to axis 4. Since (1 2)(3 6)(4 5) is the only symmetry in $G$ whose fixed point set is axis 4, it follows from the Fixed Point Theorem that (3 4 5 6) conjugates (1 2)(3 4)(5 6) to (1 2)(3 6)(4 5), as you can check.

Similarly, the rotation (3 4 5 6) maps axis 3, the fixed point set of (1 2)(4 6), to axis 5. Since (1 2)(3 5) is the only symmetry in $G$ whose fixed point set is axis 5, it follows from the Fixed Point Theorem that (3 4 5 6) conjugates (1 2)(4 6) to (1 2)(3 5), as you can check.

We conclude that there are five conjugacy classes: those listed in part (a).

**5.1** **(a)** This matrix has determinant $2(\neq 0)$ and so is invertible; its inverse is

$$\tfrac{1}{2}\begin{pmatrix} 1 & -1 \\ 0 & 2 \end{pmatrix} = \begin{pmatrix} \frac{1}{2} & -\frac{1}{2} \\ 0 & 1 \end{pmatrix}.$$

**(b)** This matrix has determinant 1 and so is invertible; its inverse is

$$\begin{pmatrix} 0 & 1 \\ -1 & 0 \end{pmatrix}.$$

**(c)** This matrix has determinant 2 and so is invertible; its inverse is

$$\tfrac{1}{2}\begin{pmatrix} 2 & -3 \\ 0 & 1 \end{pmatrix} = \begin{pmatrix} 1 & -\frac{3}{2} \\ 0 & \frac{1}{2} \end{pmatrix}.$$

**(d)** This matrix is not invertible because it has determinant 0.

**(e)** This matrix is not invertible because it has determinant 0.

**(f)** The determinant of this matrix is $ad$, which is non-zero provided that both $a$ and $d$ are non-zero. Hence the matrix is invertible if $a \neq 0$ and $d \neq 0$; in this case, its inverse is

$$\frac{1}{ad}\begin{pmatrix} d & -b \\ 0 & a \end{pmatrix} = \begin{pmatrix} 1/a & -b/ad \\ 0 & 1/d \end{pmatrix}.$$

**5.2** **(a)** We show that the three subgroup properties hold.

SG1 Let $\mathbf{A} = \begin{pmatrix} a & 0 \\ 0 & d \end{pmatrix}$ and $\mathbf{B} = \begin{pmatrix} x & 0 \\ 0 & z \end{pmatrix}$ be any two elements of $H$; then $ad = xz = 1$.

Now

$$\mathbf{AB} = \begin{pmatrix} ax & 0 \\ 0 & dz \end{pmatrix}.$$

This is a diagonal matrix with determinant $(ax)(dz) = (ad)(xz) = 1 \times 1 = 1$, so $\mathbf{AB} \in H$. Thus $H$ is closed under matrix multiplication.

SG2 The identity matrix $\mathbf{I} = \begin{pmatrix} 1 & 0 \\ 0 & 1 \end{pmatrix}$ is a diagonal matrix with determinant 1, so $\mathbf{I} \in H$.

SG3 Let $\mathbf{A} = \begin{pmatrix} a & 0 \\ 0 & d \end{pmatrix} \in H$; then $ad = 1$.

Now

$$\mathbf{A}^{-1} = \begin{pmatrix} d/ad & 0 \\ 0 & a/ad \end{pmatrix}.$$

This is a diagonal matrix with determinant $(1/ad) = 1/1 = 1$, so $\mathbf{A}^{-1} \in H$.

Hence $H$ satisfies the three subgroup properties and $H \subseteq V$; so $H$ is a subgroup of $V$.

**(b)** We show that the three subgroup properties hold.

SG1 Let $\mathbf{A} = \begin{pmatrix} a & b \\ 0 & a \end{pmatrix}$ and $\mathbf{B} = \begin{pmatrix} x & y \\ 0 & x \end{pmatrix}$ be any two elements of $N$; then $a \neq 0$ and $x \neq 0$.

Now

$$\mathbf{AB} = \begin{pmatrix} a & b \\ 0 & a \end{pmatrix}\begin{pmatrix} x & y \\ 0 & x \end{pmatrix} = \begin{pmatrix} ax & ay + bx \\ 0 & ax \end{pmatrix},$$

and $ax \neq 0$, since $a \neq 0$ and $x \neq 0$; thus $\mathbf{AB} \in N$.

SG2 The identity matrix $\mathbf{I} = \begin{pmatrix} 1 & 0 \\ 0 & 1 \end{pmatrix}$ is of the required form (with $a = 1$ and $b = 0$), so $\mathbf{I} \in N$.

SG3 Let $\mathbf{A} = \begin{pmatrix} a & b \\ 0 & a \end{pmatrix} \in N$; then $a \neq 0$.

Now

$$\mathbf{A}^{-1} = \begin{pmatrix} a/a^2 & -b/a^2 \\ 0 & a/a^2 \end{pmatrix} = \begin{pmatrix} 1/a & -b/a^2 \\ 0 & 1/a \end{pmatrix}$$

and $1/a \neq 0$, so $\mathbf{A}^{-1} \in N$.

Hence $N$ satisfies the three subgroup properties and $N \subseteq U$; so $N$ is a subgroup of $U$.

**(c)** Consider the matrix $\mathbf{A} = \begin{pmatrix} 2 & 1 \\ 1 & 1 \end{pmatrix}$; then $\mathbf{A} \in X$, but

$$\mathbf{A}^2 = \begin{pmatrix} 2 & 1 \\ 1 & 1 \end{pmatrix}\begin{pmatrix} 2 & 1 \\ 1 & 1 \end{pmatrix} = \begin{pmatrix} 5 & 3 \\ 3 & 2 \end{pmatrix}$$

and this is not in $X$: thus $X$ is not closed under matrix multiplication.

Hence property SG1 fails, so $X$ is not a subgroup of $M$.

**5.3** **(a)** $H = \left\{\begin{pmatrix} a & 0 \\ 0 & d \end{pmatrix} : a, d \in \mathbb{R},\ ad = 1\right\}$ and

$$\begin{pmatrix} 1 & 2 \\ 0 & 1 \end{pmatrix}^{-1} = \begin{pmatrix} 1 & -2 \\ 0 & 1 \end{pmatrix},$$

so

$$\begin{aligned}
&\begin{pmatrix} 1 & 2 \\ 0 & 1 \end{pmatrix} H \begin{pmatrix} 1 & 2 \\ 0 & 1 \end{pmatrix}^{-1} \\
&= \left\{\begin{pmatrix} 1 & 2 \\ 0 & 1 \end{pmatrix}\begin{pmatrix} a & 0 \\ 0 & d \end{pmatrix}\begin{pmatrix} 1 & -2 \\ 0 & 1 \end{pmatrix} : a, d \in \mathbb{R},\ ad = 1\right\} \\
&= \left\{\begin{pmatrix} a & 2d \\ 0 & d \end{pmatrix}\begin{pmatrix} 1 & -2 \\ 0 & 1 \end{pmatrix} : a, d \in \mathbb{R},\ ad = 1\right\} \\
&= \left\{\begin{pmatrix} a & -2a + 2d \\ 0 & d \end{pmatrix} : a, d \in \mathbb{R},\ ad = 1\right\}.
\end{aligned}$$

This subgroup is not the same as $H$ because, if we take $a = 2$ and $d = \frac{1}{2}$, for example, we get

$$\begin{pmatrix} 2 & -3 \\ 0 & \frac{1}{2} \end{pmatrix},$$

which is not in $H$ since it is not a diagonal matrix.

**(b)** $H = \left\{ \begin{pmatrix} a & 0 \\ 0 & d \end{pmatrix} : a, d \in \mathbb{R},\ ad = 1 \right\}$ and

$$\begin{pmatrix} 1 & 0 \\ 1 & 1 \end{pmatrix}^{-1} = \begin{pmatrix} 1 & 0 \\ -1 & 1 \end{pmatrix},$$

so

$$\begin{aligned}
&\begin{pmatrix} 1 & 0 \\ 1 & 1 \end{pmatrix} H \begin{pmatrix} 1 & 0 \\ 1 & 1 \end{pmatrix}^{-1} \\
&= \left\{ \begin{pmatrix} 1 & 0 \\ 1 & 1 \end{pmatrix} \begin{pmatrix} a & 0 \\ 0 & d \end{pmatrix} \begin{pmatrix} 1 & 0 \\ -1 & 1 \end{pmatrix} : a, d \in \mathbb{R},\ ad = 1 \right\} \\
&= \left\{ \begin{pmatrix} a & 0 \\ a & d \end{pmatrix} \begin{pmatrix} 1 & 0 \\ -1 & 1 \end{pmatrix} : a, d \in \mathbb{R},\ ad = 1 \right\} \\
&= \left\{ \begin{pmatrix} a & 0 \\ a-d & d \end{pmatrix} : a, d \in \mathbb{R},\ ad = 1 \right\}.
\end{aligned}$$

This subgroup is not the same as $H$ because, if we take $a = 2$ and $d = \frac{1}{2}$, for example, we get

$$\begin{pmatrix} 2 & 0 \\ \frac{3}{2} & \frac{1}{2} \end{pmatrix},$$

which is not in $H$ since it is not a diagonal matrix.

**(c)** $U = \left\{ \begin{pmatrix} a & b \\ 0 & d \end{pmatrix} : a, b, d \in \mathbb{R},\ ad \neq 0 \right\}$ and

$$\begin{pmatrix} 1 & 1 \\ 0 & 1 \end{pmatrix}^{-1} = \begin{pmatrix} 1 & -1 \\ 0 & 1 \end{pmatrix},$$

so

$$\begin{aligned}
&\begin{pmatrix} 1 & 1 \\ 0 & 1 \end{pmatrix} U \begin{pmatrix} 1 & 1 \\ 0 & 1 \end{pmatrix}^{-1} \\
&= \left\{ \begin{pmatrix} 1 & 1 \\ 0 & 1 \end{pmatrix} \begin{pmatrix} a & b \\ 0 & d \end{pmatrix} \begin{pmatrix} 1 & -1 \\ 0 & 1 \end{pmatrix} : a, b, d \in \mathbb{R},\ ad \neq 0 \right\} \\
&= \left\{ \begin{pmatrix} a & b+d \\ 0 & d \end{pmatrix} \begin{pmatrix} 1 & -1 \\ 0 & 1 \end{pmatrix} : a, b, d \in \mathbb{R},\ ad \neq 0 \right\} \\
&= \left\{ \begin{pmatrix} a & -a+b+d \\ 0 & d \end{pmatrix} : a, b, d \in \mathbb{R},\ ad \neq 0 \right\}.
\end{aligned}$$

This subgroup is equal to $U$ since $-a+b+d$ can take any real value.

**5.4** **(a)** We guess that $D$ is not a normal subgroup of $M$.

Consider $\begin{pmatrix} 1 & 1 \\ 0 & 1 \end{pmatrix} \in M$ and $\begin{pmatrix} 1 & 0 \\ 0 & 2 \end{pmatrix} \in D$; then

$$\begin{aligned}
&\begin{pmatrix} 1 & 1 \\ 0 & 1 \end{pmatrix} \begin{pmatrix} 1 & 0 \\ 0 & 2 \end{pmatrix} \begin{pmatrix} 1 & 1 \\ 0 & 1 \end{pmatrix}^{-1} \\
&= \begin{pmatrix} 1 & 2 \\ 0 & 2 \end{pmatrix} \begin{pmatrix} 1 & -1 \\ 0 & 1 \end{pmatrix} \\
&= \begin{pmatrix} 1 & 1 \\ 0 & 2 \end{pmatrix},
\end{aligned}$$

which is not in $D$ since it is not a diagonal matrix.

Hence $D$ is not a normal subgroup of $M$.

**(b)** We guess that $N$ is not a normal subgroup of $M$.

Consider $\begin{pmatrix} 1 & 0 \\ 1 & 1 \end{pmatrix} \in M$ and $\begin{pmatrix} 2 & 1 \\ 0 & 2 \end{pmatrix} \in N$; then

$$\begin{aligned}
&\begin{pmatrix} 1 & 0 \\ 1 & 1 \end{pmatrix} \begin{pmatrix} 2 & 1 \\ 0 & 2 \end{pmatrix} \begin{pmatrix} 1 & 0 \\ 1 & 1 \end{pmatrix}^{-1} \\
&= \begin{pmatrix} 2 & 1 \\ 2 & 3 \end{pmatrix} \begin{pmatrix} 1 & 0 \\ -1 & 1 \end{pmatrix} \\
&= \begin{pmatrix} 1 & 1 \\ -1 & 3 \end{pmatrix},
\end{aligned}$$

which is not in $N$ since it is not an upper triangular matrix.

Hence $N$ is not a normal subgroup of $M$.

**(c)** We guess that $Y$ is a normal subgroup of $U$.

Let $\begin{pmatrix} a & b \\ 0 & d \end{pmatrix}$ be any element of $U$ (so $ad \neq 0$) and $\begin{pmatrix} 1 & x \\ 0 & 1 \end{pmatrix}$ be any element of $Y$.

Then

$$\begin{pmatrix} a & b \\ 0 & d \end{pmatrix}^{-1} = \frac{1}{ad} \begin{pmatrix} d & -b \\ 0 & a \end{pmatrix} = \begin{pmatrix} 1/a & -b/ad \\ 0 & 1/d \end{pmatrix},$$

so

$$\begin{aligned}
&\begin{pmatrix} a & b \\ 0 & d \end{pmatrix} \begin{pmatrix} 1 & x \\ 0 & 1 \end{pmatrix} \begin{pmatrix} a & b \\ 0 & d \end{pmatrix}^{-1} \\
&= \begin{pmatrix} a & ax+b \\ 0 & d \end{pmatrix} \begin{pmatrix} 1/a & -b/ad \\ 0 & 1/d \end{pmatrix} \\
&= \begin{pmatrix} 1 & ax/d \\ 0 & 1 \end{pmatrix} \in Y
\end{aligned}$$

since $d \neq 0$.

Hence $Y$ is a normal subgroup of $U$.

**5.5** **(a)** $\begin{pmatrix} -5 & -3 \\ 0 & 2 \end{pmatrix} N$

$$\begin{aligned}
&= \left\{ \begin{pmatrix} -5 & -3 \\ 0 & 2 \end{pmatrix} \mathbf{A} : \mathbf{A} \in N \right\} \\
&= \left\{ \begin{pmatrix} -5 & -3 \\ 0 & 2 \end{pmatrix} \begin{pmatrix} a & b \\ 0 & a \end{pmatrix} : a, b \in \mathbb{R},\ a \neq 0 \right\} \\
&= \left\{ \begin{pmatrix} -5a & -5b-3a \\ 0 & 2a \end{pmatrix} : a \in \mathbb{R}^*,\ b \in \mathbb{R} \right\} \\
&= \left\{ \begin{pmatrix} x & y \\ 0 & (-2/5)x \end{pmatrix} : x \in \mathbb{R}^*,\ y \in \mathbb{R} \right\}
\end{aligned}$$

**(b)** The matrix $\begin{pmatrix} 3 & 5 \\ 0 & 3 \end{pmatrix}$ belongs to $N$, so

$$\begin{pmatrix} 3 & 5 \\ 0 & 3 \end{pmatrix} N = N;$$

so this coset is

$$\left\{ \begin{pmatrix} a & b \\ 0 & a \end{pmatrix} : a \in \mathbb{R}^*, b \in \mathbb{R} \right\}.$$

(We could express it in terms of $x$ and $y$ as

$$\left\{ \begin{pmatrix} x & y \\ 0 & x \end{pmatrix} : x \in \mathbb{R}^*,\ y \in \mathbb{R} \right\}.)$$

**5.6** **(a)** $\begin{pmatrix} 3 & 4 \\ 0 & 5 \end{pmatrix} Y$

$$= \left\{ \begin{pmatrix} 3 & 4 \\ 0 & 5 \end{pmatrix} \mathbf{A} : \mathbf{A} \in Y \right\}$$
$$= \left\{ \begin{pmatrix} 3 & 4 \\ 0 & 5 \end{pmatrix} \begin{pmatrix} 1 & b \\ 0 & 1 \end{pmatrix} : b \in \mathbb{R} \right\}$$
$$= \left\{ \begin{pmatrix} 3 & 3b+4 \\ 0 & 5 \end{pmatrix} : b \in \mathbb{R} \right\}$$
$$= \left\{ \begin{pmatrix} 3 & x \\ 0 & 5 \end{pmatrix} : x \in \mathbb{R} \right\}$$

(As $b$ takes all values in $\mathbb{R}$, so does $3b+4$, so we have replaced $3b+4$ by $x$, where $x \in \mathbb{R}$.)

**(b)** $\begin{pmatrix} p & q \\ 0 & s \end{pmatrix} Y$

$$= \left\{ \begin{pmatrix} p & q \\ 0 & s \end{pmatrix} \mathbf{A} : \mathbf{A} \in Y \right\}$$
$$= \left\{ \begin{pmatrix} p & q \\ 0 & s \end{pmatrix} \begin{pmatrix} 1 & b \\ 0 & 1 \end{pmatrix} : b \in \mathbb{R} \right\}$$
$$= \left\{ \begin{pmatrix} p & pb+q \\ 0 & s \end{pmatrix} : b \in \mathbb{R} \right\}$$
$$= \left\{ \begin{pmatrix} p & x \\ 0 & s \end{pmatrix} : x \in \mathbb{R} \right\}$$

(As $b$ takes all values in $\mathbb{R}$, so does $pb+q$, so we have replaced $pb+q$ by $x$, where $x \in \mathbb{R}$.)

**(c)** The set of cosets of $Y$ in $U$ can be described as

$$\left\{ \begin{pmatrix} p & q \\ 0 & s \end{pmatrix} Y : p, s \in \mathbb{R}^*, q \in \mathbb{R} \right\}.$$

To simplify this description, we choose a simple element from the general coset

$$\begin{pmatrix} p & q \\ 0 & s \end{pmatrix} Y.$$

We can take $x = 0$ in the description of the general coset that we found in part (b), to give us the element

$$\begin{pmatrix} p & 0 \\ 0 & s \end{pmatrix} \in \begin{pmatrix} p & q \\ 0 & s \end{pmatrix} Y.$$

Hence

$$\begin{pmatrix} p & 0 \\ 0 & s \end{pmatrix} Y = \begin{pmatrix} p & q \\ 0 & s \end{pmatrix} Y,$$

so the set of cosets of $Y$ in $U$ can be described as

$$\left\{ \begin{pmatrix} p & 0 \\ 0 & s \end{pmatrix} Y : p, s \in \mathbb{R}^* \right\}.$$

For each coset of $Y$ in $U$, there is a *unique* pair of values $p, s$ such that the coset is $\begin{pmatrix} p & 0 \\ 0 & s \end{pmatrix} Y$, as we now prove. If $p_1$, $s_1$, $p_2$ and $s_2$ are elements of $\mathbb{R}^*$ such that

$$\begin{pmatrix} p_1 & 0 \\ 0 & s_1 \end{pmatrix} Y = \begin{pmatrix} p_2 & 0 \\ 0 & s_2 \end{pmatrix} Y,$$

then

$$\begin{pmatrix} p_1 & 0 \\ 0 & s_1 \end{pmatrix} \in \begin{pmatrix} p_2 & 0 \\ 0 & s_2 \end{pmatrix} Y.$$

By part (b),

$$\begin{pmatrix} p_2 & 0 \\ 0 & s_2 \end{pmatrix} Y = \left\{ \begin{pmatrix} p_2 & x \\ 0 & s_2 \end{pmatrix} : x \in \mathbb{R} \right\},$$

so

$$\begin{pmatrix} p_1 & 0 \\ 0 & s_1 \end{pmatrix} = \begin{pmatrix} p_2 & x \\ 0 & s_2 \end{pmatrix} \quad \text{for some } x \in \mathbb{R};$$

so $p_1 = p_2$ and $s_1 = s_2$ (and $x = 0$).

Hence the set of cosets of $Y$ in $U$ is

$$\left\{ \begin{pmatrix} p & 0 \\ 0 & s \end{pmatrix} Y : p, s \in \mathbb{R}^* \right\}.$$

**5.7** $A$ is a subgroup.

We show that the three subgroup properties hold.

SG1 Let $\begin{pmatrix} a & 0 \\ c & a \end{pmatrix}$ and $\begin{pmatrix} x & 0 \\ z & x \end{pmatrix}$ be any elements of $A$; then $a \neq 0$ and $x \neq 0$, so $ax \neq 0$.

Now

$$\begin{pmatrix} a & 0 \\ c & a \end{pmatrix} \begin{pmatrix} x & 0 \\ z & x \end{pmatrix} = \begin{pmatrix} ax & 0 \\ cx + az & ax \end{pmatrix},$$

and this element belongs to $A$, since it is lower triangular with equal non-zero elements on the diagonal. Thus $A$ is closed under matrix multiplication.

SG2 The identity element of $M$ is $\begin{pmatrix} 1 & 0 \\ 0 & 1 \end{pmatrix}$ and this is an element of $A$.

SG3 Let $\begin{pmatrix} a & 0 \\ c & a \end{pmatrix} \in A$; then $a \neq 0$.

Now

$$\begin{pmatrix} a & 0 \\ c & a \end{pmatrix}^{-1} = \begin{pmatrix} 1/a & 0 \\ -c/a^2 & 1/a \end{pmatrix},$$

and this is a lower triangular matrix with equal non-zero entries on the leading diagonal, so it belongs to $A$.

Hence $A$ satisfies the three subgroup properties, so it is a subgroup of $M$.

$B$ is not a subgroup.

For example, $\begin{pmatrix} 1 & 0 \\ 1 & 1 \end{pmatrix} \in B$ but

$$\begin{pmatrix} 1 & 0 \\ 1 & 1 \end{pmatrix} \begin{pmatrix} 1 & 0 \\ 1 & 1 \end{pmatrix} = \begin{pmatrix} 1 & 0 \\ 2 & 1 \end{pmatrix} \notin B,$$

so $B$ is not closed under matrix multiplication. Hence property SG1 fails, so $B$ is not a subgroup.

$C$ is a subgroup.

We show that the three subgroup properties hold.

SG1 Let $\begin{pmatrix} 1+m & m \\ -m & 1-m \end{pmatrix}$ and $\begin{pmatrix} 1+n & n \\ -n & 1-n \end{pmatrix}$ be any elements of $C$; then $m, n \in \mathbb{Z}$.

Now

$$\begin{pmatrix} 1+m & m \\ -m & 1-m \end{pmatrix}\begin{pmatrix} 1+n & n \\ -n & 1-n \end{pmatrix}$$
$$= \begin{pmatrix} 1+m+n & m+n \\ -m-n & 1-m-n \end{pmatrix}$$
$$= \begin{pmatrix} 1+k & k \\ -k & 1-k \end{pmatrix},$$

where $k = m+n$ is an integer.

This product belongs to $C$, so $C$ is closed under matrix multiplication.

SG2 The identity element $\begin{pmatrix} 1 & 0 \\ 0 & 1 \end{pmatrix}$ belongs to $C$ (it has $n = 0$), so property SG2 holds.

SG3 Let $\begin{pmatrix} 1+n & n \\ -n & 1-n \end{pmatrix}$ be any element of $C$; then $n \in \mathbb{Z}$.

Now

$$\begin{pmatrix} 1+n & n \\ -n & 1-n \end{pmatrix}^{-1}$$
$$= \begin{pmatrix} 1-n & -n \\ n & 1+n \end{pmatrix}$$
$$= \begin{pmatrix} 1+k & k \\ -k & 1-k \end{pmatrix},$$

where $k = -n$ is an integer.

This inverse belongs to $C$, so property SG3 holds.

Hence $C$ satisfies the three subgroup properties and so is a subgroup of $M$.

**5.8** (a) $\begin{pmatrix} 1 & 1 \\ 0 & 1 \end{pmatrix} H \begin{pmatrix} 1 & 1 \\ 0 & 1 \end{pmatrix}^{-1}$

$$= \left\{\begin{pmatrix} 1 & 1 \\ 0 & 1 \end{pmatrix}\begin{pmatrix} a & 0 \\ 0 & 1/a \end{pmatrix}\begin{pmatrix} 1 & -1 \\ 0 & 1 \end{pmatrix} : a \in \mathbb{R}^*\right\}$$
$$= \left\{\begin{pmatrix} a & 1/a \\ 0 & 1/a \end{pmatrix}\begin{pmatrix} 1 & -1 \\ 0 & 1 \end{pmatrix} : a \in \mathbb{R}^*\right\}$$
$$= \left\{\begin{pmatrix} a & (1/a)-a \\ 0 & 1/a \end{pmatrix} : a \in \mathbb{R}^*\right\}$$

This subgroup can also be written as

$$\left\{\begin{pmatrix} x & y-x \\ 0 & y \end{pmatrix} : x, y \in \mathbb{R}^*,\ xy = 1\right\}.$$

(b) $\begin{pmatrix} 0 & 1 \\ 1 & 2 \end{pmatrix} H \begin{pmatrix} 0 & 1 \\ 1 & 2 \end{pmatrix}^{-1}$

$$= \left\{\begin{pmatrix} 0 & 1 \\ 1 & 2 \end{pmatrix}\begin{pmatrix} a & 0 \\ 0 & 1/a \end{pmatrix}\begin{pmatrix} -2 & 1 \\ 1 & 0 \end{pmatrix} : a \in \mathbb{R}^*\right\}$$
$$= \left\{\begin{pmatrix} 0 & 1/a \\ a & 2/a \end{pmatrix}\begin{pmatrix} -2 & 1 \\ 1 & 0 \end{pmatrix} : a \in \mathbb{R}^*\right\}$$
$$= \left\{\begin{pmatrix} 1/a & 0 \\ (2/a)-2a & a \end{pmatrix} : a \in \mathbb{R}^*\right\}$$

This subgroup can also be written as

$$\left\{\begin{pmatrix} x & 0 \\ 2(x-y) & y \end{pmatrix} : x, y \in \mathbb{R}^*,\ xy = 1\right\}.$$

**5.9** (a) $\begin{pmatrix} 1 & 2 \\ 0 & 1 \end{pmatrix} C \begin{pmatrix} 1 & 2 \\ 0 & 1 \end{pmatrix}^{-1}$

$$= \left\{\begin{pmatrix} 1 & 2 \\ 0 & 1 \end{pmatrix}\begin{pmatrix} 1+n & n \\ -n & 1-n \end{pmatrix}\begin{pmatrix} 1 & -2 \\ 0 & 1 \end{pmatrix} : n \in \mathbb{Z}\right\}$$
$$= \left\{\begin{pmatrix} 1-n & 2-n \\ -n & 1-n \end{pmatrix}\begin{pmatrix} 1 & -2 \\ 0 & 1 \end{pmatrix} : n \in \mathbb{Z}\right\}$$
$$= \left\{\begin{pmatrix} 1-n & n \\ -n & 1+n \end{pmatrix} : n \in \mathbb{Z}\right\}$$

(b) $\begin{pmatrix} 1 & 0 \\ 3 & 1 \end{pmatrix} C \begin{pmatrix} 1 & 0 \\ 3 & 1 \end{pmatrix}^{-1}$

$$= \left\{\begin{pmatrix} 1 & 0 \\ 3 & 1 \end{pmatrix}\begin{pmatrix} 1+n & n \\ -n & 1-n \end{pmatrix}\begin{pmatrix} 1 & 0 \\ -3 & 1 \end{pmatrix} : n \in \mathbb{Z}\right\}$$
$$= \left\{\begin{pmatrix} 1+n & n \\ 3+2n & 1+2n \end{pmatrix}\begin{pmatrix} 1 & 0 \\ -3 & 1 \end{pmatrix} : n \in \mathbb{Z}\right\}$$
$$= \left\{\begin{pmatrix} 1-2n & n \\ -4n & 1+2n \end{pmatrix} : n \in \mathbb{Z}\right\}$$

**5.10** The subgroup $A$ contains only lower triangular matrices and hence it is a subset of $L$. Since it is a subgroup of $M$, it follows that it is a subgroup of $L$.

We apply Strategy 3.2.

Let $\begin{pmatrix} a & 0 \\ c & a \end{pmatrix}$ be any element of $A$ and let $\begin{pmatrix} x & 0 \\ y & z \end{pmatrix}$ be any element of $L$.

Then $a \neq 0$, $x \neq 0$ and $z \neq 0$, and

$$\begin{pmatrix} x & 0 \\ y & z \end{pmatrix}\begin{pmatrix} a & 0 \\ c & a \end{pmatrix}\begin{pmatrix} x & 0 \\ y & z \end{pmatrix}^{-1}$$
$$= \begin{pmatrix} ax & 0 \\ ay+cz & az \end{pmatrix}\begin{pmatrix} 1/x & 0 \\ -y/xz & 1/z \end{pmatrix}$$
$$= \begin{pmatrix} a & 0 \\ cz/x & a \end{pmatrix},$$

and this matrix is in $A$ since it is a lower triangular matrix with equal diagonal entries.

Hence $A$ is a normal subgroup of $L$.

**5.11** From the formula for combining cosets using set composition, the missing matrix is the matrix product in $U$:

$$\begin{pmatrix} p_1 & 0 \\ 0 & s_1 \end{pmatrix}\begin{pmatrix} p_2 & 0 \\ 0 & s_2 \end{pmatrix} = \begin{pmatrix} p_1p_2 & 0 \\ 0 & s_1s_2 \end{pmatrix}.$$

Hence the formula is

$$\begin{pmatrix} p_1 & 0 \\ 0 & s_1 \end{pmatrix}Y \cdot \begin{pmatrix} p_2 & 0 \\ 0 & s_2 \end{pmatrix}Y = \begin{pmatrix} p_1p_2 & 0 \\ 0 & s_1s_2 \end{pmatrix}Y.$$

# Index